D0923227

0
2
3
4
5
6
7

DATE DUE			
MAR 31 '70	NOV 22	DEC 1 9 1979	
JAN 27 71	DEC 6 '72 1:30	MAR 2 5 1981	
FEB 18 7		APR 2 9 1981	
SEP 18 '71	Trend	DEC - 3 1985	
SEP 22 '71 3:00 pm		OCT 1 8 1990	
AUG 31 '72	NOV 2 0 1975		
NOV 15 72 11:30	DEC 8 1975	APR - 2 1991	
NOV 15 72	NOV 2 1 1979	DEC - 9 1991	
NOV 16 72 11:30	DEC 1 2 1979	MAR 1 0 1994	

A WILEY PUBLICATION
IN PSYCHOLOGY

HERBERT S. LANGFELD
Advisory Editor

The Human Senses

The Human Senses

FRANK A. GELDARD

Professor of Psychology
Princeton University

NEW YORK · JOHN WILEY & SONS, INC.

London · Sydney

Library of Congress Catalog Card Number: 52–13881

PRINTED IN THE UNITED STATES OF AMERICA

To two good girls,
JEANNETTE and DEBBY

BOOKS BY GELDARD (F. A.)

Fundamentals of Psychology

The Human Senses

Preface

Once upon a time—not too deeply buried in the moldering past, for it falls within the memory of a generation yet alive and active—the greater portion of psychology was "sense psychology." "Experience" was psychology's proper object of study, and experience comes by way of man's senses.

The same generation has seen changes—some of emphasis, many merely of terminology, but a few of fundamental conception. Psychology has become "the science of behavior." This development has made the role of the human senses no less important, for all behavior is triggered by stimuli, and stimuli must have sense organs on which to operate. But the elaboration of a science of behavior calls for much more than variations on the simple theme provided by the stimulus-response formula. Such rubrics as learning, motive, attitude, and interest—in short, the central adjustive mechanisms generally—have taken on an air of urgency. Preoccupation with these topics naturally results in a relative de-emphasis of others. In the contemporary picture, therefore, sensation seems to have receded somewhat into the background; more "dynamic," if less mature, concepts are crowding the center of the canvas. These trends in psychological fashions partially account for the current rarity of books on sensation. In part, also, the lack is to be attributed to the circumstance that, whereas we have no dearth of specialists in vision and in audition, and even a few experts in each of the other senses, there are not many "sensory generalists" in psychology.

The basic credo underlying this book is that the highroad to the understanding of human nature is by way of an appreciation of man's senses and of the fundamental role they play in the attainment of knowledge and the regulation of behavior. If, through its auspices, students or general readers are set on the path towards such an appreciation; if, so to speak, they are "brought to their senses," the book will have realized the major aim set for it.

Were I cataloguing all the influences responsible for the genesis and final completion of the book I should certainly have to begin with

John Paul Nafe's course in systematic psychology at Clark University
in my graduate student days.   My appetite for sensory psychology
clearly came into being then.   It has been whetted, in seminars extending over a score of years, by my own students at Virginia.   In the
actual preparation of the manuscript there has been the valuable help
of several professional colleagues.   The chapters on vision were read
and criticized, at various stages, by Clarence H. Graham and S. Rains
Wallace, Jr.   The audition chapters had the benefit of critical readings
by E. Glen Wever, Frank W. Finger, and Willard R. Thurlow.   The
chapters on the chemical senses profited from the suggestions of Carl
Pfaffmann.   The entire manuscript was appraised, and improved no
little, by Professor Herbert S. Langfeld.   To all these friends I am
very grateful; my earnest hope is that they find the finished product
not too disappointing.

Finally, my thanks are due Mrs. Jane Watson, accustomed to turning out perfect copy, for a typical performance on the manuscript,
thereby lightening the labors of author and publisher alike.

FRANK A. GELDARD

Charlottesville, Virginia
January, 1953

Contents

1

Introduction

Man has ever been the most engaging object of study for man. In the behavior of his fellows he is confronted with a never-ending source of wonder and perplexity, and in his every new experience he finds a challenge to his understanding. The intricacies of human action are myriad, and it is no accident that psychology, whose business it is to cut through the complexities and disclose the broad principles governing human nature and conduct, should have been among the last subjects to attain the stature of a scientific discipline. Pre-scientific psychology has a history as long as that of human thought itself.

There is probably no topic in connection with which the average layman is more ready to pronounce a judgment or express an opinion than that of psychology. We may be content to leave the intricacies of physics or chemistry or any other of the fundamental natural sciences to experts in these fields, satisfying ourselves with a few basic ideas about the operation of the complicated world around us. But the business of living and conducting ourselves in a world of human beings is very much the concern of each of us. We are all under the necessity of acquiring and pressing into service a workable set of conceptions of human nature. Moreover, the materials with which psychology attempts to come to grips are immediately available in the form of our own thoughts and feelings and in the actions of others. We come readily to generalize from our experiences and to develop a set of beliefs concerning the operation of the human mind. The demand for working principles is so insistent that it is not surprising that hasty convictions, half-truths, even superstitions become lodged in our mental constitutions and sometimes are modified or expelled only with the greatest difficulty. We feel "from experience" that we are rather good judges of the motives of other people. We have "explanations" for the fact that some persons have good memories while others have not. We acquire beliefs as to the relative influence of nature and nurture in shaping our behavior. We do not hesitate

1

to ascribe the genesis of anomalies we observe in others to temperament and character "types." We have convictions concerning the effects of sleep, the importance of dreams, the influences of age, sex, fatigue, climatic conditions, and a host of other matters. In fact, unless we turn the searchlight of self-criticism upon these beliefs we may go on indefinitely, trusting our crude observations, never pausing to draw into question the processes whereby we form our prejudices and set up our standards.

In all ages there have been thoughtful people who have tried to bring order out of the chaos that is personal experience; the production of various philosophical "systems," of one or another degree of satisfyingness, attests the success of such ventures. In an earlier day such systematic groupings of personal observations *were* psychology, and there are many acute descriptions and cogent explanations of psychological phenomena in philosophical writings. Indeed, many such accounts have never been surpassed. The chief danger in abiding by such systems lies, of course, in the narrow factual perspective they afford. Bodies of acceptable scientific knowledge represent joint enterprises by many different people united by common purposes and concepts; modern sciences are not compounded exclusively of personal fireside speculations, however shrewd they may be.

The scientific approach to the study of psychology differs not in the least, at the present time, from that which is employed in undertaking the study of any other basic science. The details differ; the point of view is the same. As a modern science psychology employs the method of experiment, the accoutrements of the laboratory, and the procedure of objective observation, just as do all other natural sciences. Taking its cue from the imposing successes of the more mature sciences of nature, psychology adopted the experimental method only a few score years ago in the clear recognition that, while its objects of study might be vastly more complicated and correspondingly more difficult of exact experimental manipulation, knowledge meeting the rigid demands of science could be acquired in no other way. The step taken by physics in the sixteenth century was repeated, at least in all outward characteristics, by psychology in the latter part of the nineteenth.

The beginnings of scientific psychology are peculiarly bound up with our subject—the human senses—and we shall do well, for that reason, to take a brief backward glance at experimental psychology's origins. Through it we may hope to gain a perspective not obtainable in any other way. Though the senses have doubtless been the objects of interest and study since pre-history, their scientific description is a relatively recent product of the laboratory and of the experimental method.

The Origins of Experimental Psychology. We like to date experimental psychology from the establishment of the first laboratory devoted solely to the prosecution of its problems. In 1879, Wilhelm Wundt, one of the great figures of all time in psychology, formally opened at Leipzig a laboratory designed for the experimental investigation of a broad range of psychological processes. There were begun important studies of action, attention, feeling, association, memory, and, especially, sensation and perception. All these are still important rubrics in experimental psychology, and the vast influence of Wundt and his students in shaping the future course of the infant science can hardly be overestimated. Of course, experimental psychology did not spring, like Athene, "full-fledged from the forehead of Jove"; Wundt was in no sense entirely and single-handedly responsible for its inception. Even had he been a different sort of person he could not have boasted, as Napoleon is said to have done, that he was his own ancestor. The movement that had its first institutional expression in the Leipzig laboratory had been initiated by a very considerable number of worthy predecessors, chiefly physiologists, physicists, and philosophers. What made Wundt's work a "founding" effort was the fact that it gave clear expression and implementation to several converging influences in nineteenth-century science.

There had been important figures, such as Helmholtz, Fechner, Weber, and Johannes Müller, as well as a host of lesser lights, who had not only set the stage for the advent of a distinct science of experimental psychology but who, through important physiological and physical experiments, had partially determined its ultimate trajectory. Also, there had been a very real and many-sided preparation for coming events within philosophy, particularly on the part of the British empiricists of the eighteenth century and the associationists of the early nineteenth.

It has become apparent, in retrospect, that the first experimental psychology was not so much a borrowing from the more firmly established sciences and philosophy as it was an expression of a real need for a direct frontal attack, by approved scientific methods, on broad problems of human nature. One cannot go far into physics without confronting problems concerning the sensitivity and reliability of instruments, and the most commonly employed "instrument" is, of course, the human observer. Similarly, one takes few steps into physiology, studying the manner of functioning of various bodily organs and tissue systems, without encountering the most general problems of the behavior of the organism as a whole. Further, the most persistent and abiding problems of philosophy, especially those having to do with the question of how knowledge is acquired, find answers possible only when they are made specific and cast in terms of the details of human experience. Thus it is not surprising to find Ernst Mach, a physicist "unconstrained by the conventional barriers of the specialist," publishing a volume on *The Analysis of the Sensations,* Charles Darwin producing a work on *Expression of Emotion in Man and Animals,* and Bishop Berkeley giving to the world, in successive years, his *New Theory of Vision* and the *Principles of Human Knowledge.* Nor are these in any sense isolated instances. Knowledge may be partitioned only through an artifice. The most thoughtful workers in any field will come, sooner or later, to a consideration of the most fascinating of all objects of study, man himself.

The Psychophysical Law. One development of special significance in the pre-Wundtian days, important not only because it brought measurement into the service of psychology but because it supplied methods and materials destined to dominate much of the later work, was that coming from the pioneer work of Ernst Weber (1795–1878) and G. T. Fechner (1801–1887). Weber, a physiologist greatly interested in problems of sense organ functions, a field to which he made many signal contributions, came in the course of his studies to direct special attention to the then little-understood sensations originating in muscles and their attachments. A discovery which will forever be linked with his name came out of an experiment designed to disclose the role of muscle sensations in the discrimination of weights of different magnitudes. He first found that differences could be detected somewhat more readily when the weights were lifted, thus imposing strains on the muscles of the hand and arm, than when they were simply laid on the resting hand. In true experimental fashion he set out to vary systematically the various factors involved, using initial weights of 4, 7.5, and 32 oz. Adding small weights to these standards and noting the effect on the feelings of strain in the muscles, he soon discovered an interesting relationship. All his results pointed to the generality that discrimination depends, not upon the absolute size of the difference between two weights, but upon the ratio of this size to that of the weight with which one starts. The ratio proved to be a constant one and to be independent of the absolute masses involved; the "just noticeable difference" always corresponded to a constant fraction of the standard stimulus. To produce a just perceptibly increased feeling of strain it was necessary to add a weight $\frac{1}{40}$ as large as the amount already in force. Intrigued with this evidence for the relativity of human judgments, Weber tested the applicability of his formula to other kinds of sensations and found that it apparently held, the necessary increase being invariably in the neighborhood of 2% or less for the discrimination of the lengths of lines when simultaneously presented, and about 5% when shown successively. Other experiments, some less thoroughgoing than might be desired, led him to extend the law to touch and hearing, where he found pressures to be correctly discriminated if they stood in the ratio of 29 to 30, and tonal pitches to sound different to the musically trained ear if they bore the relation of 321 and 322.

Recognition of the wide applicability and basic significance of "Weber's Law" came at the hands of another, Gustav Fechner. For one whose early interests lay in the field of pure physics and whose leanings throughout a long and varied lifetime were broadly philosophical, it is a strange quirk of fate that Fechner should now be best known for the bias he gave to early experimental psychology. Yet Fechner's contribution came out of his philosophy. His general view, first expressed in his *Zend-Avesta* (1851), an odd mixture of oriental mysticism and occidental materialism, and later in his classical *Elements of Psychophysics* (1860), called for the most embracing of beliefs in the essential identity of the mental world and the physical world of matter. The transition from the one to the other would seem to be not impossible if a combining principle, involving a universal relation between the two, could be discovered. This principle Fechner believed he had found in Weber's Law. But, whereas Weber had been content with the "just noticeable difference," Fechner reasoned further that all sensations, perhaps all mental processes, must be measurable in terms of their stimuli, and he came to formulate a more general "psychophysical" law. This law stated that the intensity of sensation is proportional to the intensity of stimulation, but that the relation is not a simple direct one. As sensations increase in equal steps, the stimuli necessary to set them off increase by equal ratios. The mathematical statement is S (sensation intensity) $= k \log I$ (stimulus intensity, energy ideally).

It happens that the Weber-Fechner Law, as a later generation has named it, has been shown not to have anything like the universal applicability its originator claimed for it. Indeed, there is some doubt as to whether it is ever strictly true; certainly there are some instances in which it represents not even a fair approximation to reality. Numerous criticisms have been directed against it on logical and factual grounds, and some critics, such as William James, have attempted to discredit it entirely. The value or truthfulness of the psychophysical law need not concern us especially at this point, however. Its importance in giving direction to early experimental psychology remains unquestioned. In the light of it scores of important investigations were carried out, and the results of these studies were naturally embodied in the content of the young science. Psychology had acquired a technique of measurement, and its results could be expressed in the language of mathematics. At the same time, it was stressing heavily the content being quantified—the human senses.

The Influence of Experimental Physiology. Any inventory of the influences leading to experimental psychology's founding must include the very considerable one exerted by studies of nervous functions. From the beginning, psychologists have been intensely interested in the workings of the nervous system, and with good reason. It is truly the "organ of mind," and, presumably, no fact concerning its operation is without some value or interest in aiding the interpretation of psychological data.

The years that were formative for experimental psychology were also those of significant and spectacular discovery for its older brother, experimental physiology. The first years of the nineteenth century had seen revealed the most basic principles of operation of the nervous system, especially Sir Charles Bell's discovery that the spinal nerves were arranged in accordance with function, sensory fibers entering the posterior and motor fibers the anterior portions of the spinal cord. His "law of forward direction" in the nervous system has been considered to be as fundamental as Harvey's discovery of the circulation of the blood. Just at the time when Weber was doing his lifted weight experiments there was being disclosed the essential difference between the kinds of nervous pathways involved in voluntary actions and those responsible for purely automatic or "reflex" activities. Also, Johannes Müller was marshalling his arguments for his famous doctrine of "specific energies of nerves," an idea so basic and far-reaching that it forms the crux of many of our current disputes in sensory theory, to say nothing of its profound influence in shaping early experimental problems. The battle between "specificity" and "non-specificity" has filled many a psychological day.

While Fechner was devising his psychophysical law and performing somewhat tedious experiments in support of it, Helmholtz' brilliant measurements of the speed of nervous conduction were being made. Helmholtz' teacher, Johannes Müller, had supposed such measures to be impossible, regarding nerve impulsion to be of the order of the speed of light! The middle of the century saw also the beginnings of modern nerve cell theory and the development of techniques for staining nerves, thus permitting their more exact anatomical study. Altogether, it was a happy combination of circumstances that joined neurological discovery and interest in psychological phenomena in such a way as to provide mutual impetus to the two fields. To this day their contents, if not inextricably interwoven, are mutually complementary. Experimental psychology would be pale without the interpretative coloring provided by an expanding knowledge of nervous functions, and, at the same time, experimental neurology may count among its most conspicuous successes discoveries prompted by psychological observations.

Some of the influences responsible for the creation of a separate field of experimental psychology have been pointed out. Once established, its growth was rapid and its frontiers were greatly expanded. Its central topic, sensation, was a natural interest which continued to be prosecuted wherever the young science took root. Over half the studies issuing from Wundt's laboratory and those of his students were concerned with sensation and perception. Of these the large majority were on vision, then as now pre-eminent among the sense channels as the conveyor of the most detailed and frequently the most urgent messages. Second in popularity as a research topic was the sense of hearing; next came touch and its near relatives in the family of senses and, finally, the chemical senses, smell and taste. This order still represents the relative importance of the various classes of sensation, whether one relies on professional judgment in coming to a conclusion about it or lets the number of technical publications in each of these areas serve as a criterion. It is the order we shall follow in our systematic survey of the senses.

It would be a mistake to suppose, because its origins are so closely bound up with the study of sensation, that experimental psychology thereby has the sole proprietary right to this field. We have already seen that physiology, especially neural physiology, has a legitimate claim to the senses, as do also some other neighboring disciplines. To come to an appreciation of what interests impinge upon the human senses, considered as objects of study, we do well to attempt to get into perspective the world of scientific knowledge and its mode of organization.

The Unity of Knowledge and the Diversity of Human Interests. Scientific knowledge, painstakingly amassed by many devotees over an extended period of human history, is nothing if not unitary when viewed in the large and against the background of superstition, folklore, and rule of thumb over which it has had to triumph. Its unity derives from a commonness of purpose, a rigor of logical planning and observational procedure, and a strict fidelity to the rules governing the use of the experimental method. Science seeks out, with detachment and disinterest, the unvarnished fact. In part, its unity derives also from the circumstance that different particular sciences, all having the same reality to view but doing so from different standpoints, come to describe many of the same objects and thus develop with other sciences a community of content. How this can come about is revealed by a useful figure once suggested by Titchener (282). He pictured the "world of experience as contained in a great circle, and . . . scientific men as viewing this world from various stations on the periphery. There are . . . as many possible sciences as there are distinguishable points of view about the circle . . . no one of them in truth exhausts experience or completely describes the common subject-matter, though each one, if ideally complete, would exhaust some aspects of experience." "One and the same item of human experience may enter, as part of their subject-matter, into a large number of sciences; whence it follows that the sciences themselves cannot be distinguished, in any final accounting, by the specific character of the 'objects' with which they deal."

We know, of course, that sciences do not just "happen"; they do not find themselves in position on the circle by accident. Sciences are only slowly and arduously "constructed," and each has a history peculiar to itself. Moreover, the stuff of which sciences are compounded is "mediate," not "immediate" experience. Nevertheless, this view of the way in which the sciences are organized is helpful, not only in stressing the unity of knowledge but also in emphasizing, in the peripheral dimension, the intimacy of relation among the various approaches. One sees that it is, after all, but a step—albeit one that offers at the conclusion of it a new and different vista of reality—from psychology to physiology, say, or from pathology to physics. Nor does any particular harm come from the journeying of the individual scientist if he chooses to traverse the scientific circle. He is under no compunction to remain uncompromisingly at one position on the perimeter. Not only should he be permitted to wander from his own observation post, but, provided only that he preserve his orientation constantly, he should be encouraged to make frequent visits to his scientific neighbors. It is only necessary that he avoid too great a peripheral velocity, for that way lies superficiality, dilettantism, or even, as Boring has termed it, "epistemological vertigo."

Nowhere in science is there a content having more points of impingement on human interests than that provided by the senses of man. All knowledge, as the Sophists of ancient Greece knew, comes only through the senses, and those who would "know how they know" turn quite naturally to the contemplation of the senses as the originators of experience. "The eye," John Locke noted in his *Essay Concerning Human Understanding*, "whilst it makes us see and perceive all other things, takes no notice of itself," and it becomes the special business of the sciences arranged about the circumference of Titchener's great circle, not to mention a variety of artistic and technological concerns representing powerful springs of human action, to furnish the means whereby an understanding of the visual process—and those of the other senses—can be attained.

The range of interests brought to bear on sensation and the senses is of prodigious extent. Consider vision. The study of what and how we see is not alone the business of scientific man, though he is doubtless in the most favored position to supply a full and impartial description. The visual process is also of importance to man considered medically, artistically, economically, educationally, and even politically. Charles II of England, perhaps remembering the price on his own head in Cromwell's time, is said to have derived much amusement from Mariotte's demonstration of the blind spot of the eye (1668) and required his courtiers to repeat the experiment to observe how they would look with their heads off! The mode of operation of the human eye is of practical concern to the physician as he checks the retinal color zones for evidences of disease or malfunction, to the painter in oils as he teases depth out of light and shade, to the advertising expert as he assaults the eye with all manner of suggestions for purchase, and to the professional educator with his modern reliance on visual aids. And these are, of course, in no wise isolated examples. Man viewed militarily or legally or as an engineering or linguistic creature would yield up myriads of instances in which visual sensation is a central consideration and thus itself a natural object of study. The visual implications have to be taken into account whenever there swing into action the illuminating engineer, the stage lighting expert, the designer of aircraft instruments or submarine controls, the railroad signalman, the paper chemist, the fabricator of ceramics or textiles, the manufacturing pharmacist, the designer of automobile bodies, the blender of paints, or the optical instrument maker. The list might go on and on, for it is difficult to think of human skills or technical knowledge or artistic endeavors apart from the visual sensations on which they in such large measure depend.

Nor is the visual channel the sole one of importance in human affairs. The fields of communication, entertainment, and education make almost incessant demands on our hearing apparatus, while the housing and clothing industries are monuments to our cutaneous senses, just as the food technologies are to our chemical senses. Little wonder that philosophers throughout the ages, when they have not been exalting Reason, have been extolling Sensation as the very essence of Truth. Little wonder that the scientific study of sensation and the senses forms today, as it did in Wundt's time, the most fundamental of psychological contents.

The Senses and Human Engineering. In the chapters that follow we shall be dealing, for the most part, with the senses considered in their fundamental or "pure science" aspect. The treatment accorded them will be systematic, and the aim will be to arrive at descriptive accounts which may be expected to hold good in a variety of settings and a diversity of applications. However, the impression should not be given that sensory psychology, as presently constituted, has no "applied" or technological side, that it fails to square with the manifold human needs and interests which, we have seen, may be brought to bear on it. Indeed, in evidence of just such a meeting of practical demands there has been witnessed in recent years the very lively growth of what has been variously called "human engineering," "psychotechnology," and "engineering psychology," a central concern of which is sensation and the senses. This development is a significant one and one whose latent possibilities have not even been estimated as yet.

Human engineering, born of World War II though a lineal descendant of both pre-war experimental psychology and engineering design practices, has thus far busied itself mainly with problems of a military nature. It is a product of the times, and, whereas in a less unsettled world it could have been expected that engineering psychology would have enjoyed its most conspicuous successes in the solution of industrial problems, necessity has dictated otherwise. Military weapons and the predicaments created by warfare have been its chief preoccupations (93).

Modern military equipment and weapon systems impose an incredibly heavy burden on man's senses. We think of shipboard radar, e.g., as a device for dispensing with the masthead lookout and thus of circumventing the limitations of man's sensory endowments. Radar searches where the eye cannot see, through darkness and fog and beyond the acuity limits of human vision. However, as was repeatedly demonstrated in World War II, what radar and similar devices also do is to substitute one sensory task for another and, while effectively extending the range of exploration, also come to require discriminations that tax the capabilities of sense organs. "This recent war," writes Stevens in evaluation of the military role of human engineering (271, p. 390), "was different from other wars in the peculiar respect that it was fought largely on margin—sensory margin—where the battle hangs on the power of the eyes or the ears to make a fine discrimination, to estimate a distance, to see or hear a signal which is just at the edge of human capacity . . . and the paradox of it is that the faster the engineers and the inventors served up their 'automatic' gadgets to eliminate the human factor the tighter the squeeze became on the powers of the operator. . . ."

Principles of visual psychophysiology found ready application in the design of instrument faces and dials, radar consoles, gunsights, binoculars, stereoscopic height finders, aircraft insignia, cockpit lighting, and in a number of situations requiring optimal arrangement of men and equipment in ships, airplanes, and tanks. Auditory psychophysiology—"psychoacoustics," it came to be called—was brought to bear on problems of voice communication systems, where the study of speech intelligibility under various conditions of wave distortion and "jamming" led to important discoveries concerning the best ways to "package" speech and to improve equipment for transmitting and receiving it. Experience in audition was also put to work on underwater sound detection devices and auditory signal systems, such as aircraft radio ranges and "flybar" (flying by auditory reference).

Even the sense of touch, not ordinarily a receiver of information originating at a distance and thus of less intrinsic military importance than its more highly developed relatives in the family of senses, came in for special investigation in connection with the tactual discrimination of shapes for knobs and handles of control levers. Especially in airplane cockpits, where a plethora of instruments and controls confronts the pilot, any device or procedure which will lessen the demands on vision and audition may be counted a distinct boon. A bewildering array of levers, knobs, switches, pedals, and wheels lies about the pilot as, among other things, he adjusts engine and flight controls, landing gear, lights, "intercom," and radio (57, p. 128). To make matters worse, aircraft designers, for what must seem to them to be adequate reasons, have a way of changing the positions of vital controls from one type of airplane to another. Thorough training can, of course, be expected to automatize responses, and the properly "transitioned" pilot will normally seek out the correct lever or switch, even in an emergency situation. However, let his habit systems be-

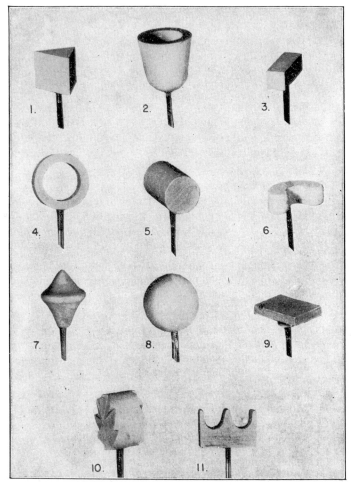

Fig. 1. Knobs found best for shape coding of controls. From Jenkins, *172*.

come overtaxed by excessive demands on his adaptability, especially in stressful circumstances, and sheer position of a control may be an insufficient cue to appropriate action.

It was with a view to reducing the hazards attending the lack of cockpit standardization that experimental psychologists undertook to determine the advantages to be derived from "shape coding" of airplane controls (*306, 172*). Plastic knobs of all conceivable shapes were devised and mounted on the ends of rods projecting vertically from the circumference of a turntable. Twenty-five different shapes were selected for use in a carefully designed experiment. In each trial the blindfolded subject was first required to feel a given knob for 1 second, the turntable orientation was changed, and the subject's task was then to find the originally presented knob by "feel" alone. Half the trials were with the bare hand, half with the subject wearing a standard flight glove. Eighty experienced pilots took part in the experiment. A record was kept both of outright misidentifications of knobs and of undue hesitation in arriving at a decision, though it turned out that the two kinds of indices led to substantially the same conclusions. Nearly all subjects made some errors, confusions between certain pairings of knobs were common, and hesitancy in decision was frequently noted. In some instances the amount of error ranged up to 40%. The more experienced pilots, those with the larger number of flying hours to their credit, were no better in this task than the less experienced. The wearing of gloves reduced accuracy somewhat but not as much as one might suppose. From an analysis of the errors of confusion and hesitation made in nearly 2000 comparisons there eventually emerged the 11 knobs displayed in Fig. 1 as representing the range of useful shapes for this purpose. All others had to be discarded as potential troublemakers. Among 8 of the knobs retained there had been no confusions whatever, and 3 additional ones were sufficiently free from error to be included as satisfactory. These are the shapes one uses when maximal tactual discriminability between neighboring controls is desired.

This account of a particular wartime experiment and of the practical setting from which it developed can hardly do more than serve as an example to suggest the flavor of the problems and interests characterizing the field of human engineering and its stake in the human senses. It is to be presumed—and certainly is devoutly to be wished—that successes of the kind already achieved in the military milieu can be duplicated, even greatly extended, among more peaceful pursuits.

2

The Visual Stimulus
and the Eye

Of the several senses giving us information about things and events in the world around us, none is richer than the visual one. The eye is the most highly developed of our sense organs, being at once the most complex in structure and the mediator of the most elaborate of our experiences. It is because vision yields the most varied sensations, setting the pattern for many analogous phenomena in other departments of sense, that we do well to consider it first.

To appreciate fully the way in which visual sensations are initiated it is necessary to understand not only the manner of functioning of the eye but also the nature of the stimuli that operate upon it. The normal or *adequate* stimulus for vision is, of course, light, but other forms of energy, properly brought to bear upon the visual apparatus, can produce visual sensations. Press upon the eyeball, and diffusely patterned "luminous" patches are seen; apply a sufficiently strong galvanic current to the closed eyelid, completing the circuit through some other part of the body, and a pinkish white or bluish white "glow" is seen at the moment of contact. Thus light is not the only possible stimulus for vision, though nearly all visual experiences are generated through its action.

Physical Conceptions of Light. Light, as at present conceived by the physicist, is either a form of energy propagated by wave motion (undulatory theory) or it consists of a barrage of emissive particles (quantum theory). The two conceptions are struggling for ascendancy, and each view has its virtues and difficulties. Both "explain" a wide variety of phenomena and both are used, somewhat indiscriminately, in aiding fresh discoveries. Interpretation requires at one time the undulatory theory, at another the emissive concept. Especially is the quantum idea needed to account for the electrical properties of light, whereas the wave conception is needed for the phenomena

14

of light interference. Fortunately, it is not necessary for us to wait
·upon the final solution; consistency of a sort is accomplished by the
modern physicist, and translations from one to the other mode of
thinking are not only possible but common.

Light Sources. Sources of light are of two kinds: incandescent bodies
("hot" sources), and luminescent bodies ("cold" sources). Practical
sources for experimental purposes have, until recently, been almost
exclusively of the incandescent variety. The sun, some kinds of flames,
electric arcs, and most electric lamps are incandescent sources. In
general, this kind of light generator is highly wasteful of energy.
However, standardization of incandescent lamp equipment has reached
a high point of development, and convenience of operation favors its
use. Within recent years there have been seen the beginnings of the
practical use of luminescent sources but the possibilities of their application to experimental needs have hardly been explored as yet.
Light may be obtained from cathode rays (electroluminescence), from
crushing and rubbing certain materials (triboluminescence), from the
chemical activity basic to certain biological processes, e.g., the flashing
of fireflies (chemiluminescence), and from the action of short-wave
radiation upon "phosphorescent" and "fluorescent" materials. It is this
last sort of luminescence that offers the most immediate possibility of
widespread commercial usefulness. Fluorescent materials are those
that glow during activation; phosphorescence is an effect continuing
after the cessation of activation. The future will doubtless witness
important changes in the direction of more common use of luminescent
sources because their efficiency is so relatively high. The light output
from standard commercial fluorescent tubes is more than five times
that from corresponding tungsten filament lamps.

For many experiments in vision "daylight" is an ideal source. Light
from the sun is, of course, a natural standard, but only those observations that can be made relatively quickly can utilize this illuminant.
Not only are there likely to be wide intensive variations from moment
to moment, when reflected daylight is used, but the wavelength composition changes with the elevation of the sun. Inconstancies may be
minimized with "north" light and a moderately overcast sky; the illumination favored by artists is also the best for the laboratory. For
extended experiments involving repeated observations, especially those
of a quantitative sort, it is better to employ an artificial illuminant,
the characteristics of which will remain invariable throughout the experiment. Several such illuminants have become standard and are
used in the most careful visual research. They utilize suitably filtered

light from a lamp, the "color temperature" of which is specified. However, in most experiments reproducibility is assured if only the type of lamp and the power supplying it are known. One is ordinarily not so much interested in the source as in the illumination yielded by it, and this may be measured with accuracy.

The Visible Spectrum. Light waves of significance for vision occupy but a relatively short range of the total electromagnetic spectrum (Fig. 2). The entire range of radiations extends from the extremely

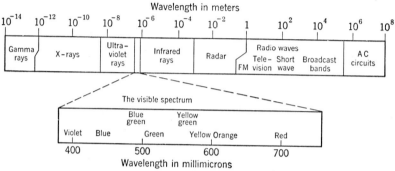

FIG. 2. The total electromagnetic spectrum. That portion of it normally affecting the eye, occupying a relatively narrow band of wavelengths, has been enlarged in the lower part of the diagram. From Chapanis, Garner, and Morgan, 57.

short cosmic rays (10 trillionths of an inch), at one end, to the long radio waves (many miles), at the other. Under usual conditions visual stimulation involves less than $\frac{1}{70}$ of this range, waves whose lengths vary from about 380 mμ (millimicrons, millionths of millimeters) to about 760 mμ. Below the shortest visible ("violet") waves lie the chemically active ultraviolet ones, and above the longest ("red") are the thermally active infrared waves. Nearly all light sources emit waves belonging to one or the other neighboring region or to both. Actually, under some special conditions, the eye is capable of responding to waves coming from the infrared and ultraviolet regions. Reliable measurements of visible light, involving very high energies, have extended into the ultraviolet to wavelength (λ) 312.5 mμ and into the infrared to λ1050 mμ. The calculation has been made (289, p. 129) that λ310 mμ and λ1150 mμ represent the approximate theoretical limits of light absorption by the eye, assuming presently available sources of radiation. To see a light of λ1000 mμ, say, there is required a source 10 billion times as strong as that needed to see a light of λ562 mμ.

While most visual objects send to the eye an elaborate mixture of waves of various length, it is possible with suitable apparatus to confine the waves to a narrow band and thus produce relatively "pure" stimuli. One way is to mask out all but a narrow wavelength band by the use of an adjustable slit placed over the spread-out spectrum. Spectrometers and monochromators employ this principle. Another method is to utilize filters which, by absorbing a great proportion of light incident to them, pass only a short range of waves. Such filters, made either of dye dissolved in glass or of colored gelatine films (ordinarily protected by optical glass), are said to be "monochromatic," though in any literal sense the term is obviously a misnomer. They are "monochromatic" only in the sense that a single color is seen when looking through them. Filters are available for many specific uses, and a wide range of transmission characteristics may be obtained.

Far more common than exposing the eye to light transmitted directly from the source is the practice, in visual experiments, of using reflected light as the stimulus. Light impinging on any object meets one of three fates: it is transmitted, absorbed, or reflected. Whatever is transmitted or reflected produces no change in the object. If the object absorbs *visible* light it is, by definition, a pigment. Colored papers and other pigmented surfaces, commonly used in visual experiments of a qualitative nature, owe their "color" to the fact that they selectively absorb light, reflecting those waves which, when sensed, yield sensations of color. It is vital that the concept of "color" be reserved for the sensation. Light, physically speaking, has no color; a color is not a color until it is seen. At the stimulus level we are dealing only with light waves which, to be sure, may vary among themselves in important respects, but color is not one of their physical properties.

Light Units. A physical dimension of light stimuli, of the utmost importance for our consideration, is that of intensity. The potential stimulating value of an object reflecting or transmitting light is in large measure determined by its intensity. There are four fundamental concepts concerned here: luminous *flux*, luminous *intensity* or candlepower, *illuminance*, and *luminance* or photometric brightness. Luminous flux, measured in units of *lumens*, is the basic concept, and the remaining three are defined in terms of it. Luminous flux is the rate of flow of light energy and is thus analogous to power in other energy systems. Since the rate of flow is constant, for practical purposes, luminous flux may be regarded as an entity which varies only in amount. The lumen, the unit of flux, is defined as the amount of light emitted in a unit solid angle by a standard candle. Thus the amount of light falling on an area of 1 m² situated 1 m distant from a standard candle (or an area of 1 ft² at a distance of 1 ft), would be 1 lumen. A point source of one candle emits a total flux of 4π lumens.

The intensity of a *source* is measured in candlepower, 1 candlepower being the intensity of the accepted "standard" candle. From time to time there have been in use many variously defined "candles," but current practice is based on the *international candle*, adopted by England, France, and America in 1909 and defined in terms of electrical consumption in a lamp.. Secondary standards are readily set up by matching the primary one, and it is convenient to refer to these. Incandescent lamps, calibrated by some certifying agency such as the National Bureau of Standards, constitute our actual "reference" standards, and "working" standards can be reproduced quite simply by the methods of photometry.

The concept of illuminance (illumination intensity) involves the idea of interception of light flux by a surface. Illuminance is measured in terms of the density of flux falling on a surface. There are several available illuminance units of which the *foot-candle* is perhaps the most commonly used. The foot-candle is defined as the illumination received on a surface 1 ft² in area when this surface is supplied by a uniformly distributed flux of 1 lumen. Most illuminometers, portable devices for measuring illuminance, are direct-reading in foot-candles. An important relation, the inverse square law, applies to illuminance. This states that illumination intensity is inversely proportional to the square of the distance from the source, E (ft-candles) $= I$ (candles)$/D^2$ (ft²). Knowing the intensity of the source in candlepower we may compute the illuminance at a given point, or, conversely, illuminance having been measured at a surface, the candlepower of the source may be calculated.

Ordinarily, we are less interested in specifying the intensity of illumination incident to an object than we are in stating the flux proceeding to the eye from a *unit area* of its surface. In the latter case the *luminance* (photometric brightness) of the surface is determined. Specifications of luminance are made in terms of candles per square centimeter. Numerical conversions into other units of luminance are possible, and there will be found in the literature of vision a veritable plethora of such units, including the lambert (lumens/cm²) and millilambert (0.001 lambert), the foot-lambert or apparent foot-candle, and many others. There is a somewhat common practice, in visual science, of expressing stimulus intensities in terms of actual illuminance of the retina, once the light has reached the eye and its amount has been cut down by the pupil. In such cases intensity is specified in terms of *trolands,* a troland being defined as a luminance of one candle per square meter passing through a pupil of 1 mm². This unit was formerly called the "photon," a designation which was perhaps unfortunate since the term has wide currency in physics, where it designates the ultimate and indivisible unit of visible radiation in the quantum theory of light. The context ordinarily keeps the two meanings apart, of course.

Photometry. Photometers, the instruments with which light intensity measurements are made, exist in a profusion of designs. How-

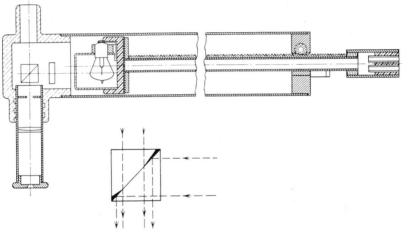

Fig. 3. Schematic diagram of the Macbeth Illuminometer. The little carriage housing the standard lamp may be moved back and forth with a rack and pinion, and thus, by utilizing the inverse square law of illuminance, there may be brought about an equation with the unknown light. The standard illuminates the outer field, the unknown the inner one. The Lummer-Brodhun cube, shown in the head of the instrument and enlarged in the lower diagram, makes possible juxtaposition of the two lights to be compared. Reproduced by courtesy of Leeds and Northrup, Philadelphia.

ever, many of them are basically similar in that they provide two or more neighboring fields of view which permit the direct comparison of two luminances, the unknown and a known standard (Fig. 3). The greatest accuracy in light measurement is associated with the use of the Lummer-Brodhun type of photometer, though there are several others only a little less sensitive. The Macbeth Illuminometer, a portable photometer using a Lummer-Brodhun cube, is perhaps the best known of the precision instruments for intensity measurement. Since the development of the generating type of photoelectric cell, there has been a wide application of this device to photometry. In visual photometry the eye can only tell us when two adjoining surfaces are equal, or approximately equal, in brightness. It cannot tell us directly *how* bright the surface is. Since the electrical output of a photocell is proportional to the intensity of light falling on it, a meter connected to the cell can be calibrated to read directly in foot-candles (or some other unit) of illuminance. However, as yet, visual photometry yields more delicate measures than does any photoelectric method.

Intensity Control. It is one thing to measure light intensities and another to control them in visual experiments. Several different principles may be used, however, to effect the necessary control. A simple expedient in changing light intensity is to vary the distance of the source, thus taking advantage of the inverse square law. However, more often than not, this method is inconvenient, and other devices have to be resorted to. If continuous or "smooth" variation is demanded, one may use diaphragms, "wedges," or polarization of light. If it is necessary only to alter intensity in gross steps, diffusion plates, sectored discs, or "neutral tint" filters are of value.

Since, in many optical systems, lenses are employed to direct, gather, or focus light, one simple way to vary the light flux is to insert in the system an adjustable diaphragm of the type used in cameras, preferably near a lens, since control is more critical at such a point. The optical wedge consists of a long strip of film, underexposed at one end and greatly overexposed at the other, there being a continuous graduation of density along its length. Suitably mounted in glass and supplemented by a small "balancing wedge" to cut down all parts of the light beam equally, it provides a convenient method of varying intensity over a wide range. A third device is the Nicol prism. Its use as a polarizer of light, and hence its employment in polarimeters, saccharimeters, and similar instruments, is familiar. Since, for visual purposes, it makes no difference whether light is vibrating in only one plane or in all, a pair of Nicol prisms ("polarizer" and "analyzer") in a light path can be used to vary light intensity smoothly. The recent development of polarizing sheets ("Polaroid") for the same purpose is useful, since the great disadvantage of the ordinary variety of Nicols is their small size.

For changing intensity in steps a simple method is to diffuse light, thus effectively losing a portion of it, by inserting in the light path one or more ground glass sheets or other uniform translucent material. An improvement is to employ variously exposed and developed photographic slides; the geometrical relations of an image being transmitted by the optical system are thus preserved. Ruled glass sheets of the type used by photoengravers are excellent as diffusion plates. Rotating sectored discs, driven at speeds sufficiently high to eliminate all perceptible flicker, are sometimes of service. A general relation, known as *Talbot's Law,* applies here. The brightness of a surface supplied by light passing through a rapidly rotated sectored disc is the same as it would be if it were illuminated by a beam whose intensity was the same fractional part of the original beam as the angular opening in the disc is of the total 360°. Thus a disc having open sectors totaling 180° will halve the intensity, one of 36° would transmit but 10% of the incident light, etc. A number of prepared discs which can be slipped on and off a motor shaft thus provide a readily reproducible series of intensities. Two such sectored discs, used together and capable of being locked together at any one of a variety of settings, comprise the so-called *episcotister.* This is especially useful where one wishes quickly to equate two intensities in photometry. Finally, "neutral tint" filters in a wide range of transmission values are commercially available. These, like wedges, are made of non-selective film and thus appear satisfactorily "gray," are housed between optically flat glass, and are extremely stable as to transmission. Combinations of such filters and optical wedges, in tandem, are especially useful.

There are other physical properties of light and features of its control that are advantageous to know about but which need not be discussed generally. We shall encounter some of them in their specific settings. It is important that we go on to consider the anatomical and physiological properties of the eye so that we may understand the bases of light reception by the organism.

The Gross Anatomy of the Eye. The structure of the eye has been frequently compared to that of a camera, and in a very general way the analogy is a sound one. Like the camera it admits light through an adjustable "diaphragm" and focuses images by means of a lens on a sensitive surface. But the details of the two differ in many important respects, and the human eye appears, upon detailed study, to be much more complex in construction and operation than the most elaborate camera ever conceived.

The main features of the eye's form and its chief components may be seen in Fig. 4. It will be noted that, in the main, three layers are present. The outer covering, the *sclera,* forms a tough, fibrous, protective coat for the delicate layers within. The cornea is continuous with the sclerotic coat but, being transparent, forms one of the refracting media of the eye. Loosely attached to the sclera and forming the second of the layers is the *choroid*, consisting largely of blood vessels freely interlaced with each other. The choroid is the great nutritive structure of the eyeball, but in addition it contains brownish black pigment cells, probably important in light reception. The choroid becomes modified in the front of the eye to form the iris. The innermost layer, the *retina*, is of utmost importance for our consideration, since it is the retina that contains the terminations of the optic

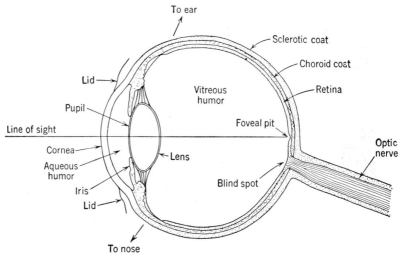

FIG. 4. Gross structure of the human eye. From Judd, *Color in business, science, and industry*. New York: Wiley, 1952.

nerve and hence is the locus of light reception. The retina extends nearly as far forward as the ciliary body, the latter composed largely of muscular tissue and situated at the junction of the iris and choroid.

The *crystalline lens* of the eye, a remarkable body whose shape may change and thus have its focal length altered, is attached to the ciliary body by ligaments. The lens is completely encased within a membranous capsule, and tension exerted on the capsule by the ciliary muscle brings about a change of curvature, more especially of the anterior surface, which is at all times less rounded than the posterior surface. The space between the front of the lens and the cornea is filled with a dilute salty solution, the aqueous humor ("watery substance,") while the great bulk of the eyeball, the space between the back of the lens and the retina, is composed of transparent vitreous humor ("glassy substance"). The latter gives "body" to the eyeball and preserves its nearly spherical shape.

The *iris* has important properties for vision. The tissue comprising it is largely muscular, one set of muscle cells being arranged circularly to make a "sphincter," the other set forming radial muscles which, when they contract, enlarge the central opening of the iris, the *pupil.* The two sets of muscles are thus mutually opposed in their action and, at any moment, represent a fine balance of forces. Because the iris muscles are both directly and indirectly connected with many parts of the nervous system, pupil reactions come to be of special symptomatic interest. Pupil responses can reveal not only certain events within the eye itself but may serve to indicate quite remote happenings in the body.

The pupil opening determines the amount of light flux that will fall on the retina and is capable of a considerable range of adjustment. Its major response is a reflex one, controlled almost exclusively by the sense cells situated at and near the center of the retina (50). When bright light strikes the retina the pupil may be constricted to an opening of less than 2 mm diameter. In the absence of light the pupil may dilate to over 8 mm diameter. Such a change represents about a seventeenfold increase in the area of the opening. The pupil is thus a primary determiner of the effective stimulus at the retina and, since its response is a prompt one, serves as an emergency device to help bring about an adjustment of the organism to fluctuations in light intensity (243).

Two other features of the gross anatomy of the eye are important. One is the occurrence of a small indentation at the back of the eye known as the *fovea centralis.* The fovea has special functional properties which we shall have occasion to consider. The other area to be noted is the colliculus or *optic disc,* situated about 3 mm to the nasal side and 1 mm below the fovea. Here the nerve fibers from all parts of the retina are collected and leave the eye as a bundle, the second cranial or *optic nerve.* Functionally, the area of exit is known as the "blind spot" because no nerve terminations exist here and there is no way whereby incident light may become effective.

The Structure of the Retina. The larger picture of the eye, then, is of three coats or layers: the sclera (protective), the choroid (nutritive), and the retina (sensitive). The retina must now be considered somewhat more intimately. Figure 5 shows, in schematic form, the plan of the retina. It is seen to have a somewhat complicated structure, though not an unintelligible one. The first fact to note is that two different types of nerve endings are present, *cones* and *rods,* so named from their conical and cylindrical tips. The next is that they are oriented away from the source of light, the front of the eye, their tips pointing toward the choroid. It is for this reason that the human eye, in common with the eyes of other vertebrates, is said to have an "inverted" retina. A third general feature concerns the type of connection the cones and rods make with the fibers of the optic

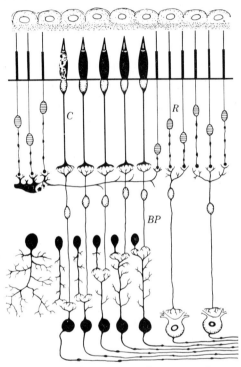

FIG. 5. Detailed structure of the retina. The cones, *C*, are connected individually to bipolar cells, *BP*, while the rods, *R*, show multiple connection. From Detwiler, 78. By permission of the editor, *American Scientist*.

nerve. By and large each cone connects, through a bipolar cell, with its own optic nerve fiber. This is invariably the case with foveal cones. Rods, on the other hand, are said to be connected molecularly; i.e., several of them impinge upon a single bipolar. The innervation of the cones would thus seem to favor discreteness of response of the single elements, while the lateral connections of the rods make for cooperative action among them. The cones of the human eye vary in length between 0.028 and 0.085 mm, and, over most of the retina, they vary in width between 0.0025 and 0.0075 mm. Rods are 0.040 to 0.060 mm long but have an average width of only 0.002 mm.

Rods and cones are not haphazardly distributed throughout the retina. At the center of the retina, the fovea centralis, there can be found only cones. In that region the cones are tightly packed together and, in consequence, are longer and thinner (0.001 mm) at the fovea than elsewhere. In fact, were there not so many proofs to the contrary, we should suppose from their appearance that they were rods.

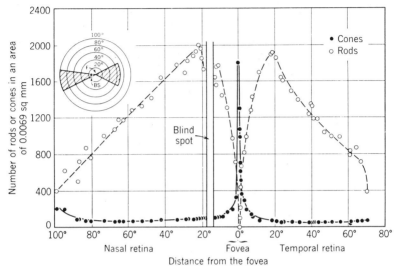

FIG. 6. Distribution of rods and cones throughout the retina. The number of end organs per unit area from the fovea to the extreme periphery has been plotted. Cones are represented by solid, rods by open, circles. The inset shows the regions sampled by Østerberg (225) in obtaining the counts. From Chapanis, 56. Courtesy of the National Research Council and the author.

The fovea itself is of very small area, subtending an angle of but 1.5°. Surrounding the fovea, and including the fovea within it, is a larger area likewise devoid of rods. This is the *macula lutea* ("yellow spot"), so called because of its appearance when viewed through an ophthalmoscope. The macula subtends about a 3° angle. Just outside the macula, rods begin to put in their appearance, and as one goes further into the periphery of the retina the population of rods becomes progressively denser. The concentration of cones falls off rapidly just outside the macula and, at a distance of about 20° from the fovea, reaches a low value which remains fairly constant throughout the rest of the periphery. There has been only one careful count of retinal rods and cones and that in only a single human. In 1935, Østerberg took the tally, examining 164 different sample areas of the retina (225). The plot of his findings appears in Fig. 6; the shaded area of the inset shows where the counts were made.

In the human retina there are about 6½ million cones and upward of 100 million rods. In any given area of the retina the number of functioning end organs (under a specified set of stimulus conditions) determines the fineness of detail that can be seen, just as in the photographic plate the intimacy of detail in the picture depends on fineness of "grain" in the emulsion. Whereas, on the average, there are 140,000 to 160,000 cones per square millimeter in the human retina, it must be that not all are functioning at one time except under conditions of maximal stimulation. Otherwise variations in light intensity would not bring with them corresponding changes in the acuteness of seeing.

Rods and cones differ from each other not only in anatomy and distribution; chemical differences between them are known to exist. Either contained within them or closely associated with rods is a material known as *rhodopsin* or "visual purple." The characteristics of rhodopsin are by now well known, since it may be extracted from the vertebrate retina and used experimentally. Visual purple is found to be sensitive to all but dim red light and will bleach when exposed to light from all other parts of the spectrum. Its absorption curve has been determined, and its bleaching properties correspond well with those predicted from a knowledge of the behavior of rods in the visual process. Rhodopsin has been subjected to a careful chemical analysis and is found to be one of the so-called conjugated carotenoid proteins and, like all similar substances, has a large molecule. A recent determination shows rhodopsin to have a molecular weight of 45,600.

The material of the cones has not been isolated as yet, but its existence has been amply demonstrated. There are good reasons for believing that it is also a carotenoid protein. It has been given the name *iodopsin* or "visual violet" by its discoverer, George Wald.

The Optic Nerve Pathway. There remains for consideration the course taken by the optic nerve as it leaves the eyeball and proceeds to the brain. The bundles of fibers from the two eyes converge to join and apparently cross at the *optic chiasma* (from the Greek *chi,* a cross). But the complete crossing is only apparent. At the chiasma there occurs instead a half-crossing, or hemidecussation, one part of the fibers crossing to the opposite side of the brain, the other continuing on its own side. The fibers which cross over in each optic nerve are those originating in the inner half of the retina. The effect of this arrangement is to include in the right optic tract, behind the chiasma, all fibers coming from the right halves of the two retinae.

Fibers from the left halves terminate in the left side of the brain. Beyond the chiasma the fibers proceed to the thalamus and terminate chiefly in the lateral geniculate body of that center. Other fibers, arising at this point and connecting with the optic nerve fibers, convey impulses to the occipital lobes of the cerebrum.

In the main, there is a preservation of an anatomical point-to-point conduction in the entire pathway. Pathological studies and especially nerve degeneration experiments on animals (195) prove this to be the case. Distinctly favored, in the entire scheme, are the fibers coming from the central portions of the two retinae. It appears that the macular region either has special representation in the brain or it sends fibers to both hemispheres. The point is still disputed, but it is definitely known that, in those brain injuries where an entire occipital lobe is put out of commission, the resulting damage to the visual field, oftener than not, spares the macula.

The consequences of this arrangement of fibers for interpretation of visual phenomena are many. The design of the optic pathways must be kept in mind in the setting of visual experiments. Light stimuli impinging on corresponding points of the two eyes must release optic nerve impulses that find a common final path, while those from opposite sides of the retinae presumably cannot do so.

3

Basic Visual Phenomena

The Absolute Threshold. Light may be thrown into the eye at such a low level of energy as to produce no detectable response on the part of the visual apparatus. A general phenomenon, encountered in all sense departments, is that of the threshold; a certain minimum amount of energy must be delivered to the sense organ before sensation can be aroused. This value is known as the *absolute* or *stimulus threshold*.

Of what order is the minimum energy necessary to elicit a visual sensation? This question has been raised experimentally many times, and several answers are available. However, a set of determinations by Hecht and his co-workers (*159*) is superior to earlier ones, with respect to both technique of measurement and control of the several complicating factors encountered in such experiments. A small patch of light, of variable intensity but of constant wavelength composition, was thrown into the eye so as to fall on a small area, containing perhaps 500 rods, situated outside the macula. The exposure time was held constant at 0.001 second (1 msec). In successive trials the intensity was varied with an optical wedge, and the observer's task was simply that of reporting whether or not the light flash was seen. Over a large series of trials the average intensity necessary to produce a just visible flash was determined. From the intensive measurement the liminal energy was calculated. This value varied from 21 to 57 hundred billionths of an erg in different observers, extremely small values indeed. Not all the light emitted by the test patch was effective, of course, and a series of corrections had to be applied. A small amount, about 4%, was lost through reflection back from the surface of the cornea and another 50% was lost by scattering through the optic media of the eyeball, while perhaps 80% of the remainder failed to be absorbed by the rhodopsin of the rods. Cones, as we shall see later, presumably did not participate in such low-intensity reactions. Allowance being made for all these, it turns out that the effective light energy

28

at the threshold is of the order of a few hundred billionths of an erg. Stated otherwise and in terms of quantum calculations, it appears that between 5 and 14 light quanta (average of 7) are necessary to stimulate the visual organ. Assuming each rod to act when a single quantum is absorbed, it must require the release of but 1 molecule of rhodopsin in each of only 7 rods to initiate a visual effect. From these measurements an important conception may be reached. The visual apparatus is apparently tuned to the highest possible degree consistent with the nature of light energy. If man's eyes were much more sensitive to light than they are the "shot effect" in photon emission would be perceived, and "steady" light would no longer appear steady! A similar state of affairs obtains in hearing, as we shall see: if man's ears were any better attuned they would be assailed by noises coming from the "dance of the molecules" in the very air in which he lives.

Cast in terms of luminance, rather than energy units, the absolute threshold for vision in the peripheral part of the field is about 0.000001 millilamberts. The precise value varies with the size of the stimulus and the location of the retinal area on which it falls. It also varies with the duration of the stimulus, but for the present we are considering relatively long exposures rather than short flashes. A light spot projected on the macula and filling it would require a luminance ten thousand times as great, or about 0.01 millilambert, to reach threshold.

The Differential Threshold. If we begin with an illumination just sufficient to stimulate, i.e., with threshold intensity, and determine the increment of intensity (ΔI) necessary to increase the seen brightness by the least perceptible amount, we shall have passed through a distance on the intensive scale corresponding to a "just noticeable difference" (j.n.d.). The experiment is performed by the use of a divided light field, the two parts of which are capable of independent manipulation. Either a field presenting a bisected disc or two concentric fields (a so-called disc-annulus arrangement) may be used. Obviously any other intensity, except that yielding maximum brightness, may be taken as a starting point and ΔI determined. If the initial intensity on one side of the field is designated I and the just noticeably different intensity on the other is called $I + \Delta I$, we should find that the ratio $\Delta I/I$ would vary in a systematic way over the range of visible intensities. The Weber fraction, $\Delta I/I$, was originally thought to be a constant one ("Weber's Law"). It is roughly so for the middle ranges of illuminations but deviates very considerably at the two ends of the scale. At the lowest intensities the fraction is nearly $\frac{1}{1}$, while at the highest intensities it decreases to as little as $\frac{1}{167}$.

The first extensive determinations of the relation of $\Delta I/I$ to I were those made by Koenig and Brodhun in 1888. Since that time there have been many remeasurements of ΔI, and several factors influencing the function in one direction or another have been isolated and studied.

Among the best-controlled of such experiments are those of Smith (*264*) and Steinhardt (*267*). The latter's curves connecting $\Delta I/I$ and

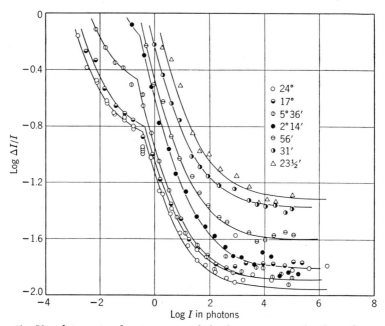

FIG. 7. Visual intensity discrimination of the human eye. The dependence of $\Delta I/I$ on intensity of illumination, for seven different sizes of test field, is shown on a double logarithmic plot. From Steinhardt, *267*. By permission of the Rockefeller Institute for Medical Research and the author.

I, for several different sizes of test field, are given in Fig. 7. For convenience in scaling both variables have been plotted in logarithmic units. Were Weber's Law to hold rigidly, all lines connecting the points in the figure should be straight; that they are far from such, and that, moreover, they show some interesting regular deviations is obvious. One irregularity that should especially pique our curiosity is that occurring at relatively low intensities in the curves for the larger area test fields and giving a jointed appearance to the function.

Duality of the Receptive Process. A distinction, based upon anatomical differences and distribution, has already been made between rods and cones. That the two types of end organs actually subserve different visual functions as well seems certain. On the basis of studies made by him on the vertebrate retina, Max Shultze in 1866 came to the important conclusion that the eye is not one sense organ, but two. The notion remained neglected for some years but was found useful by Parinaud (1881) to account for certain pathological phenomena of vision, notably night blindness. He restated at that time the "theory of the double retina." The idea gained wide currency only when von Kries, in 1895, brought together a variety of evidences pointing to duality of the receptive process. Since his time we have spoken of the "duplicity" or "duplexity" theory of vision. Rods function differentially at low intensities only and initiate colorless sensations; cones operate at higher intensities and are responsible for sensations of color.

It is interesting that the evidence first advanced for a duplex visual sense, the anatomical, should now be the least convincing proof we have. Indeed, further histological examination of the retina reveals a diversity of structure not originally suspected. Because there are to be found in the retina sense cells that are "rod-like" but not true rods and others that are merely "cone-like," some scientists have gone so far as to deny the validity of the duplicity theory (288). However, the distinction between rods and cones is commonly supported by histologists, and there are well-known characteristic differences between the two.

But, even if anatomy did not clearly demand a duplex retina, there can be no doubt that other considerations definitely do. Perhaps the most convincing evidence is that, at different levels of illumination, the retina possesses two distinct sets of absorption characteristics. These are revealed in *spectral visibility curves* of which there are two separate ones for the normal human eye. The curve obtained for a high-intensity spectrum is known as the *photopic* or "daylight" curve, that for a very dim spectrum as the *scotopic* or "twilight" curve. A high-intensity spectrum appears to the eye colored; if the intensity is lowered beyond a certain point the spectrum is still seen, but as colorless. A landscape viewed at dusk presents the same appearance. As twilight pervades the scene colored objects first lose their brilliance, then become hueless. As a folk saying has it, "At night all cats are gray."

Photopic visibility curves are obtained by measuring the relative energy in different spectral regions needed to produce a match with a standard high brightness. The classic measurements are those made at the National Bureau of Standards by Gibson and Tyndall (118) on some 50 observers. Maximum visibility is realized at $\lambda 555$ mμ in the greenish yellow part of the spectrum. Scotopic visibility curves are obtained by a method similar to that used for photopic curves except that the brightness to be matched is very close to the absolute threshold. The best measures here are those of Hecht and Williams

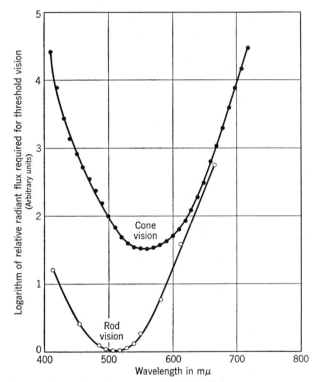

FIG. 8. Photopic (cone) and scotopic (rod) visibility curves compared. The relative amounts of energy needed to reach absolute threshold as a function of wavelength. The cone curve is derived from the data of Gibson and Tyndall (*118*); the rod curve, from those of Hecht and Williams (*160*). From Chapanis, *56*. Courtesy of the National Research Council and the author.

(*160*). As compared with the photopic one, the low-intensity curve shows a shift toward the short wavelength (violet) end of the spectrum. The scotopic maximum is at λ510 mμ in what appears photopically as the green region. The measurements entering into both photopic and scotopic curves are very accurate, and there is no possibility of confusing the two. Curves combining the two sets of data are shown in Fig. 8.

Thus far it has only been demonstrated that there are two sets of visibility functions. But, fortunately, identification of one set with the operation of the rods can be made. As we have seen, rhodopsin can be extracted and its absorption determined. Many such measurements have been made, and the best of them demonstrate unequivocally that the scotopic curve is that belonging to the rods. Thus far "visual violet," the substance of the cones, has not yielded to similar treatment, but it may be confidently predicted that the photopic curve will describe its absorption. There are complications here, for it is quite probable that the photopic curve is the sum of at least three slightly different curves. When we come to the question of color theory we shall see the wisdom of thinking in terms of more than one cone substance.

There are several other facts that fit into the picture of photopic and scotopic vision. Since twilight vision involves only the rods, it should be true that the central part of the retina is incapable of being stimulated by very dim light. Such proves to be the case; a *central scotoma* or blind macula is present in dim illumination of the retina. A simple way to test for its presence is to attempt to search out a very dim star at night. If one looks at it directly, i.e., with its image falling on the fovea, it will disappear from view. The French physicist, Arago, gave this advice: "Pour apercevoir un objet très peu lumineux, il faut ne pas le regarder."

Another phenomenon, known for over a century, demands the rod-cone distinction. If two quite different colors are matched for brightness at high intensity, then are compared under low illumination, it will be found that the match no longer holds. The same is true for an intensity change in the reverse direction. Colors at the red end of the spectrum drop precipitously to black, as light energy is reduced, while those at the violet end lose brilliance more gradually. This effect is known as the *Purkinje phenomenon*. It is, of course, entirely consistent with the direction of shift of the visibility curves in passing from daylight to twilight vision. Moreover, the Purkinje phenomenon cannot be demonstrated within the rod-free macula. In all other parts of the eye a "colored" light is seen at the absolute threshold as colorless; then as the intensity is gradually raised and the light appears brighter, a point is finally reached where color is seen. This happens when the cone threshold has been passed. The point of acquisition of color differs for various wavelengths and retinal areas; for white light the abrupt change to cone vision occurs at a brightness of about 0.003 candle/ft². When colored light is used, the intensity range over which only gray is seen, i.e., the distance between the rod and cone thresholds, is known as the *photochromatic interval*. As would be predicted from the relative positions of the photopic and scotopic visibility curves, the photochromatic interval is small in the red part of the spectrum and relatively large in the violet.

Evidences from comparative anatomy and the behavior of lower organisms also support the idea of duplexity. In general, it is the case that nocturnal animals, such as rats and mice, bats, certain lizards (e.g., the gecko), and birds that migrate only at night possess either pure rod retinae or have a great preponderance of rods. Those animals which have only cones, such as the pigeon, hen, and other "day birds," as well as the turtle and the majority of other reptiles, have strictly diurnal habits. Forms of vertebrates which, like man, possess a double retina show two visibility curves, one for low illuminations, another for high. Fish are known to have both rods and cones, and in them the Purkinje shift has been demonstrated.

A final line of proof comes from abnormalities of vision. Hemeralopia or "night blindness" is a condition in which, under dim illuminations, vision is poor. It may be so incapacitating as to prevent its sufferer from getting about at night. Apparently there are two different forms, one congenital and permanent, the other temporary and due to vitamin A deficiency. Measurements of spectral visibility on nightblind individuals reveal their eyes to have lost one-half their dual function. The remaining one yields the typical high-intensity cone visibility curve. "Day blindness" also exists, though it is of rare occurrence. The symptom most obviously present is total color blindness, and it is in connection with the latter difficulty that such cases are usually investigated. The visibility curves of a few totally color-blind individuals have been determined, and, even though the measurements be made at relatively high brightness, the function is clearly that belonging to the rods. In fact, the agreement with the scotopic visibility curve of Hecht and Williams is extremely close (see Fig. 28).

A backward glance at the origins and development of the idea of the dual function of the retina makes one wonder why we should now speak of the *theory* of duplicity. It was a "theory" at the turn of the century; now we should do well to treat it as established fact. In the light of it a number of things become explicable. For one, there is the peculiar "break" in the intensity discrimination data, already noted. Obviously there are two branches of the curve, a low-intensity rod portion mediating the lowest 30 j.n.d.'s, and a high-intensity cone section covering upwards of 500 such steps. For areas involving more than the pure cone macula it would be surprising if the transition from one to the other did not occur. And there are other phenomena demanding similar interpretation, as we shall see.

Adaptation. It was noted earlier that the pupil serves as an emergency device, reflexly controlling to a considerable degree the amount of light striking the retina. But there is another, slower-acting but fully as important, means of bringing the retina into equilibrium with the environment. Under stimulation by light the retina progressively loses its sensitivity and in the absence of light recovers it. The process occurring in the presence of light is known as *light adaptation* or retinal fatigue; the reverse change is called *dark adaptation*. The range of response due to adaptation is very extensive. After a stay in the dark

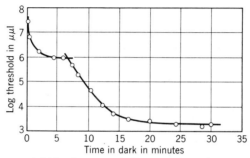

FIG. 9. The course of dark adaptation following a high level of light adaptation. The first section of the curve is for the cones, the second for the rods. The test light was restricted to the short waves, below λ460 mμ, and appeared violet to the cones. Threshold values are in micromicrolamberts ($\mu\mu$l). From Hecht and Shlaer, *158*. By permission of the editor, *Journal of the Optical Society of America*, and Dr. Shlaer.

of a half-hour's duration the retina may become responsive to light of only 1/100,000 the intensity originally necessary to stimulate it.

Dark adaptation has been known since its first description by Aubert in 1865. The earliest measurements were those of Piper, in 1903, who set the pattern for such experiments by determining the absolute threshold after various periods in the dark. Piper spoke of the "two phases" of dark adaptation, an initial rapid stage followed by a slower one, but incorrectly ascribed the entire process to the rods. Considering the eye as a whole, it is true that the most extended sensitivity change is due to rod adaptation. The cones do adapt, however, though they do so relatively rapidly and their range of adjustment is not nearly as extensive as that of the rods. Excellent modern measurements of dark adaptation are available. Figure 9 shows a set of measures obtained with the "adaptometer." The first section of the curve is for the cones. The test light was restricted by a filter to waves below λ460 mμ and appeared violet. The larger segment results from rod adaptation, and, though the same test light was used in procuring it, no color could be seen. Again we have the fact of the dual retina evidenced.

The form of any curve representing the course of dark adaptation is determined by several different variables, and any particular curve is the result of a group of specific conditions. The important variables are: (1) *Size and location of the retinal area tested.* A small field (1–2 degrees) situated centrally can obviously possess only the cone section, while the larger or more peripheral the test field, the more will the rods be involved. A large field, the center of which is fixated, will naturally show both branches. (2) *The wavelength composition of the test light.* With extreme red light, to which rods are quite insensitive, only the cone portion appears. As the wavelength is shifted towards the violet the rod section becomes increasingly more prominent and appears earlier. (3) *The duration of the test light.* Intensity and time operate reciprocally in threshold measurements. Below a "critical duration" the Roscoe-Bunsen Law, $I \times t = K$, holds. This relation, also known as the "reciprocity law" and the "photographic law" (because of its application to the behavior of film emulsions), results in very brief exposures giving high threshold values as compared with those yielded by longer ones. (4) *The intensity of the pre-adapting light.* If the eye has been previously adapted to a very bright light the cone section will be extensive, and the rod portion may not appear as a separate branch for a considerable time in the dark. The less bright the pre-adapting light, the sooner does the rod branch appear. If the pre-adapting light is dim enough the cone section may be suppressed entirely. In all determinations of dark adaptation curves the pre-exposure brightness must, therefore, be specified. (5) *The duration of the pre-exposure.* The longer the pre-exposure, within limits, the greater will be the "fatigue" and, therefore, the more prominent will be the cone segment.

One detail of the dark adaptation process merits special attention. Some evidence exists for dual rates of dark adaptation, quite apart from the typically different properties of the rods and cones in this respect. Data obtained by Wald and Clark (*290*) show that exposure of the eye to a brief, intense, pre-adapting light is followed by a rapid dark adaptation process, whereas long pre-exposure results in a relatively slow rate of dark adaptation. This phenomenon suggests that rhodopsin, which presumably is broken down during light adaptation and restored during dark adaptation, may be synthesized in two different ways. Photochemical studies tell us that this is indeed the case. Rhodopsin is rapidly resynthesized from retinene, into which it **is** changed when light acts on it, but is only slowly formed from vitamin A, a reduction product of retinene.

All the experimental facts point to "light" and "dark" adaptation as obverse processes. It is well to think of adaptation this way. At any given moment there is either an equilibrium at some point on the dark-light adaptation scale or a progression from one point to another on it. The eye is either "adapted" to the illumination to which it is exposed or is in process of becoming so.

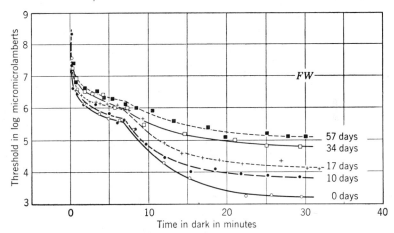

FIG. 10. Effect on dark adaptation of avitaminosis A of various durations. From Hecht and Mandelbaum, *156*. Courtesy of the American Physiological Society.

Recently there has been evinced much interest in dark adaptation data as a result of the discovery that variations in the curves may be associated with deficiencies of vitamin A. Subjects put on a diet deficient in this necessary food element show, more often than not, a rise in threshold at all points of both the cone and rod portions of the curve. Some of the changes are quite extreme. Figure 10 shows the progressive raising of thresholds at all levels of dark adaptation for one subject having experimental avitaminosis A. This subject showed the most severe alteration of 17 people studied by Hecht and Mandelbaum (*156*). That the effect was specific to vitamin A is attested by the fact that the daily diet was supplemented by plentiful quantities of all other vitamins. In some starved subjects, a single large dose of vitamin A was sufficient to lower thresholds measurably, though complete recovery was a matter of weeks and months in all cases. The clinical value of this discovery is obvious. Even a single threshold measure taken after, say, 20 or 30 minutes of dark adaptation may reveal a diet deficiency, once the "norms" have been adequately established.

The course of light adaptation can be ascertained by any of several techniques. The obverse of the method used in measuring dark adaptation is one possibility. After varying periods of exposure to light and with a return to complete dark adaptation between trials, the absolute threshold can be determined and the decline in sensitivity charted. This is the technique used originally by Lohmann (163, p. 324) and, more recently, by Wald and Clark (290). The drop in sensitivity, as revealed by such measures, is most rapid in the first few seconds, then progressively slower for many minutes. Depending on light intensity, the adaptation process seems to continue on for a period ranging from 10 to 80 min. This method possesses one inherent defect. To measure the absolute threshold it is, of course, necessary to extinguish the adapting stimulus. Then, some time is required to make the threshold determination; meanwhile, the light-adapted retinal area has undergone some dark adaptation. Since dark adaptation is most rapid at the onset of the process, the error of measurement introduced by this circumstance may be very considerable.

Another, and somewhat more direct, approach to the problem can be made by "fatiguing" one area of the retina with a known intensity of light for a definite period, then quickly effecting a brightness match by means of a comparison light falling in an unfatigued area. The selection of a suitable array of adaptation times will reveal the course of the process for the intensity used. Such measures were made by von Kries, with the crude apparatus then available, as early as 1877. More extensive determinations have been made by the author (107), and these, in turn, have been repeated by Wallace (291, 292, 293). Representative results for macular cone adaptation, taken from Wallace's work, are shown in Fig. 11. As the adapting light continues to act, the retinal area under stimulation loses more and more sensitivity until, after perhaps a minute's fatigue, an equilibrium point is reached. The amount of loss, while very considerable under all conditions of stimulation, is found to be a function of the intensity of the adapting light; the higher the intensity, the greater the relative loss in brilliance. It is noteworthy that the course of light adaptation, as revealed by the comparison light technique, seems to have run to completion within a relatively short period of time. Whatever the initial light intensity, a 3-min interval would appear to be sufficient to accommodate the process. This result contrasts sharply with that obtained by the "instantaneous threshold" method, which shows an hour or more to be necessary to reach a final equilibrium state (154). Whether this discrepancy can be attributed solely to differences of method is a question not yet resolved.

To complicate matters, a third and more recently devised technique, that introduced by Baker (*16*), yields a somewhat different kind of result. This method utilizes ΔI as a measure of sensitivity. As light adaptation proceeds, a small increment of luminance is periodically

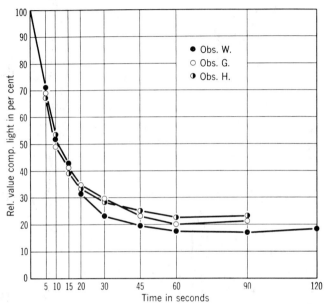

FIG. 11. Light adaptation of the cones. The course of the sensitivity loss resulting from steady illumination of the macula has been charted with the aid of the comparison light technique, the measuring light being thrown into the unfatigued eye. The three observers are obviously in close agreement. From Wallace, *291*. Permission of the Journal Press.

flashed into the adapting area. The size of the increment is systematically varied until ΔI has been determined for a long series of adaptation times. It is found that sensitivity improves (ΔI gets smaller!) throughout the first 3 min of light adaptation, then declines slowly to a level intermediate between this and that of the original dark-adapted state. It is clear that different measures of sensitivity give different pictures of the adaptation process. Just as there are many dark adaptation curves, each representing a particular combination of experimental conditions, there are many curves of light adaptation, each having clear meaning only insofar as the operations performed in establishing it have been defined unambiguously.

It would be difficult to conceive of a process of greater fundamental importance to sensory psychophysiology than is adaptation. The phenomenon is a very general one, occurring in all the sense departments. Moreover, it reveals the basic mode of action of the sense organ. It is not surprising, therefore, that the interpretation put upon adaptation determines, in large measure, the direction any theory of vision will take. We cannot, at this point, review the many conflicting conceptions, but we shall have to bear in mind that adaptation must be accounted for in a satisfactory manner if visual theory is not to remain pale and incomplete.

Hue Discrimination. We have seen that the eye is capable not only of utilizing very small physical energies but of making fine distinctions between intensities. Another aspect of the physical stimulus calling for discriminatory response on the part of the eye is that of wavelength.

At the extremely long wave end of the spectrum the normal eye sees red (in photopic vision). Progressing through the spectrum there is seen successively orange (about $\lambda 610$ mμ), yellow ($\lambda 580$ mμ), green ($\lambda 510$mμ), blue ($\lambda 470$ mμ), and violet ($\lambda 420$ mμ), as well as a large number of intermediate hues. Some of these we name, such as yellow-green and blue-green; for others, occurring less familiarly, we have no adequate common designations.

It should be said straightway that the correspondence between wavelength and visible hue is not an entirely constant one. Hue is partially determined by intensity. Except for certain invariable points in the spectrum all colors, upon being brightened, shift slightly towards either yellow or blue. This phenomenon is known as the *Bezold-Brücke effect*. If the brightness of a red of $\lambda 660$ mμ is reduced from 2000 to 100 trolands it becomes necessary to decrease wavelength by 34 mμ to maintain the original hue. A green of $\lambda 525$ mμ calls for an increase of 21 mμ under the same conditions. These are extreme examples, but some such adjustment is needed for most colors. Three spectral points, $\lambda 572$ mμ (yellow), $\lambda 503$ mμ (green), and $\lambda 478$ mμ (blue), are "invariable" ones, displaying no apparent alteration at all. In addition, there is a specific mixture of long and short waves (purple, lying outside the spectrum) which is likewise uninfluenced by brightness change (237, 238). Figure 12 shows a set of constant hue contours.

What is the capacity of the eye to detect small changes in wavelength? In raising the same question for intensity discrimination we were interested in seeing the size of ΔI and in determining in what systematic way the size of ΔI varied. Now we need to know the magnitude of $\Delta \lambda$.

If we throw into both sides of a bisected field red light of $\lambda700$ mμ, then change one side by gradually shifting the wavelength downward, we shall arrive at a point where the two hues, the original red and the new slightly orange-red, can be distinguished in hue. As with intensive changes, we shall have passed through one j.n.d., in this case equivalent

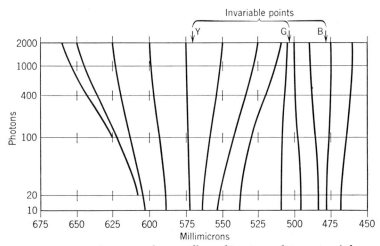

FIG. 12. Contours of constant hue. All combinations of intensity (photons = trolands) and wavelength lying along a given contour appear to be of the same hue. Three spectral points, $\lambda572$ mμ (yellow), $\lambda503$ mμ (green), and $\lambda478$ mμ (blue) yield constant hue regardless of intensity. All other points are subject to variations in accordance with the Bezold-Brücke phenomenon. From Purdy, 238. Courtesy of the *American Journal of Psychology*.

to $\Delta \lambda$. The first step, according to the determinations of Jones (*174*), will be 22 mμ in length. If the two sides of the field are again equated (at $\lambda678$ mμ) and the next j.n.d. measured, it will this time cover a distance of but 13 mμ. In the passage through the spectrum in this manner, it will be found that 128 j.n.d.'s will be traversed, some discriminable differences· being but 1 mμ and most of them less than 3 mμ in length. The size of $\Delta \lambda$ in various parts of the spectrum can be read from Fig. 13. The function is seen to be a complex one and to have several inversions in it. It should be added that, whereas these measures represent excellent technique, other sets of data, equally good (*194, 266*), show relatively large individual differences among observers possessing normal color vision. The *form* of the function is well established, however.

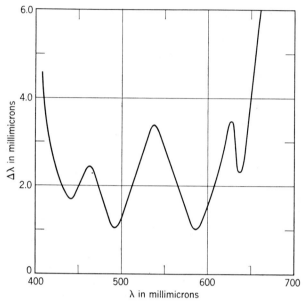

Fɪɢ. 13. Wavelength discrimination by the human eye. The change in wavelength which can be just detected ($\Delta\lambda$) is plotted as a function of wavelength (λ). The data are from Jones, *174*.

Saturation Discrimination. Besides intensity and wavelength, still a third aspect of spectral light can be discriminated. This is the *purity* or *saturation* of the color yielded by it. We commonly speak of spectral red and blue as saturated colors and orange, yellow, and yellow-green as unsaturated. Saturation has been defined as "that attribute of all colors possessing a hue which determines their degree of difference from a gray of the same brightness." Saturation is thus a third variable in color experience; it may be thought of as the relative absence of grayness in colors. The most direct measurements are those of Jones and Lowry (*175*), who stepped off j.n.d.'s of saturation along eight different hue lines, all intersecting at a gray of the same brightness. The least saturation was found in yellow ($\lambda575$ mμ), where but 16 j.n.d.'s could be found. Red of $\lambda680$ mμ and violet of $\lambda440$ mμ each gave 23 steps, and other colors were intermediate. Much the same relation between wavelength and the number of saturation steps comes from the less direct but more detailed study of "colorimetric purity" by Priest and Brickwedde (*236*).

Electrical Signs of Visual Activity. Our world of visual objects is describable in several dimensions, as we have seen. The phenomena thus far considered are, for the most part, concerned with the more fundamental of them, such dimensions as brightness, hue, and saturation. The data on these are available to direct observation, and we obtain them directly, or at least only as indirectly as the rules of laboratory experimentation require.

There are other ways of obtaining valuable basic information about visual processes, however. Instead of dealing directly with the end product of the visual mechanism's action, the visual perception, we may study the various physiological and neural events underlying it. By taking successive cross sections, so to speak, of the retinal and nervous precursors to central excitation we may hope to gain some insights as to how the direct observational data come into being.

Nerves, during the passage of impulses along their lengths, give evidences of the changes occurring within them. The optic fibers responsible for reporting the state of affairs in the rods and cones are no exception. Nerve impulses consist in progressive local disturbances of fibers and display several interesting chemical and physical properties. Oxygen is used up and carbon dioxide is given off, detectable quantities of heat are emitted, and measurable electric currents are generated. It is this last effect that has proved to be of the greatest service in providing a picture of nervous functioning. The electrical change promptly signals the passage of the impulse; its magnitude is a true reflection of the extent of the alteration within the fiber; and, especially since the development of vacuum tube amplification and the perfection of electrical recording methods, it may be measured with considerable precision. The technique consists in placing one electrode on the nerve tissue at the point from which the record is desired and connecting another, so-called "neutral" electrode to an inactive region. A difference of electrical potential between the two is created as the impulse passes, and it is this small voltage, the "action potential," which is picked up, amplified, and recorded. Placement of the electrodes is, of course, the primary determiner of what changes will be registered. In animal preparations, if they are attached to the front and back of the eyeball itself there is obtained a record of the complex events in the retina, known as the *electroretinogram* (ERG). If they are spaced along the optic nerve bundle its summed activity is represented in the record. If the "active" electrode is inserted into the tissue of the occipital cortex of the brain the most elaborate of all visual responses are recorded.

Typical electroretinograms are shown in the solid lines of Fig. 14. Consequent upon light stimulation, the first response is a very small negative deflection known as the *a*-wave. This is followed immediately by a large and abruptly ascending *b*-wave, then by a slower *c*-wave, and finally by a characteristic "off-effect," the *d*-wave, before the original condition of zero potential is resumed. At low-stimulus intensities the *a*- and *d*-waves are not discernible. For many years the shape of the ERG was thought to be an accident of the way the recording was done; it remained for Granit (*127*) to disprove this conjecture and to make an interesting analysis of it. It is his belief

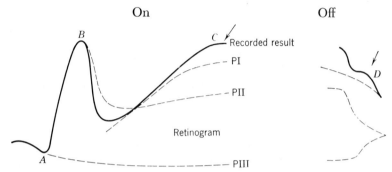

Fig. 14. The electroretinogram (ERG) and its analysis. The four prominent features are: *A*, the first negative deflection, the *a*-wave; *B*, the rapidly following positive *b*-wave; *C*, the slower *c*-wave; *D*, the "off-effect," or *d*-wave. Granit's analysis (*127*) into the three components, PI, PII, and PIII, is shown by the dotted lines. From Bartley, *17*. By permission of the *Psychological Review* and the American Psychological Association.

that there are three separate processes summed in the ERG and that certain influences, such as ether anesthesia and asphyxia, affect the three components differently. Process I (PI) is eliminated first during progressive anesthesia, PII is affected next, and PIII, the negative or "inhibitory" component, is most resistant. The dotted lines of Fig. 14 indicate the form of each of the components; the ERG is the algebraic sum of the three processes acting simultaneously.

The temptation has been strong to identify each of the components of the total ERG with three kinds of activity in the retinal layers, and various suggestions have been made (*17*), but at present we know with complete certainty only that the three responses are intermingled in the ERG as recorded, that PII is a necessary forerunner of the discharge in the optic nerve (since its obliteration by drugs eliminates the nerve response), that PI seems to add nothing to the nerve message, and that PIII, accounting as it does for the first downward deflection of the *a*-wave, is presumably connected with the operation of receptor cells of the retina themselves.

Relatively recent investigations of the ERG, especially those performed with human subjects and using the ingenious technique developed by Riggs (*249, 248, 173*), in accordance with which the electrical connection to the eye is supplied by a silver electrode embedded in a contact lens, have quite convincingly demonstrated that the principal *b*-wave results from the operation of the scotopic mechanism. Several lines of evidence combine to force this conclusion: (1) During prolonged dark adaptation the *b*-wave, in response to a periodically repeated standard stimulus, continues to increase in amplitude for an hour or more, paralleling the rods' dark-adaptation performance. (2) When the retina is progressively light adapted to higher levels of field luminance the magnitude of the *b*-wave is markedly reduced, and the response is eliminated altogether at a moderately high adapting intensity. (3) The sensitivity of the eye to colors, as measured by the relative intensities needed to produce a standard amplitude of *b*-wave, agrees well with the measures yielded by the conventional scotopic luminosity curve derived from brightness matches. (4) Extreme red light, which is ineffective as a rod stimulus, produces a waveform consistently different from that obtained with light from the short-wave end of the spectrum.

There is some evidence that the *c*-wave is an artifactual component of the ERG. If the eye is atropinized the *c*-wave drops out without otherwise influencing the course of the total ERG. The *c*-wave probably arises from the muscle action potential supplied by the iris or ciliary body in consequence of the pupillary or accommodatory reflexes set in motion by the light flash that also arouses the other components of the electrical response. In any case, there has not been much research interest in the *c*-wave. It arrives on the scene too late in the sequence of events to be represented in the final nerve discharge.

Whether the *a*-wave is a true photopic component, as its invariable appearance in the red response suggests, or is inevitably coupled with the *d*-wave to form the inhibitory PIII component, as Granit believes, remains to be settled. Our present state of information about the ERG is incomplete but challenging. A more intimate picture of electrical responses at the retinal level, especially one that can be correlated with changes further along in the catenary chain of events, would dispel some major mysteries of the visual mechanism.

There is ample reason for regarding the retina to be a true nervous center. It follows that its electrical response is of a complex sort. When recordings are made from beyond the retina, in the optic nerve, it is possible to get a little more intimate picture of the events transpiring there. The optic nerve in some animal preparations may be

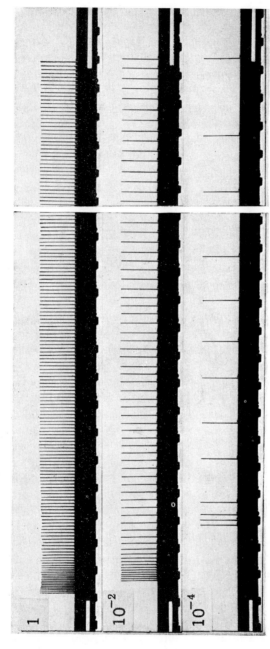

FIG. 15. Impulses in a single fiber of the optic nerve. Action potentials from the eye of Limulus, the king crab, in response to steady illumination. Records for three different intensities varying in the ratio 1.0:0.01:0.0001 are shown. Time is marked off in ⅕-sec intervals. From Hartline, *147*. Courtesy of the editor, *Journal of the Optical Society of America*, and the author.

"shredded," thus making possible the isolation of a single fiber for test. The first such records were obtained as recently as 1932, by Hartline and Graham (148). They singled out individual fibers still attached to functioning receptor cells, in the eye of the king crab Limulus, and recorded the impulses generated by light flashes. As had been found a few years earlier for single tactile fibers (7), the response to steady stimulation consists of a succession of spaced electrical discharges. The responses are uniform with respect to size, in accordance with the "all-or-nothing" principle. The only variation is one of frequency (see Fig. 15); the greater the intensity of the stimulus light, the higher the frequency. A decline in rate of discharge with a continuation of the stimulus is to be noted also. This is, of course, the accompaniment of light adaptation and presumably is the correlate of reduced brightness following steady exposure.

The crab's eye is of relatively simple construction. There is apparently only one general type of receptor, each unit being attached to a single nerve fiber, and there have thus far been found no lateral connections to complicate things. The functional picture should be correspondingly simple. Actually, however, some fairly complicated effects are producible in even so comparatively simple a retina. Thus Hartline has been able to demonstrate, e.g., spatial interaction phenomena of both an inhibitory and disinhibitory variety between neighboring units of the king crab's eye.

When a more complex, vertebrate eye is investigated the electrical effects become more elaborate. Three kinds of responses found in individual fibers of the frog's optic nerve are displayed in Fig. 16, taken from the work of Hartline (147). Some fibers respond very much as do those of the crab's optic nerve, maintaining periodic discharges so long as the stimulus light is falling on their attached receptor cells. Others respond only briefly at the onset and cessation of the stimulus (or whenever the light is abruptly increased or diminished in intensity). The third variety of fiber does an even stranger thing; it bursts into activity for a second or two when the light is cut off. Reilluminating the retina immediately suppresses activity in these fibers.

Again, as with the ERG, it would be convenient if clear meaning could be attached to these findings for the optic nerve, but as yet they are extremely perplexing. Recordings from large numbers of samples reveal that only one-fifth of the fibers are concerned with the maintained type of discharge. Apparently the optic nerve is better organized for reporting the disappearance of a stimulus than for registering its presence! Such are the absurdities one is led to when information is sketchy and incomplete.

Simultaneous recordings from the eye (ERG) and the optic nerve bundle to repeated flashes of white light have been managed by Adrian (2) in several different vertebrate preparations (rabbit, cat, and guinea pig). Figure 17, taken from his work, shows the great discrepancy between the form of the optic nerve discharge and that of the retinal response. Whereas this picture of the visual mechanism's

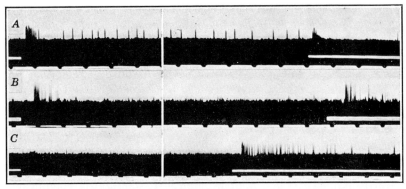

Fig. 16. Responses of three types of fibers in a vertebrate eye (frog). The presence of a light stimulus is signaled by the disappearance of the white line just above the time record. Time units are ⅕ sec. (A) response of a fiber of the type found in the crab's eye (Fig. 15). This shows regular discharge in the presence of light. (B) an "on-off" type fiber. Only the onset or cessation of the stimulus produces a response. (C) the "off" type fiber, which discharges only when the light goes out. From Hartline, 147. What appears to be an "off" response in the A record is in reality the normal response of the fiber, a single spike which happened nearly to coincide with the cessation of the stimulus, combined with several smaller spikes from a nearby fiber of the "off" variety. This was clearly explained by Dr. Hartline in his original description of the record but has not always since been understood. Courtesy of the editor, *Journal of the Optical Society of America,* and the author.

action may represent a considerable simplification of that present in the human case—the guinea pig has no cones, while the cat and rabbit possess relatively few—it is clear that the events transpiring in the optic nerve bundle are vastly complex as compared with those recorded from the eye itself. Separation of the cone and rod contributions may be present in the ERG (if that is what the *a*-wave and *b*-wave are about), but there is no hint of a simple dichotomy in the nerve message. As Adrian himself observes: "It is presumably the function of the eye to furnish the brain with a coherent account of visual events, and, although it may employ two kinds of receptor, it has abundant synaptic connections for welding their twin messages into one" (2, p. 35).

If the electrical events in the retina seem intricate they are simplicity itself compared to those obtained when leads are taken off
the cortex of the brain. The higher cortical centers, in their very
construction, provide maximal opportunity for free interplay of excitations. It is therefore not surprising that electrodes placed in this
region, particularly if their area is large, pick up many interacting
impulses and reveal, in the final record, only summed activity difficult
of detailed analysis.

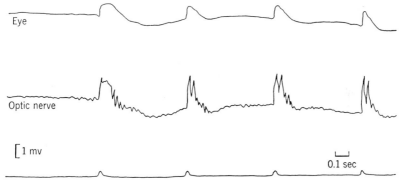

Eye

Optic nerve

[1 mv

0.1 sec

Fig. 17. Comparison of electrical responses of the retina and optic nerve of the
rabbit. The top record is the ERG, while the middle one is the optic nerve response, recorded simultaneously with the ERG. The discrepancy between the two
is obvious. The time marker (bottom) reveals that flashes of light were being
repeated at half-second intervals. From Adrian, 2. By permission of the Cambridge University Press, the *Journal of Physiology*, and the author.

Records of brain action potentials (*electroencephalograms,* EEG)
may be obtained in humans without the necessity of contacting the
cortical tissue directly. Electrodes collodioned or otherwise attached
to the scalp will detect the presence of rather large disturbances, so-
called alpha-waves or the "Berger rhythm," having an average frequency of 10 per second. Smaller ones, occurring at rates as high as
30 or more per second (beta-waves), and very slow but large undula-
tions (delta-waves), as low as 4 per second in frequency, are also
present in the complex. Whatever the exact mode of origin of these
rhythms (and this question is as yet unsettled) it is clear that they are
in large part spontaneous on the part of the brain. They have been
shown to occur in many isolated cell masses. The interesting thing
about them, for our immediate concern, is their sudden diminution or
even complete abolition with the onset of visual stimulation. Many
other sensory stimuli have the same result, but excitation of the visual
centers seems to be most effective in producing the depression. An

explanation offered by Adrian and Matthews (5) seems to fit the facts well. It is their belief that the presence, in the resting state, of regular large waves implies synchronized discharge from many cortical cells. The visual stimulus initiates a series of specific responses and thus breaks up the synchronous activity. But there have been other and conflicting views, and we seem as yet to be but at the threshold of information of this sort.

A few studies have dealt a little more intimately with brain action potentials than it is possible to do by the method just discussed. Small and carefully placed electrodes pick up potentials complex in form and suggestive of multiple origin, like the ERG. Different rates of conduction in fibers of different size make for apparent confusion, and the masking effect of ever-present spontaneous discharges confound the picture. It is too early to attempt broad generalizations concerning cortical potentials, but it has been amply demonstrated that the methods which have yielded so many valuable facts concerning nervous changes in peripheral parts of the body are equally applicable to the study of central nervous functions.

4

Color Vision
and Color Blindness

Visual Quality. We saw in Chap. 3 the manner in which three different dimensions of the physical stimuli for vision can be separately discriminated. It would be very convenient if there could be found a strictly analogous set of dimensions of visual experience corresponding to the stimulus properties of intensity, wavelength, and colorimetric purity. But to claim such correspondence would be to oversimplify things considerably. It is better to drop our *psychophysical* attack on the problems of vision for the time and assume a *phenomenal* viewpoint. What sort of order comes into the picture if we forget what we know about the physical dimensions of light and attempt a direct description of visual experience?

If the largest possible range of visible objects were to be examined we should see that certain uniformities of light and shade, color tone, and resemblance to gray run through them. There would be textural variations and differences of shape also, but we have raised no question of the geometry of physical objects, and we shall do well here to sidestep the somewhat vexing problem of form perception. One way of representing the variations in visual sensation is to make use of the *color spindle* (Fig. 18). Visual qualities occupy its entire surface, while a multitude of intensive series radiate out in all directions from the middle point, neutral gray. The central rim represents all the different hues found in the spectrum and, in addition, a series of hues compounded of red and violet—the purples. White and black are also obviously distinct qualities and are represented at the tips of the spindle. From each noticeably different hue there runs a series of qualities terminating in white; similarly, a series exists between black and each point on the hue circle. Integrating the entire surface we have a qualitative "shell," all possible colors having positions on its surface.

51

It is clear also that various series exist within the spindle, but the points on these lines seem to be *intensitively* rather than *qualitatively* different. There is such a series between neutral gray and white and another between gray and black. It is well to note that this makes black a positive sensation which can vary in degree. There has been a good deal of controversy on this point, since the naive view would make black the simple accompaniment of lack of stimulation. But the experience in looking at physical "blackness" is not black, nor is black the lack of sensation! Perhaps due to autonomous processes working in the brain one gets, in the dark room, not black but gray or purplish gray. This is sometimes called "brain gray" or the *self-light of the retina*. It appears that gray may be a constant background process and that all stimulation must "break through" it, or perhaps "modulate" it, for visual quality to be experienced.

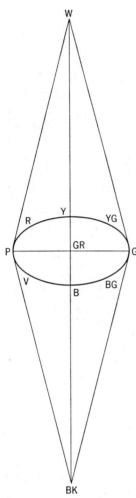

FIG. 18. The color spindle in its simplest form.

Other intensive series radiating from neutral gray to the surface of the spindle must, of course, terminate at colors. These are lines of increasing saturation, and it is perhaps clearer now why saturation is defined in terms of lack of grayness. The outside boundaries of the spindle are not determined by the saturations experienced in viewing the spectrum; under special conditions of observation colors may appear even better saturated than do spectral ones.

There are other ways of representing color sensations and other interpretations to be put on the spindle. Some have stressed the unique character of certain salient hues and have made of the hue circle a square. The figure thus becomes a double pyramid, bases joined, with psychologically "unique" red, yellow, green, and blue at the corners (*80, 81*). The point is well taken; there does seem to be something special about these particular hues. Orange resembles red and yellow, but yellow does not resemble red and green. The question is an old one and long debated (*45*, pp. 145 ff.), but too often the location of special "primary" hues at the corners of the pyramid have provided the impetus for commitment to some special theory of color vision which, in our present state of knowledge, may not be entirely healthy.

If attention is paid to the actual number of observable stages of hue, saturation, and brightness, that is, to the number of just perceptible differences of all kinds within the world of color, one does not come

FIG. 19. A psychological color solid. The model on the right differs from that on the left in having its vertical dimension increased by a factor of 4. The two models have the same horizontal dimensions. From Nickerson and Newhall, *223*. Photograph by courtesy of Dr. Nickerson and the U. S. Department of Agriculture.

out with a neat geometrical arrangement like the spindle or double pyramid. There results the irregular figure illustrated in Fig. 19 (*223*). From the measurements that went into the construction of this model there may be made a simple computation of the total number of distinguishable colors. The number is a surprisingly large one—7,500,000!

Both the spindle and pyramid are conceived by many to be "qualitative solids" in the sense that all points within the figure, as well as on the surface, are *qualitatively* distinct from each other. It has remained for Boring (*43*, Chap. 2) to show that the figure is, in fact, a solid, but qualitative only on its outer surface; within, it is representative of a host of intensive differences. This view appears to be more in line with present trends of theory in that it unites qualitative and quantitative concepts. But whatever the form of color solid adopted and whatever the details of its interpretation, it represents a useful conception. Observed color is clearly describable in the three dimensions of the figure: brightness, hue, and saturation.

Color Nomenclature and Specification. The names given colors are notoriously arbitrary. Color vocabularies we acquire in the course of a multitude of varied experiences with colored objects are pretty much fortuitous affairs. It is not alone the layman who uses color names inaccurately. A study of the color designations used by chemists and druggists revealed the greatest variety of names for description of a single fluid. But we cannot give up our color names; they are too useful. It is better to attempt standardization of them and thus bring order out of relative chaos. A method of color designation which has been carefully worked out with a view to practical usefulness as well as to theoretical correctness is the system devised by the Inter-Society Color Council, an organization serving as a clearinghouse for color problems of all sorts. The ISCC system is built on nine basic hue names (red, orange, yellow, green, blue, purple, brown, pink, and olive) coupled with eleven modifiers, such as light, vivid, weak, very, deep, etc. By joining one or more modifiers with hue names, 312 separate designations of color are possible. The system has the advantage that common color names are used, but used in such an unambiguous manner that reference to some external standard becomes unnecessary. This set of color names now has the official sanction of several influential organizations concerned with color and vision, and there is every expectation that it will come into more common use.

Another way to specify colors is to utilize the principle, long known, that any color may be matched by three suitably chosen spectral colors. Such a "tristimulus specification" represents the most exact procedure we now possess. An analysis of any color into three components can be made quickly and accurately with the recently developed Hardy recording spectrophotometer. We shall return later to some of the details of tristimulus color specification, after we have learned something of the color mixing process upon which the method is based.

Still a third method of making color specifications is to set up acceptable material standards. Various sets of solutions, pigmented or dyed surfaces, and filters have been used in conjunction with a known illuminant. The advantage in such a system is its great convenience. The best known of these systems are the Lovibond tinted glasses, the Maerz and Paul "color dictionary" containing 7000 color samples keyed to 4000 color names, and the Munsell system. The last is of special interest in that it has been so constructed as to conform as nearly as possible with the basic idea of the "color spindle." A revision of the Munsell system in 1943 (*221*) greatly improved its general utility.

Color Mixture. If the light reflected from the surface of a colored paper were to be analyzed with a spectrometer there would be found present a great variety of waves, probably extending over the entire spectrum, though having a strong maximum in some one region. Yet the surface appears, upon direct viewing, to have only a single "color." A unitary effect is thus being produced from a complex stimulus. Most of the colors we see are produced in this way; only under very special circumstances are "pure" colors encountered. Obviously, color mixture plays a very important role in everyday seeing.

Color mixtures are produced by two distinct processes, color *subtraction* and color *addition*. The subtraction process is the less common, though it accounts for the results found in mixing paints and other pigments. We all know, from blending water colors, that green can be produced by a suitable mixture of yellow and blue, and, because it is a derived color, green is not regarded as an artistic "primary." It is surprising to learn, therefore, that green (but not yellow) is regarded as a primary in visual science. The confusion disappears when it is disclosed that the production of green by mixing yellow and blue is an accident of the subtractive process. The yellow pigment absorbs all but yellow and green light, reflecting these. Similarly, the blue pigment reflects blue and green, absorbing all other waves. From the incident white light, itself a mixture of all visible waves, a double subtraction has been made. The remainder is green, the only color reflected in common by the two originals. Precisely the same results would be obtained in passing white light successively through color filters having transmission characteristics like the reflectance values of these pigments. Color filters, then, also operate on the subtractive principle.

By far the majority of color mixtures are, however, additive. Especially is this true of color mixing in the laboratory. Combine, by superposing them on a single screen, two spectral samples such as red and green, and an intermediate hue, yellow, will be seen. Blend green and blue in the same way, and an intermediate green-blue is the result. The experiment may be done systematically for all possible color combinations. If so, it will be found that there is nothing fortuitous about color mixtures but, on the contrary, that they are entirely regular and lawful in operation.

If we select from the long-wave end of the spectrum a red and combine with it green in different proportions, the resulting mixtures will
vary continuously through orange, yellow, and yellow-green. A particular red (lithium) of λ671 mμ, when mixed with green (thallium)
of λ536 mμ, yields a yellow indistinguishable from λ589 mμ. This is
the so-called Rayleigh equation, often used for testing color vision. If
the color to be mixed with the initial red is selected further down in

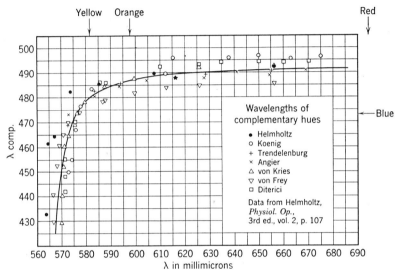

Fig. 20. Complementary color pairs. The data of seven different investigators
have been combined in a single plot. The curve, one branch of an equilateral
hyperbola, is the locus of a large number of pairs of complementary wavelengths.
From Priest (235) after Helmholtz, 163. Courtesy of the editor, *Journal of the
Optical Society of America.*

the wavelength series still other intermediates are possible, though
the more remote in the spectrum the two components, the less saturated, i.e., the whiter or grayer, the mixture will be. If the second
component is taken as far down as λ493 mμ there will be no hue at
all; if intensities are properly chosen this mixture will appear white.
The two components in this case are said to be *complementary* colors.
This pairing of red (λ671 mμ) and blue-green (λ493 mμ) is but one
instance among a great many such complementary combinations. The
data gathered from several independent determinations of complementary pairs are shown in Fig. 20. The curve best fitting the points
is one branch of an equilateral hyperbola.

If, in the selection of a second component to be combined with
lithium red, one goes beyond λ493 mμ to the shorter waves, he finds

another series of hues. This is the group of colors made up of non-spectral purple and the purplish reds. It has been determined that this series of hues contains 28 j.n.d.'s, which, added to the 128 found in the spectrum, brings to 156 the total number of discriminable hue steps (263). Thus one may complete the "hue circle," already familiar from the color spindle. The details of this circle are shown in Fig. 21.

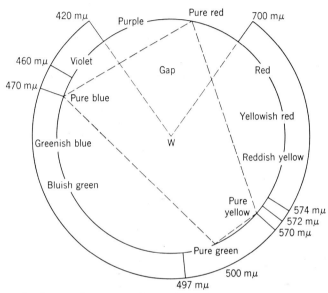

Fig. 21. The hue circle. Spectral stimuli from λ420 mμ to λ700 mμ are arranged in sequence about the circumference. Complementary colors lie at opposite ends of diagonals. The positions of psychologically "pure" yellow, green, and blue in the series are noted, as is also that of "pure" red, which lies in the gap beyond spectral red. From Southall, 265. By permission of the Oxford University Press and the author.

Here complementary pairs lie at opposite ends of each diameter. It will be noted that psychologically "pure" red lies in the gap between the two ends of the spectrum; all spectral reds are judged to be somewhat yellowish.

If one were devising a system for reproducing all possible hues as well as white, three basic components would be necessary. It has long been known that all colors can be obtained through the suitable mixture of "primaries" selected from the long-wave, medium-wave, and short-wave parts of the spectrum. The primaries in question are red, green, and violet. A general color equation can be written: $C = xR + yG + zV$, where x, y, and z are coefficients varying in size for different colors, C. For two-component mixtures, one of the coefficients becomes 0. For white or gray, x, y, and z are equal.

The sizes of the coefficients necessary to reproduce all the colors of the spectrum are shown in Fig. 22. Here the primaries have been selected as follows: red, λ650 mμ; green, λ530 mμ; violet, λ460 mμ. So long as only the hue relations among different color sensations are being considered there are several sets of primary wavelengths that

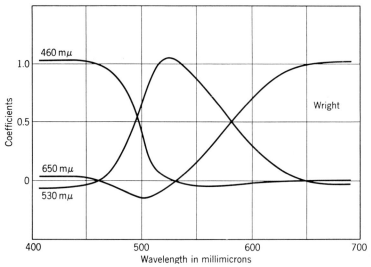

Fɪɢ. 22. Reproduction of spectral colors by three primaries. The curves represent the average readings for 10 observers and show the sizes of coefficients necessary to reproduce all spectral points when the primaries selected are: λ650 mμ, red; λ530 mμ, green; λ460 mμ, violet. After Wright, 326. By permission of the Howe Laboratory of Ophthalmology, Harvard University.

will answer quite well (265, pp. 313–337). When other aspects of color (e.g., saturation) are also taken into account, however, the number of possibilities becomes definitely limited (152).

Color mixtures, as additions of excitations, have been discussed as though there were but a single means of producing them, viz., the combining of spectral samples. There is little doubt that, for the most exact results, this method is the best. A high point of instrumentation has been reached in the Helmholtz color mixer, which does exactly this (265, p. 314). But there are more convenient ways of seeing the qualitative relations between colors in mixtures. One is to make use of Lambert's method. Two sources, such as colored paper squares, are placed at right angles to each other. A piece of clear glass, bisecting the angle between the papers, now transmits one color to the eye and, through partial reflection, "mixes" the second with the first. Changing the direction and amount of light incident to the papers makes possible a wide range of mixtures.

The most commonly used device for color mixing is the sectored disc or color wheel. Two or more interjoined colored papers, the relative proportions of which can be varied, are rapidly rotated at speeds sufficient to eliminate flicker. A single mixed color results. The effect depends upon the property of the retina whereby an impression, once being set up, requires an appreciable time of "decay" to be eliminated. Two rapidly successive impressions thus "fuse" to yield a unitary one. It is interesting that this mode of color combination, used more uncritically than any other, involves the most elaborate retinal and cortical events and, for its strict interpretation, would require the most complicated account.

A third procedure in color mixing is to take advantage of the fact that we have two retinae, independent in their action, and to present two different colors to the two eyes. Binocular mixtures thus arrived at are notoriously unstable, and yet some facts important for theory can be gained through this method. Two colors very similar in wavelength composition and luminance can be made to combine quite readily; they yield a single fused impression intermediate to the originals in hue. However, two colors from quite separate regions on the hue circle will show only transient mixtures. Steadily viewed, they struggle in *rivalry*, first one and then the other having the upper hand in the conflict. Hecht has questioned a large number of observers on the "mixture" obtained by viewing a bright source through Wratten filter 29 (red), in front of one eye, and filter 58 (green) before the other. Yellow was quite uniformly reported, and from this experiment it becomes possible to dispense with yellow as a primary. It appears to be a "brain" mixture, since only in the brain could the two excitations come together. Hecht's account (150) leaves out a description of the more obvious action occurring under these conditions, the intense rivalry between red and green, but the point is well taken that if yellow is even momentarily and unstably formed in this way it can be regarded as a derived rather than a primary color. Much the same kind of result comes from the binocular mixture of blue and yellow; "brain" white is transiently produced in the struggle.

Now, with the chief facts of color mixture before us, we may return to the question of the specification of colors. It has been seen that the additive combination of three lights—any three, so long as no one of them can be formed by a mixture of the other two—is sufficient to produce a match with any color whatever. This being the case, given

(1) the specifications of the spectrum in terms of three suitably selected primaries, and (2) a spectral analysis of an unknown light, it should be a relatively simple matter to arrive at a "tristimulus specification" of that unknown.

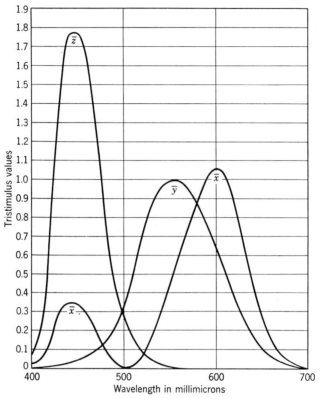

Fig. 23. The "standard observer," according to the agreements of the International Commission on Illumination in 1931. The values of $\bar{x}$, $\bar{y}$, and $\bar{z}$ have been so selected as to match, for the average observer, a unit amount of radiant energy at each wavelength. The $\bar{y}$ curve is of special interest, since its values have been chosen to duplicate the photopic luminosity curve for the normal eye. From Hardy, *143*. By permission of the Technology Press, Massachusetts Institute of Technology.

The exact specification of the various parts of the spectrum in terms of three primaries is no longer an arbitrary matter. An important step was taken by the International Commission on Illumination in 1931 in settling on the color mixture data already carefully compiled by Wright and Guild, working independently in England, to form the basis of a standard tristimulus spectral analysis (*143*). The data, as adopted, are based on the color matches of a sufficient number of subjects whose settings were in excellent agreement. These data have been given the designation "the I.C.I. standard observer"; they are displayed in Fig. 23. The values of $\bar{x}$, $\bar{y}$, and $\bar{z}$ indicate the amount of each of the I.C.I. primaries needed to match a unit amount of radiant energy at each spectral wavelength. The curve labeled $\bar{x}$ represents a reddish purple primary, $\bar{y}$ is a green resembling a spectral green of $\lambda520$ mμ but more saturated, and $\bar{z}$ is a blue of somewhat greater colorimetric purity than a spectral blue of $\lambda477$ mμ. At each wavelength the amounts of the three primaries needed, in additive combination, to match the spectral band at that wavelength may be found by simply adding the ordinates of all three curves at that spectral position. Thus, at $\lambda578$ mμ, there are required approximately equal amounts of reddish purple ($\bar{x}$) and green ($\bar{y}$) to match the yellow seen by the normal observer. In the region of $\lambda475$ mμ, a large component of blue ($\bar{z}$) joins with small, roughly equal amounts of $\bar{x}$ and $\bar{y}$ to match the particular blue seen there. Other combinations suggest themselves.

The green primary curve ($\bar{y}$) is of special interest in that, in selecting the characteristics of the primaries, $\bar{y}$ has been made equivalent to the photopic luminosity curve for the normal eye. This has been done with a view to permitting one of the primaries to specify completely the luminous aspect (brightness) of the color quite apart from its chromatic aspects (hue and saturation). Luminosity of a color is thus known if Y (a particular value of $\bar{y}$) is known.

The chromatic features may also be specified exactly, but a little less directly. This is done by reference to the so-called "chromaticity diagram," a useful construction which tells us a great deal about a color and its relations with all other colors. A typical chromaticity diagram is shown in Fig. 24. The axes, x and y, are called "chromaticity coordinates," and the following relations define them: $x = X/(X + Y + Z)$; $y = Y/(X + Y + Z)$. Because $x + y + z$ must necessarily equal unity, it is sufficient to specify a color in terms of two of these coordinates, usually x and y. The solid curved line of Fig. 24 is the locus of the colors of the spectrum between its "practical" limits, $\lambda400$ mμ to $\lambda700$ mμ. All colors possible with real stimuli are represented by points within the area bounded by this line and the lower straight line connecting extreme violet and extreme red (the purple series). The point C, near the center of the diagram, shows the location of "daylight," the light supplied by I.C.I. Illuminant C.

The points G and P are non-spectral color samples such as might be
encountered in paints. Sample G may not only be specified in terms

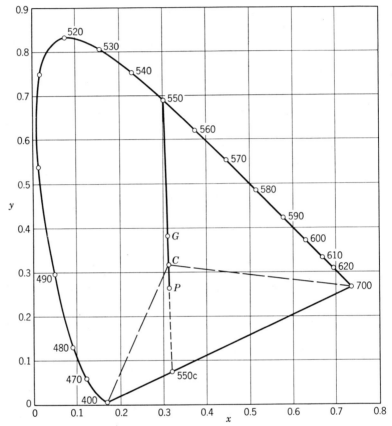

FIG. 24. A chromaticity diagram. The sample, G, lies on the line between the
illuminant, C ("daylight"), and λ550 mμ. This identifies its color as yellowish
green and as highly unsaturated (since it lies about 17% of the distance from C
to the spectral curve). Sample P may be specified, as to dominant wavelength,
as the complement of λ550 mμ, hence "550c." Its purity may be judged to be
about 20%, since its position is about ⅕ of the distance between Illuminant C
and the line connecting λ400 mμ and λ700 mμ (the purple series). From Hardy,
143. By permission of the Technology Press, Massachusetts Institute of Technology.

of its coordinates, x and y (and, by subtraction of the sum of these from
1.00, z as well), but its position on the diagram permits two other
·things to be said about it. Its "dominant wavelength" and its "purity"
may also be specified. A line drawn from the illuminant, through the
sample, to the spectral locus (the vertical line of the diagram) inter-

sects the boundary of the color area at λ550 mμ. This is the sample's dominant wavelength. Since λ550 mμ lies in the yellowish green part of the spectrum, this reveals that the sample will appear yellowish green in daylight. Moreover, a numerical specification for the purity of the sample can be arrived at by determining, on the chromaticity diagram, the relative distances of the sample and the corresponding spectral point from the point at which the illuminant is situated. Our sample G lies about 17% of the distance from C ("white") to spectral green, and it therefore has a purity of 17%. Similarly, sample P is a purple whose specifications can be given exactly in terms of x, y, and z. However, purples lie outside the spectrum, and an artifice has to be resorted to in defining dominant wavelength and purity of all purples. The convention is to specify the wavelength of the exact complement of the purple sample, in this case λ550 mμ, and to write it "550c." Perfectly saturated purples are regarded as occupying the straight line connecting the ends of the spectrum. This particular purple sample is situated about one-fifth of the way from the illuminant to the purple line; its purity turns out to be 21%.

After-Images. When light is allowed to fall but briefly on the retina, the excitation does not cease abruptly with the termination of the stimulus. Indeed, we have seen that this phenomenon may be put to work and that it is basic to one of the common color mixing methods (not to mention that it is basic to the entire motion picture industry!). The sensation invariably lags behind the stimulus, sometimes not even noticeably, but under some special conditions it may persist for a matter of minutes.

After-images are usually classed as *positive* and *negative*, the terms being used very much as they are in photography. A positive after-image has the same qualitative characteristics as the sensation of which it is an outgrowth. A negative after-image, developing as a final stage of the same process, is of antagonistic or complementary quality. The conditions favorable to the observation of one are not the best for the other, though presumably every visual act has potentialities for after-image production. Positive images are best observed after brief intense stimulation of the dark-adapted eye. Thus, switching on and off a colored light after a prolonged stay in the dark will yield a brief image of the same hue as the light. A quick glance at the setting sun will often result in a good positive image, so intense is the stimulation. One of the best ways to observe positive after-images is to expose the eye repeatedly to a well-lighted landscape through a fast-acting camera shutter. Here the details of differently colored and variously shaded parts of the view are seen to fade at different rates.

Negative images are not as fleeting as positive ones and thus are easy to obtain under a wide variety of conditions. However, for their favorable observation a sufficient period of initial stimulation must be given; i.e., light adaptation to the stimulus is a prerequisite to the appearance of the negative after-image. In an experiment designed to produce a negative image it is well to think of two sets of stimuli, the primary one fatiguing or "tuning" the retina, and a secondary one giving the conditions essential to its appearance. Ordinarily, one looks first at a colored light or surface, then after a half-minute or so substitutes a gray or white background on which the complementary image will develop. The secondary stimulus is obviously important. If it is identical with the primary one there is only a continuation of light adaptation, and no after-image can appear. If it is complementary in hue to the primary stimulus high saturations of the complement are experienced. The most vivid colors possible are obtained by projecting the after-image of one spectral color on its complement. Thus an eye previously adapted to purple light will see "supersaturated" spectral green on looking at the middle of the spectrum. It was this situation to which reference was made when, in considering the dimensions of the color spindle, it was said that the spectrum does not define saturation limits. Spectral colors, therefore, really lie inside the hue rim of the spindle.

The phenomena observed against darkness after a brief intense flash of white light are elaborate and not easy to explain as yet. The after-image of such a stimulus is made up of a sequence of many colors, dark intervals being interspersed in the series. This is known as the "flight of colors" and may consist of successive images of purple, blue, yellow, green, red, and bluish green. This series is merely a commonly reported one, and there is no guarantee that it will be reproduced by all observers under all conditions. In fact, it is known that the number of phases observed in the flight as well as the total duration of the flight is determined by the intensity of the initial flash. Berry and Imus (34), conducting a systematic experiment on the two variables of flash intensity and flash duration, were able to show that as $\log I \times t$ of the flash varies arithmetically both flight duration and the number of color changes observed vary geometrically. Bright flashes of colored lights yield sequences somewhat similar to those yielded by white light, and it is not at all clear why this should be so. In particular, well-saturated purples show up in the "flight." Why this color should be favored above others is likewise not clear.

A certain "objectivity" inheres in after-images. Since the effect is due to adaptation of a local area of the retina, the image moves with change in direction of regard. Also, its apparent size varies with fixation distance. Look at a small colored square at reading distance sufficiently long to develop a negative image, then change fixation to a distant wall. The colored square now assumes huge proportions. Shift back to a short focus, and the square becomes tiny. In the fading process an image tends to have its form changed, also. The corners

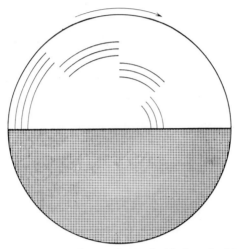

Fig. 25. Benham's top. Though providing only black and white stimuli in various temporal sequences colors, notably reddish yellow and blue, are seen upon rotating the disc at the proper speed. From Southall, 265. By permission of the Oxford University Press and the author.

of a square become rounded, and a complex outline is smoothed in the direction of simpler shape. This is a general tendency in unstable forms throughout nature, as the Gestalt psychologists have correctly noted.

Some especially curious effects may be obtained if spatial variations of the stimulus are allowed to complicate the arousal of after-images. In viewing "Benham's top" (Fig. 25) the innermost rings take on a yellowish or reddish appearance, while the outer ones are seen as bluish, and yet there is given only alternate black and white stimulation. A reversal in direction of spinning moves red to the outer and blue to the inner rings. The speed of rotation is critical; above and below an optimal range of speeds the effect disappears. Another phenomenon, revealing an undulating process to underlie the after-image, is that known as "Charpentier's bands." An illuminated radial slit, rotated against darkness at the rate of 2 revolutions per second, has the appearance illustrated in Fig. 26. The pulsating nature of the after-image, which here trails after the excitation proper like the tail of a comet, is clearly revealed by the presence of the dark bands. The size and prominence of the bands change with variations in speed, intensity, and slit width. McDougall has gathered similar evidence, from a study of stationary images, of an undulating decay of the sensation (206).

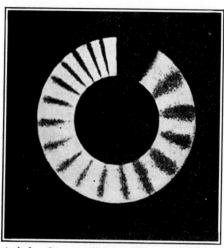

Fig. 26. Charpentier's bands. An illuminated slit, moving in a clockwise direction at a rate of 2 rpm and viewed against darkness, has a reported appearance somewhat like this. The dark bands and progressive dimming of the trailing after-image attest the undulating character of visual excitation. After McDougall, 206.

Color Zones and Perimetry. Not only are images falling on the extreme peripheral retina vague in outline and lacking in detail, but they are likely to appear colorless as well. In fact, the peripheral retina may be said to be normally relatively color blind.

A small colored test object, brought into the visual field from its peripheral limits and moved steadily toward the point of fixation, will at first be seen as gray. At a certain visual angle it will take on hue, though not necessarily the "correct" one. Finally, approaching the center of the field it will be clearly and correctly recognized. Different colors behave differently in this regard. Red and green are likely to appear yellowish before assuming their proper hue, while blue is rarely misidentified. The exact point of correct identification varies with a number of stimulus characteristics: wavelength, intensity, wavelength composition (saturation), size, exposure time, and contrast between test object and background, as well as conditions of retinal adaptation. All other variables being held constant, however, there remains a characteristic effect of wavelength variation. Blue and yellow have more extensive retinal fields than do red and green, and, as between

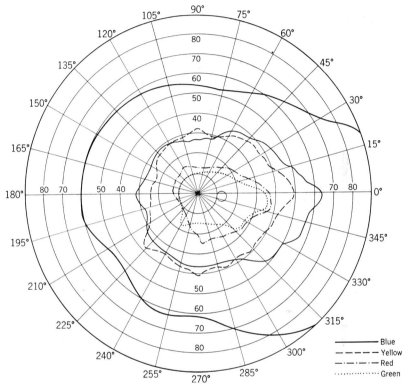

FIG. 27. Chart of the retinal color fields. The limits of the visual field of the right eye for each of the colors blue, yellow, red, and green when the test object is a small, homogeneous patch of light of moderate intensity. From Dimmick, 79.

the pairs, the blue field is slightly more extensive than the yellow, and the red is considerably larger than the green (Fig. 27).

The devices used to determine the extent of the various color "zones" are the *perimeter* and the *campimeter*. Both employ the same principle, the perimeter consisting essentially of a graduated arc along which a colored disc is moved, and the campimeter being simply a plane surface having meridional lines to serve as guides for the test object. In the case of the perimeter the arc is capable of rotation about the fixation point, thus providing several meridians for test. The campimeter possesses only the inconvenience of requiring computation of the tangent relations to establish the visual angles at which the colors are recognized.

The classic study of the color sensitivity of the peripheral retina is that of Ferree and Rand (91). They determined chromatic thresholds for red (λ670 mμ), yellow (λ581 mμ), green (λ522 mμ), and blue (λ468 mμ). Their results fail to confirm the older belief that the zones for red and green are coincident and that blue and yellow fall together in an outer zone. In fact, when sufficiently high intensities are used, the peripheral limits for red, yellow, and blue are identical with that for mixed white light and are hence coincident with the extreme outer limits of vision itself. Green sensitivity is considerably less than that of the other colors; although very high brightnesses were employed, green could never be seen in the extreme periphery. These results have been substantiated, in the main, by later studies (250).

Color Blindness. The inability to distinguish between simple colors has long been a matter of curious interest. As early as 1777 an account was given of a certain Mr. Harris of Cumberland, England, who at the age of four, "having by accident found in the street a child's stocking, he carried it to a neighboring house to inquire for the owner; he observed that the people called it a red stocking, though he did not understand why they gave it that denomination, as he himself thought it completely described by being called a stocking" (170). In his later life there was abundant proof that he was indeed color blind, and this appears to be the first recorded instance of the defect. A score of years later the anomaly was being called "Daltonism" after the famous English chemist who was himself "red blind" and who gave a remarkably accurate description of the defect. Dalton said, in 1798: "I found that persons in general distinguish six kinds of colour in the solar image. . . . To me it is quite otherwise. I see only two, or at most three, distinctions. These I should call yellow and blue, or yellow, blue and purple. My yellow comprehends the red, orange, yellow, and green of others; and my blue and purple coincides with theirs. . . . Woolen yarn, dyed crimson, or dark blue is the same to me." The English-speaking world has long since given up the intimate association of color blindness with the name of John Dalton, preferring to remember him for his part in the establishment of the atomic theory of matter, but the French name for color blindness is still "daltonisme."

There are several different kinds of color defect, ranging from simple color "weakness" to the complete incapacity to detect hue differences. The common classification of the various forms, originated by von

Kries, comes out of considerations due to color theory (the trichromatic theory of Young and Helmholtz) and is, therefore, not free from prejudice. However, it accommodates well the most frequently encountered forms. The von Kries classification is as follows:

    I. Anomalous trichromacy (color "weakness")
        A. Protanomaly (red weakness)
        B. Deuteranomaly (green weakness)
    II. Dichromacy
        A. Red-green blindness
            1. Protanopia (red blindness)
            2. Deuteranopia (green blindness)
        B. Blue-yellow blindness
            1. Tritanopia
    III. Monochromacy (total color blindness)

Concerning the first class of color disturbances, the "weaknesses," it is difficult to make general statements; too little is known about individual differences in "normal" hue sensitivity. We have already seen that different observers characteristically get different results in the spectral hue discrimination experiment. However, some people have extraordinarily high $\Delta\lambda$ values in either the red or the green region and, especially in dim illuminations, may confuse reds and greens. If low discriminability is in the red they are said to be *protanomalous,* if in the green *deuteranomalous.* There is in these cases no absolute absence of red or green sensitivity; the loss is merely a relative one, and hence higher intensities are needed to permit correct color recognition. Instances of anomalous trichromacy are encountered fairly commonly, though with what frequency and to what degree it occurs in the general population we cannot know until a comprehensive program of careful color testing has been launched. The practical urge to settle the question is not as great as with the true color blindnesses, and an adequate survey has never been made. Perhaps color weakness exists in all gradations; perhaps it exists in distinct "types."

In the case of *dichromacy* we can be more definite. The two forms of "red-green" blindness, *protanopia* and *deuteranopia,* occur quite commonly. Some surveys place the incidence as high as 8% of the male population. Deuteranopia is the more common of the two. Red-green blindness is one of those sex-linked biological traits which, like hemophilia and several others, is transmitted by the plan of alternation of generations. In successive generations it is transmitted from the male, through the female (who, however, is not likely to be afflicted with it), to the male. Thus if one is red-green blind he has his maternal grandfather to hold responsible. Theoretically, a female may be red-green blind if both her father and her maternal grandfather are afflicted.

In a general way the two forms of red-green blindness are alike. Both protanopes and deuteranopes confuse red and green, seeing both as poorly saturated yellow. They have, then, only two colors remaining in their spectrum, yellow and blue, and hence they are "dichromats." However, each type can detect errors of matching on the part of the other, for there are important detailed differences between them. Protanopes have a fore-shortened spectrum at the long wave end; deuteranopes are able to see hue (yellow, to be sure) out to the normal limit of the red. The brightest part of the spectrum is, for the protanope, shifted about 15 mμ towards the violet, as compared with the normal, whereas the deuteranope has a very slight displacement of the high point towards the red end. In the blue-green, close to λ500 mμ, a "gray band" is seen in the deuteranope's spectrum, comprising a neutral point in the transition from yellow to blue. A similar neutral point exists for the protanope (at λ493 mμ), but it is barely noticeable in the spread-out spectrum. These differences between the two forms, though minor, are definite and measurable and must be taken into account in any final theory of color vision.

The question may fairly be asked as to how one knows what colors are seen by a color-blind individual. Mental content is reputed to be private, and color names, after all, are used by the color deficient very much as they are by those with normal color sensibility. The protanope sees a muddy yellow on looking at a red brick building, but, since the word "red" seems to be used quite universally by other people in describing bricks, the muddy yellow is for him "red" and so he calls it. Similarly with green, the particular yellow he sees on looking at the lawn is for him "green." It is because color blinds ordinarily possess a good color vocabulary (and also because many color normals have a poor color education!) that tests of color vision cannot be based on color naming if they are to separate successfully the color defective from the normal. The one way to be sure what colors are seen by the color blind is to find instances of unilateral color defect, people with one normal and one color-defective eye. Such cases do exist, and a few have been competently studied (262).

An important feature of red-green blindness is the retention, despite the color defect, of normal visual acuity. Details of objects can be detected as well by protanopes and deuteranopes as by the normal. This is of the utmost significance and must mean that there are no non-functioning end organs in these eyes. Attempts to account for red-green color blindness on the grounds of the lack of some set of receptors should be immediately discouraged. Obviously protanopes and deuteranopes have a full complement of sense cells, as otherwise their acuity would be cut down by some constant large fraction.

The other form of dichromatism, *yellow-blue blindness*, occurs rarely and seems always to be associated with some pathological condition of the retina or optic tract. This being the case it is difficult to arrive at generalities; each case has its own idiosyncrasies. About the only symptom all tritanopes have in common is the characteristic confusion of blue and yellow without, however, any loss of red-green discrimination. A neutral transition appears in the spectrum of the tritanope, as in other forms of dichromacy. In those cases successfully measured in this regard there is fair agreement that the gray band occurs in the neighborhood of λ570 mμ, longer waves appearing red, shorter ones green or bluish green.

A final form is monochromacy, in which there is no hue discrimination whatever. Cases of total color blindness are rarities, only a few ever having been studied with any thoroughness. The monochromat sees the entire spectrum as varying shades of gray; objects can be discriminated only on the basis of brightness differences. Total color blindness is inevitably complicated by other symptoms, some of them quite incapacitating. One such accompaniment, greatly reduced acuity in normal illuminations, either forces the monochromat to seek the protection of dark glasses or requires that he adopt half closure of the lids to prevent being dazzled. More or less constant nystagmic movements, rapid sidewise and vertical oscillations of the eyeballs, vastly complicate seeing and suggest that the central retinal region is being avoided in fixation. Pupil reactions are sluggish and greatly diminished in extent.

All these characteristics of monochromacy concur in pointing towards the simple explanation that the entire visual function is here mediated exclusively by the rods. All behavior is in line with the supposition that cones are either missing or failing in function. There is, of course, one way of settling the question. That is to make spectral visibility determinations on the eye of a totally color-blind individual. One such set of measurements has been made by the author (*110*). The visibility curve is reproduced in Fig. 28. It will be seen that it coincides almost perfectly with the accepted scotopic curve. Thus there seems to be no doubt that vision in the monochromat is entirely the concern of rods; cones, at least functional ones, are completely missing from the picture. Whether the cone structures are present is not known. Only one totally color-blind eye has even been subjected to post-mortem histological examination, and the findings were uncertain.

The foregoing account of color blindnesses represents something of an oversimplification in that several additional forms, all of them rare, have been encountered since the von Kries classification was devised. Thus, there has been recognized since about 1925 a third kind of anomalous trichromacy, the "tritanomalous" type. Just as the protanomalous may be described as those who require too much red, in a

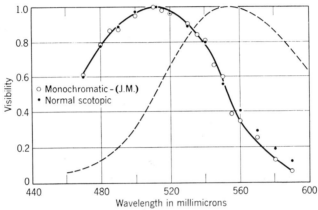

FIG. 28.   Spectral visibility in total color blindness. The visibility curve for a monochromat is shown as a solid line. The black dots are scotopic visibility values as determined by Hecht and Williams (*160*). The normal photopic visibility curve is shown as a dotted line. From Geldard, *110*.

red-green mixture, to match yellow, and the deuteranomalous as those needing too much green in the same circumstance, the tritanomalous use too much blue in creating standard blue-green mixtures. Tritanomaly thus lies between normal trichromacy and tritanopia and, like its partners, exists in various degrees.

Another form of yellow-blue blindness has been distinguished, a variety known as *tetartanopia*. To the tetartanope the spectrum appears red at the long wavelength end, green in the middle region, and red again in the short wavelengths. Two neutral bands separate the three segments, one at λ580 mμ and the other at λ470 mμ. This type contrasts with tritanopia as classically described. The tritanope has a red-green spectrum also, but typically he has a single neutral band, near λ570 mμ.

In addition to the congenital variety of total color blindness, itself rare, two acquired forms have been recognized. Both show some degree of cone vision to have been retained; there are thus not the disabling symptoms found in the congenital type. In one form the luminosity of the spectrum has a high point where the normal's is, in the region of λ560 mμ. High-intensity acuity is also good, but there are no colors; all differences are those of shading. The other type has a protanopic luminosity curve with, therefore, a peak of sensitivity at about λ540 mμ. The most reasonable explanation of this set of symptoms is that an inherited dichromatism, protanopia, has become compounded by disease of the retina or optic nerve, acquired tritanopia reducing the state of vision to the monochromatic. It goes without saying that this combination of events occurs extremely rarely.

If we now bring together the salient features of all kinds of color weakness and color blindness discussed we have the condensation provided by Table 1.

TABLE 1. CHARACTERISTICS OF THE VARIOUS FORMS OF COLOR DEFECT

After D. B. Judd (176)

Type of Color Defect	Hue Discrimination Remaining	Peak of Spectral Sensitivity (mμ)	Position of Neutral Point ("Gray Band") (mμ)
Anomalous trichromacy			
Protanomaly	Y-B, R-G (weak)	540	None
Deuteranomaly	Y-B, R-G (weak)	560	None
Tritanomaly	R-G, Y-B (weak)	560	None
Dichromacy			
Protanopia	Y-B	540	493
Deuteranopia	Y-B	560	497
Tritanopia	R-G	560	572
Tetartanopia	R-G	560	470, 580
Monochromacy			
Congenital	None	510	All
Acquired	None	560	All
Combined protanopia and tritanopia	None	540	All

Theories of Color Vision. In approaching the matter of suitable theories of color vision it is well to raise the more fundamental question of what can reasonbly be expected of theories in general. A theory does not pretend to be a set of facts. We can only ask of a theory that it provide the possibility of interpreting in a satisfactory manner the facts already in existence and that, in addition, it be sufficiently embracing to point the way to the discovery of new facts. The color theories most actively discussed at the present time meet these criteria very inadequately, though each has its virtues and defects.

The most profitable line of thought in color theory stems from Thomas Young (1807). Beginning with the fact that all colors may be reproduced by the suitable mixture of but three primaries, Young supposed that there existed three distinct sets of nervous fibers, one set sensitive to red, one to green, and the other to violet. The expansion of the theory at the hands of Helmholtz and his followers is classic. Figure 29, taken from Helmholtz' great *Physiological Optics*, represents the degree of excitation assumed to occur in each of the three kinds of nerve fibers when stimulated by light from various parts of the spec-

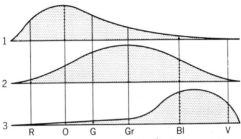

Fig. 29. The original excitation curves of Helmholtz. These three diagrams, entirely imaginary in their construction, "indicate something like the degree of excitation of the three kinds of fibres, No. 1 for the red-sensitive fibres, No. 2 for the green-sensitive fibres, and No. 3 for the violet-sensitive fibres" (*163*, p. 143).

trum. It will be noted that all fibers are responsive in some measure to all waves, though the "red" fibers (those that report "red" when stimulated) are excited most by long waves, "green" fibers respond best to those of medium length, and "violet" fibers are maximally stimulable by short waves. It should be noted that the peak of the "violet" curve is in a spectral region that may as well be called "blue." The designations "blue" and "violet" are therefore used indiscriminately in discussions of the trichromatic theory. All sensations of color result from these three simultaneous excitations, and one need only know the relative strengths of the components in the stimulus light to predict what color will be seen. Thus yellow, e.g., involves approximately equal responses on the parts of the red and green fibers, a small violet component slightly desaturating the mixture. Greenish blue results from equal excitations of the green and violet fibers, a little red "graying" it. White consists of simultaneous and equal activity by all three sets of fibers.

Nowadays we conceive the mechanism to be three different sets of cones, each with its own light-sensitive material and its own absorption characteristics, but Young's basic idea of three additive processes is retained in the modern statement of the theory.

It has been amply demonstrated that several different sets of curves will satisfactorily care for all the facts of color mixture. The three components may be relatively widely separated, as in Fig. 29, or they may overlap to a great extent. It is only when one considers other quantitative relations, such as those coming out of hue discrimination and spectral saturation measurements, that the possibilities become limited. Figure 30, taken from Hecht's theorizing, shows three sets of cone primaries designed to meet slightly different demands. The upper set of curves describes color mixture and photopic visibility exactly but only approximates the data of hue discrimination and saturation. The middle set has been adjusted to the "colorimetric purity" (saturation) data of Priest and Brickwedde. The lower curves describe better than the others the detailed facts of hue discrimination but slightly distort the other relations. The differences need not be stressed to the exclusion of the similarities, however. It is apparent that Young's trichromatic theory may still, about a century and a half after its inception, accommodate modern color measurements to a remarkable degree. Even if slight concessions were to be made here and there in the construction of the curves and an average of them taken, it is apparent that most of the basic facts of color vision—mixture, spectral visibility, hue discrimination, complementary colors, and spectral saturation—would be cared for tolerably well. In view of the fact that these several sets of measurements were made by different investigators, at different times, and with various equipment and observers, the agreement must be considered truly striking.

One startling thing coming out of a study of the cone primaries is the realization that the spectrum does not yield much "color"! Since white results from equal excitations of all three elements, it follows that the "whiteness" at any point in the spectrum is given by a value three times the ordinate of the lowest curve at that point. The curves for the three primaries lie very close together, and only that vertical distance extending above the lowest curve can be representative of the addition of "hue" to the white. This means that the spectrum is really very poorly saturated, and the fact, which we have already encountered, that there can be saturations far better than those of the spectrum seems entirely reasonable.

Three kinds of color-receiving elements having been assumed to exist in the retina, it would be very convenient if we could stimulate one set of cones independently of the others. As Maxwell has said (209, p. 448), "This would be truly a primary colour, whether the

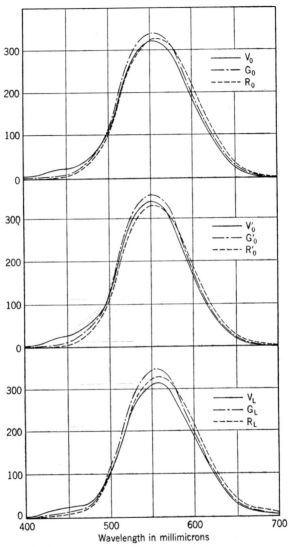

Fɪɢ. 30.   Spectral characteristics of three hypothetical sets of cone primaries. The top set of curves satisfies the facts of color mixture and photopic visibility exactly, the middle set accommodates the data of saturation discrimination, while the lower set fits hue discrimination data better than do the others.   From Hecht, *151*.   By permission of the Howe Laboratory of Ophthalmology, Harvard University.

nerve were excited by pure or by compound light, or even by the action of pressure or disease." But the cones are so small and, especially in the center of the retina, so closely packed together and, moreover, there is so much light scattered throughout the ocular media, that it has never been found possible to direct a beam of light, however finely adjusted, on a single element. Were this possible it is still highly probable that the threshold of sensation would never be passed

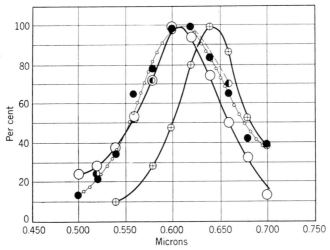

Fig. 31. Relative magnitudes of electrical responses from different receptors in the retinae of tenches (European fresh-water fish). From Granit, 128. Courtesy of the editor, *Journal of the Optical Society of America*.

by so meager a stimulus. One would suppose that microscopical study of retinal tissue might reveal peculiarities of the three types of cones, but there is no "tag" whereby one set may be judged to "say red," another "green," and a third "violet" when excited. Presumably the differences are photochemical and neural, not anatomical.

However, some beginnings have been made in the proper direction. Using an ingenious microtechnique, Granit (*128*) has been able to record the electrical changes accompanying activity of single retinal elements in several species of animals known to be capable of color vision. Distinct types of receptors were found. Figure 31 shows the relative magnitudes of electrical response from different receptors in the eye of the tench, a fresh-water fish possessing "visual violet" (Wald's cone substance) in the retina.

Further direct support for the trichromatic theory comes from studies of nerve degeneration in the lateral geniculate body, the center through which the majority of optic nerve fibers pass in the projection of the retina on the cortex. There are known to be six distinct layers of fibers in the lateral geniculate body, three from each eye. Destruction of tissue at a local area of the retina leads to degeneration *in all* three pathways through the geniculate body (59). The conclusion seems inescapable that three processes are associated with a particular retinal locus. The idea is strengthened by the added knowledge that such threefold representation in the geniculate body obtains only for the central region of the retina, the only place where color recognition is distinct.

Despite its many advantages the trichromatic theory of Young and Helmholtz has not always had a clear field, nor have its fundamental tenets remained undisputed. Two other theories, that of Ewald Hering and that of Christine Ladd-Franklin, have contended for prominence, and the weight of opinion, especially in psychological circles, has sometimes favored one or the other. The chief objection of both Hering and Ladd-Franklin to the trichromatic theory is that it fails to recognize the cardinal fact that yellow and white are as elementary and simple in experience as are red, green, and blue. Ladd-Franklin complained that "the Young-Helmholtz theory is at most three-fifths of a colour theory." This point has been encountered before, and we have seen that it has been met, at least formally, by the demonstration that yellow and white may be "brain" processes, since they may be synthesized through binocular mixture.

Whereas the principal facts prompting the trichromatic theory were those of color mixture, it was a purely psychological consideration, the apparent unitariness of the six sensations, white, black, red, green, yellow, and blue, that served as the inspiration for Hering's theory of color vision. He supposed the primaries to be arranged in pairs and thus also arrived at the idea of a three-component mechanism. There are for Hering three complex substances, one mediating white-black vision, another accounting for red and green, and a third responsible for yellow and blue. Each substance, in its unstimulated condition, is in a state of equilibrium and yields gray (the "self-light of the retina"). The white-black material is more plentifully supplied and is more readily excitable than the others. When activated it gives purely achromatic brilliance and can be depressed in the direction of black only through light adaptation and contrast. The other two substances behave somewhat differently, having their activity either depressed (catabolism) or augmented (anabolism) by the action of light. The red-green substance yields red when "torn down" by

light, and green when "built up." Similarly, in the yellow-blue substance catabolism produces blue, whereas anabolism results in yellow.
Spectral light falling on a system of this kind will excite all three
substances in varying degree, and the single sensation elicited will
be the resultant of the three processes acting jointly, as in the trichromatic theory.

Hering was never very clear about the location of his metabolic
substances, always referring vaguely to the *Netzhaut*, the entire optical
nervous apparatus, as responsible for light reception. It remained for
Troland (*286*), the outstanding modern exponent of the theory, to
restate it and place the substances in three types of cones. He has,
at least qualitatively, shown the adequacy of the theory to the main
facts of color mixture (albeit a little wastefully, since three components are enough), hue discrimination, saturation data, adaptation, and
after-images. Special assumptions are needed to care for the color
"zones" and contrast phenomena, as indeed they are for the Young-
Helmholtz theory. A serious difficulty in the Hering theory lies in
its basic postulate that anabolism can be brought about by the direct
action of an external stimulus. This notion runs counter to all modern
physiological conceptions of metabolic reactions.

The Ladd-Franklin theory represents in a sense a compromise, being
trichromatic for mixture purposes but tetrachromatic in its insistence
on the primacy of yellow. The distinctive feature of this theory is
the stress it lays upon the possible development of the color sense;
it is therefore sometimes spoken of as a "genetic" theory of color vision.

It is supposed that our present capacity to discern colors has evolved
from a primitive mode of seeing in which only blacks, whites, and
grays could be discriminated. Vision was mediated exclusively by a
white "mother substance" which, in two subsequent cleavages, has
first split into blue and yellow materials, and then the yellow has
further differentiated into red and green substances. The end products
of this evolution are thus the components of the trichromatic theory:
red, green, and blue. It should not surprise us if the theory is able
to interpret color mixture data adequately.

The greatest appeal of the Ladd-Franklin theory lies in its apparent
ease of interpretation of the facts of color blindness and those of the
retinal color zones. Red-green color blindness would appear to be an
atavistic phenomenon, a "throwback" to a more primitive stage of
color vision in which only blue and yellow are present. But why,
then, the distinct differences between protanopia and deuteranopia?

Are there two atavistic paths—and leading to what variations of the yellow substance?

The color "zones" might reasonably represent the present state of evolution of the color sense. The primitive white substance is present throughout the entire retina, and hence brightness discrimination occurs out to the limits of the visual field. The blue and yellow sub-stances, being the first decomposition products, have not yet invaded the extreme periphery but are more extensively distributed than the red and green, which, being relatively recent acquisitions, are restricted to the inner zone. It would be convenient for the theory if the red and green fields were more nearly coincident and if the limits for blue and yellow similarly fell together.

A more serious difficulty arises from the failure to "house" the sensitive substances. The theory does not lend itself to the picture of discrete types of cones. This in itself is not necessarily bad, but the alternative is to suppose that three or more different kinds of messages may be conveyed over identical nerve fibers. This does violence to some very well-established neurological ideas which, until we are in possession of better ones, we would do well not to discard.

Certain color phenomena are not handled at all adequately by any existing theory. The satisfactory explanation of the common varieties of color blindness has, in particular, been a stumbling block. It will not do to assume, as some proponents of the Hering theory have done, that R-G blindness represents simply the absence of the R-G substance. Again, why protanopia and deuteranopia? The R-G substance cannot be "missing" now one way and now another. Acuity, we have noted, is normal; presumably nothing is missing.

If an explanation of color blindness is to be based on a purely retinal mechanism the most nearly adequate one would appear to be that of Fick (92). Reasoning within the framework of the Young-Helmholtz theory, he supposed protanopia to result from the substitution in the "red" cones of the green receiving substance with, however, a retention by the fibers attached to the red cones of their normal capacity to report "red." There would then be a shortening of the spectrum at the long-wave end, and the red cones would respond simultaneously with, and to the same extent as, the normal green cones. Neither "red" nor "green" could be reported in isolation, and all spectral lights down to about $\lambda 500$ mμ would appear yellowish. Similarly, deuteranopia involves the substitution in the "green" cones of the red receiving material. No shortening of the spectrum would be occasioned, and, owing to the manner of crossing of the red and blue curves, an appreciable "gray band" should appear in the deuter-anopic spectrum in the region of $\lambda 500$ mμ. As with the protanope, all visible waves longer than this should yield yellow, since there is no way in which the "green" and "red" could be elicited singly.

This special modification of the trichromatic theory explains the two forms of R-G blindness remarkably well and is clearly in advance of all other color theories in this regard. A difficulty appears, however, when one attempts to relate it to the quantitative facts of spectral visibility in red-green blindness. There is no trouble with deuter-anopia; the relations are as predicted. The protanope, however, sees the spectrum as too bright in the blue and violet and too dim in the long waves to accommodate the theory precisely, however ingenious it may be.

There is, of course, no necessity for adhering to the idea of a strictly retinal mechanism in attempting to account for color phenomena. It is perhaps short-sighted of the classical theories of color vision that they have so little to do with the optical pathway and optical brain. It is as though these organs were not participants in the visual response. One theory, which is reasonably adequate to the facts of color blind-ness, takes some account of processes other than the photochemical ones of the retinal receptors. This is the formulation of G. E. Müller (177). It is made up of the chief elements of the Young-Helmholtz and Hering theories and is sometimes spoken of as a "zone" or "stage" theory of color vision. The first stage is the photochemical one of light reception by the cones. For this initial step Müller supposes the pri-maries of the Young-Helmholtz theory (red, green, violet) to be pres-ent. A second stage is chemical and involves two pairs of antagonistic processes, the red-green and yellow-blue balanced reactions of the Hering theory. The final stage is that of excitation of the optic nerve; here may be aroused the six "psychological primaries": red, yellow, green, blue, black, and white.

The implication of the Müller theory is that a most elaborate mechanism is at work, but perhaps color vision does involve this de-gree of complexity. At any rate the theory does what none of the simpler ones does—it predicts in some detail the characteristics of all the forms of color blindness listed in Table 1, including the rare types. Like its progenitors, however, it is not a complete theory in that many color phenomena other than those of color-defective vision go un-explained by it.

What shall we say now in evaluation of the current available theories? Is one clearly right and the others wrong? If we thought so we should never have regarded them as theories in the first place. All have demonstrated their worth in setting problems and aiding in their solution. Until a master generalization is unearthed which will make one or more of the theories completely untenable it is the part of wisdom to retain them, view them critically, and be constantly ready to revise or abandon them.

5

Visual Acuity, Contrast, and Interaction

Spatial Visual Acuity. Under usual conditions of illumination an object may be seen with the greatest distinctness if we "turn our eyes" toward it, i.e., if the image is made to fall on the fovea. Peripheral regions of the retina have little power to discriminate particulars of form. The appearance of the whole visual field has been likened to a "picture the details of which are finely etched in the center as in a steel engraving while the outlying parts are only roughly sketched in as in a charcoal drawing."

Visual acuity, the capacity of the eye to resolve details, thus normally varies greatly in different regions of the retina. The precise definition of acuity is given in terms of the reciprocal of the angular distance separating two contours when they are just distinguishable as two. Because it conveniently represents average performance of the "good" eye, the unit is taken to be one minute of arc. A person with normal acuity would be able to discern as distinct two points separated by as little as 1' of arc and, if this represented his best performance, his acuity would be 1.0. Actually, some eyes have a resolving power of as much as 2.0 or even 3.0.

Test objects most commonly used for determining visual acuity are the Snellen letters (the familiar letter chart of the oculist's office), Landolt rings (broken circles), ruled gratings, and variations of these. The convention is to employ as a standard an object subtending a 5' angle, the detail to be discriminated being 1' in width. Ideally, the 5:1 ratio should be maintained throughout a set of different-sized test objects. With block letters, such as those of the Snellen series, this requirement can only be approximated, since only a circular form could meet it rigidly. The Landolt "broken circles" (or the Ferree-Rand "double broken circles") are superior and should in time supplant the Snellen letters. Gratings consist of glass plates having equidistant parallel lines ruled on them; their great advantage lies in the fact that transmitted rather than reflected light may be used with them. Grids and checkerboard designs have been employed by some. Acuity measurements have also been made with single fine wires suspended in a uniformly illuminated field, the thinnest wire to be resolved determining the acuity level. Clearly, the concept of acuity has here been given a different definition, there being no interspace to be discriminated, and we should not expect exact agreement between results gained by the two methods. Indeed, experiment proves the results to differ in the two cases. Measures of the *minimum visible* (single-fine-line technique) typically show the least width of line that can be detected to subtend an angle of the order of 1″. Acuity as measured by the *minimum separable* (interspace between contours) requires an angle of the order of 1′, as we have seen.

Still other kinds of visual tasks may be used as a basis for measuring acuity. *Vernier acuity* involves the detection of a break in a single vertical line, the displacement being a lateral one. The smallest "jog" in the line that can be seen thus establishes the magnitude of vernier acuity. Acuteness of vision measured in this way is more nearly related to the minimum visible than to the minimum separable, giving optimal values around 5–10″ of arc. *Stereoscopic acuity* brings in the binocular relation. It is defined in terms of the least perceptible depth displacement of two objects. The objects may be presented separately to the two eyes, as in the stereoscope, or real distance separations may be effected, as in the "three-rod" (Howard-Dolman) test, familiar as a test for depth perception in the armed services. Visual acuity determined stereoscopically gives optimal values close to those for monocular vernier acuity (5–10″ of arc), though the psychophysiological processes concerned in the two are patently different. In a well-controlled experiment employing a stereoscope to present a stationary vertical line to the left eye and a movable one to the right, Mueller and Lloyd (217) found stereoscopic acuity to vary systematically with intensity of illumination, averaging around 10″ of arc for high intensities and about 25″ for low.

Acuity, however measured, varies with illumination in an interesting way. We know from everyday experience that small print, difficult to discern in dim light, may be read with ease under higher illumination. The relation has been worked out systematically, and the data gathered by Koenig, at the turn of the last century, are still standard. They are reproduced in Fig. 32. The S-shaped curve should by now be suggestive. As suspected, the function is really compounded of two. The lower branch is representative of rod mediation; above an acuity of about 0.1 the cones take over the task.

One interpretation that accords well with other phases of visual theory requires us to suppose that both rods and cones vary among themselves with respect to threshold.   At the lowest illuminations only a few rods are stimulated.   Since they presumably have a "chance" distribution (with respect to threshold), this amounts to a sparse func-

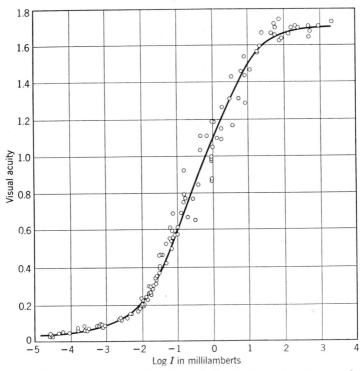

FIG. 32.   Relation between visual acuity and illumination intensity, according to the data of Koenig (1897).   From Hecht, *151*.   By permission of the Howe Laboratory of Ophthalmology, Harvard University.

tional population.   If the active elements are far apart the resolving power must be poor, just as in a "grainy" photographic film in which the elements are relatively far apart.   As light intensity is increased, more and more rods have their thresholds passed, bringing a greater number into play and thus reducing the average distance between functioning receptors.   At a certain point (acuity of 0.1, approximately) the cones enter the picture and shortly are exclusively mediating the visual response.   Vision is now best foveally, and it improves steadily with continued increase in illumination.   Only when the thresholds of all cones have been passed will a further intensity increase be ineffective. If illumination is extremely high, reflectance from all objects, "black" and "white" alike, will be great. Receptors can no longer function differentially, all will be stimulated maximally, and "glare" will be the result. The inability to discern any objects when subjected to the dazzling light of a snow field in the full sun is a case in point.

The mechanism assumed by this account is, of course, identical with that postulated for intensity discrimination. And why not? Visual acuity may be thought of as a special case of intensity discrimination. To test the resolving power of the eye one sets up a situation which requires the subject to make a darkness-lightness judgment: to detect the light interspace between two dark contours, to distinguish a dark line against a bright background, to tell when two points of light, seen in the dark, fuse into one or break apart, etc. Any interpretation of visual acuity, to be acceptable, must be in full accord with one's basic account of intensity discrimination.

There has been much speculation concerning the anatomical basis of visual acuity (295, 256). Measurements of the diameter of foveal cones yield suggestive values. According to Polyak's determinations (234) the average cone in the center of the fovea centralis is of such size as to subtend a visual angle of 24″, though some are even a little smaller. This value includes the sheath separating adjacent cones. For the minimum separable such a value would serve. It need only be assumed that between two groups of stimulated cones there are two or three unstimulated rows. For the minimum visible, however, the cone diameters are too great to permit of an explanation in terms of end-organ separation.

As matters now stand this kind of thinking about visual acuity proves to be quite unprofitable. One need only recall the many events transpiring between the entrance of light rays into the eye and their final representation in the brain to see that the geometrical features of a test object are unlikely to be preserved without change throughout this elaborate process. To begin with, there is not even complete preservation of the optical image within the eyeball itself. A variety of influences operate to blur it. Light is diffracted by the edge of the pupil and scattered by the dioptric media through which it must pass to reach the retina. The eye, in common with most optical instruments, is subject to both chromatic and spherical aberration. As though these factors making for indistinctness of the image were not enough, the entire eyeball, it turns out, is only unstably held in position. The line of regard, in fixating an object, actually dances about slightly. Careful measurements of the eye's fixational movements ("physiological nystagmus," it is sometimes called) have been made by Riggs (242), using an ingenious technique in which a plane mirror mounted on a contact lens is the main element in a sensitive optical lever. Four different kinds of motion are found to be going on when the eyes are being "held still." There are: (1) very rapid movements occurring at frequencies ranging from 30 to 70 per second. These rarely embrace excursions of as much as 1' of arc, having an average extent of 17.5", but may occasionally be as large as 2' of arc; (2) relatively slow motions, highly variable from moment to moment and from one subject to another, occurring generally 2 to 5 times a second and ranging from 1' to 5' in extent; (3) slow drifts extending as much as 5' in any direction and on which both of the above described motions are superposed; and (4) irregular rapid jerks, ranging from 2.2' to 25.8' of arc (average of 5.6'). These jerky motions often seem to be compensatory for the slow drifts. If all these movements of the eye are now combined it is seen that "fixation" of the eye is a very lively event and must be thought of in dynamic, rather than static, terms. In fact, it would appear that the eye is never really motionless. Over a period of 3 to 4 sec, even though their owner is making every effort to maintain steady fixation, the eyes are totaling up movement that amounts to 10–20' of arc. In all this activity light from any given point of an object being "fixated" must be impinging successively on 25 to 50 different receptor cells and can be expected to remain on one cone for only a few hundredths of a second, at most.

In view of all these influences making for non-correspondence between the visual acuity test object and a particular pattern of cells in the retinal mosaic, one sees how fruitless it is to speculate about the minimum separable or the minimum visible in relation to the width of optic nerve endings. Acuity must eventually find an adequate explanation in its underlying neural anatomy and physiology, but the suspicion is that the relevant nervous structures and functions will be those of the optic nerve and visual cortex of the brain. At least, considerations other than those having to do with the peripheral end organ will be important.

Temporal Acuity; Flicker. When a series of equally spaced flashes strikes the retina, flicker is likely to result. Whether flicker will be seen and what its appearance will be are primarily determined by the flash frequency. When it is low the contrast between darkness and the flash is great. As frequency is increased there is a reduction in contrast, and at a sufficiently high rate of repetition the individual flashes will not be sensed at all. The point at which flicker just disappears is known as the *critical fusion frequency*. It is convenient to

Visual Acuity, Contrast, and Interaction

provide the flashes by interrupting a steady light with a sectored disc and, by convention, one having equal open and closed sectors. In making a critical fusion frequency determination it is necessary only to increase disc speed until the last vestige of flicker has just been eliminated, leaving a smooth and steady field, and express frequency in terms of the number of flashes (or cycles of light and dark) per second.

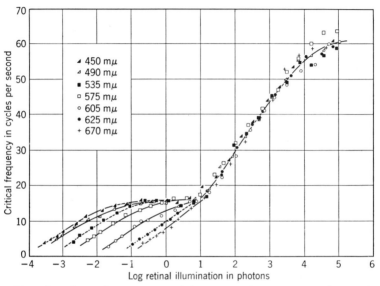

Fig. 33. The relation between critical frequency of fusion, in cycles (flashes) per second, and intensity of illumination, in photons (trolands), for seven different spectral regions. From Hecht and Shlaer, *157*. By permission of the Rockefeller Institute for Research and Dr. Shlaer.

Critical fusion frequency proves to be a variable quantity, though precisely measurable for a given set of conditions. It depends upon the intensity of the stimulus, its wavelength composition, stimulus size, the state of adaptation of the eye, the retinal locus of the image, whether or not there is excitation of neighboring retinal areas, and probably other factors. If all but one of these variables is held constant and the effect of the remaining one is systematically investigated, accurately reproducible curves may be obtained. The relation between fusion frequency and intensity of illumination is of special interest and has been determined many times. Figure 33 gives some typical results. This graph has the additional advantages of showing the dependence on wavelength and the now familiar characteristic break between the rod and cone segments of the function. The main relationship, however, is that between intensity (log I) and fusion frequency. From about 15 flashes per second, the practical lower limit at which fusion may be maintained with the dimmest foveal light, to about 60 flashes per second, above which flicker cannot be detected even in the brightest test patch, there is an approximately linear relation with log I. A series of such lines obtains for lower intensities visible in the periphery, ranging upwards from about 3 flashes. It was originally thought that the relation was a strictly logarithmic one, and the Ferry-Porter law, formulated in 1892, stated this to be the case. We now see that this relation, like that for $\Delta I/I$, has a curvilinear form.

It is not immediately clear why the fusion point-log I curve should run in the direction it does. One might suppose that a bright flash, arousing a more vigorous response on the part of the retina, would "carry over" farther into the dark interval and thus require a lower flash rate to produce continuity. The positive after-image of a dim light would not persist as long and would seem to require a high critical fusion frequency. The mystery is dispelled when one comes to think of flicker in terms of successive brightness discriminations (Fig. 34). Flicker can be seen only when excitation level fluctuates outside the limits of one j.n.d. of brilliance. An intense flash precipitously raises the excitation level to a high point, but its decline is also sharp. A series of dim flashes yields a more gradually changing excitation curve, and a new flash is not required so promptly to maintain the undiminished level.

Because fusion frequency is accurately determinable and because it varies regularly with a number of influences affecting visual sensitivity, it may itself be used as an index of sensitivity. The author has elsewhere urged (*111*) that in the critical fusion point we have a measure of visual *temporal* acuity, analogous to visual *spatial* acuity measures, already discussed.

One of the puzzling features of the critical flash rate is the manner in which it varies, under standard conditions, from one individual to another. For a given moderate illumination it is possible to find values ranging between 35 and 45 flashes per second among a dozen different observers. For a single individual this would correspond to an illumination change of 1:100, a very considerable one indeed. It is not a matter of unreliable measurement. Ten successive settings from the same subject will show a very narrow range of values; as has been said, great precision attaches to such determinations. An extensive study by Tice (*281*) involving large numbers of measures, not only of fusion points but of other timed visual phenomena, has failed to provide any correlations suggesting an adequate answer to this question.

Another curious effect associated with flicker is that appearing when rotation speed is reduced below the fusion point and the successive flashes begin to be seen as somewhat discrete. Under these conditions there is a great enhancement of brilliance, that of the individual flashes

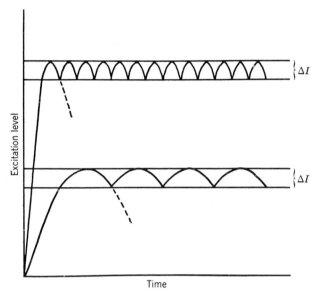

FIG. 34. The theoretical course of flicker. The lower curve represents the fluctuations in brilliance evoked by a dim light at the critical fusion frequency. The upper curve similarly represents the effect created by a bright light. For the more intense stimulus the rise in excitation is quite abrupt, but so is the decline. The stimulus flashes must be repeated more frequently to maintain excitation within the limits of ΔI and render the flickering light "steady" in appearance.

increasing far above the level they would reach with steady light of the same intensity. This is known as the *Brücke effect* and has been extensively investigated by Bartley (*17*). There is considerable evidence to show that subjective flicker rate is not "locked" to objective flash rate, especially at low frequencies of the latter. Autonomous brain processes, revealed by electrical brain waves, apparently enter the picture to modify flicker phenomena.

Contrast. Another lack of exact correspondence between stimulus and sensation is revealed in contrast. Broadly stated, contrast occurs in any field in which differential stimulation occurs. Since a homogeneous field filling the entire retina is encountered but rarely, contrast is seen to be a very general phenomenon, affecting practically all visual experiences. Two lights, closely adjacent in the field, alter the appearance of each other in a predictable way. If the lights are colorless we are dealing with an instance of *brightness contrast*, and the effect is in the direction of increasing the observed difference between them. If the lights possess hue *color contrast* intervenes also to augment the difference but, in this instance, to shift each one in the direction of the complement of the other. A simple way to observe the contrast effect is to place a gray square on a colored surface. The gray immediately becomes tinged with the hue complementary to the background. Pieces of gray paper cut from the same sheet appear almost unbelievably different when compared on several different well-saturated colored backgrounds.

Very vivid contrast effects can be produced by the "colored shadow" technique. If general illumination is supplied to a surface by a colored lamp and an opaque object, such as a rod, is held so as to cast a shadow on the surface, the area on which the shadow falls will be found to possess the hue of the complement of the light. If, now, accessory white general illumination is made to fall on the surface, the contrast color in the shadow will be quite vivid. It is a general rule of color contrast that it is at a maximum when unaccompanied by brilliance contrast, and the white light here tends to equalize brightness. The elimination of contours between two contrasting areas also favors maximal color effects.

Color contrast is so undeniable and "real" a phenomenon as to lead to the conviction, on the part of the naive observer of it, that its explanation is to be given in physical terms, that it represents something happening "out there" in the stimulus. The author has seen a student, working in the laboratory on the contrast effect, attempting to recombine, by an ingenious prism arrangement, contrast colors in shadows! Pedagogical principles dictated that the experiment not be interfered with, and the results were instructive if disappointing.

Many explanations of contrast have been offered. They range from the fantastic suggestion that a rapid "circulation" of decomposed photochemicals goes on in the retina (Ladd-Franklin) to the notion that contrast always represents an "illusion of judgment" (Helmholtz). Both of these are almost certainly wrong, but, of all the hypotheses thus far offered, there appears to be none that is clearly correct. Most speculation as to the "seat" of the process places it in the brain, but it can be demonstrated that, if so, it is presumably not identified with activity of the highest centers. A reinterpretation by Graham (*124,* p. 861) of an old experiment by Hering on binocular color mixture shows conclusively that contrast must be induced before the arrival of impulses at the visual cortex.

It is urgent that a satisfactory theory of contrast be devised; it has proved the greatest possible stumbling block for general color theory. None of the current theories, successful though they may be with a considerable range of other facts, has any adequate account to offer of color contrast.

Spatial Interaction. While contrast may eventually turn out to be a subcortical brain process, there is little doubt that the retina itself provides the possibilities for interaction of excitations. When we were considering the structure of the retina, it was noted that many lateral connections are present. The supposition is that the retina can operate as a nervous *center*. Prompted partly by this suggestion and to some extent by the desire to quantify the relations in brilliance contrast, a large number of studies have been directed towards interaction phenomena.

It is known that, in the relatively simple nervous centers found in the spinal cord, neighboring pathways interact with each other to provide a variety of effects: facilitation, summation, inhibition, "recruitment," etc. (63). Is the retina capable of any of these? It appears that it is.

The problem has a brief but busy history, and the "classic" experiment in this field is that of Adrian and Matthews in 1928 (6). Their work was on the eye of the conger eel, a record being made of the electrical changes in the optic nerve. The "latent period," the time between the application of the stimulus and the initial response on the part of the nerve, was taken as the measure of sensitivity. Latency of response to four closely grouped light spots falling on the retina proved to be shorter than that to any single spot. When the illuminated areas were separated by greater distances and "summation" no longer appeared, bathing the retina with strychnine (known to permit ready spread of nervous impulses) once more brought about a relative reduction of latency to the "four-spot" stimulation.

A technique used widely for studying interaction is the flicker method. There are good reasons for believing that flicker measurements provide an index of purely retinal events, and the assumption that they do has been widely accepted (124, pp. 844–845; 254). Using flicker, Granit and his colleagues have demonstrated that summation occurs in the periphery of the human eye. A repetition of the "four-spot" experiment yields results which are best interpreted as evidence for summation on the part of the rod mechanism (126). Absolute threshold determinations in the periphery, made with two interacting stimuli present in various degrees of separation, point to the same conclusion (28).

That spatial summation should occur in the periphery of the human eye, where many rods converge on a single ganglion cell, is probably to be expected. The functional and anatomical facts are in agreement. However, it is not so clear why summation should operate within the rod-free macula where the arrangement of nerve fibers is quite different. Yet abundant experimental evidence indicates that it does (129, 111, 108). Nor is it apparent what mechanism is responsible for bringing about a facilitation of macular vision when an additional stimulus is thrown into the periphery. It is known that foveal sensitivity, both absolute and differential, is improved by using a bright "surround" encompassing the central field. Foveal fusion points are raised also by adding a steady light to the periphery (109). It has likewise been shown that peripheral sensitivity is enhanced by simultaneous macular stimulation (294); interaction apparently works in both directions.

Not all interaction effects are those of facilitation, however. Under some conditions (125, 100) inhibition can be demonstrated. Results and interpretations of many interaction experiments are as yet conflicting, and the full meaning of the phenomena is by no means apparent. But it seems certain that the retina behaves like a nervous center in displaying such variations, and the main word should be one of caution against oversimplifying our picture of the eye's action.

6

Sound Energy and the Ear

The procedure was found useful, in studying the visual process, of first becoming acquainted with the characteristics of the stimuli and with the anatomical and physiological features of the receptor organ before considering the various phenomena of seeing. A similar approach to the subject of hearing will prove fruitful. We need to know something of the nature of sound energy and of the manner in which it affects the tissues of the ear before the phenomena of hearing can most profitably be examined.

The Physical Nature of Sound. If uncertainty exists as to what conception of light energy is most useful for experimental purposes there is none concerning sound energy and its manner of propagation. Sound is generated only by vibrating bodies and is transmitted by wave motion of a material medium. Air is usually the medium, though sound may be conducted by other gases and by liquids and solids. Wherever an elastic material exists there are the potentialities for sound transmission. Sound will not travel in a vacuum, as is amply demonstrated by the bell jar demonstration of elementary physics (213), first entirely convincingly performed nearly three centuries ago by Robert Boyle. A ringing bell, suspended under a jar, will become inaudible when the air of the container is exhausted by a pump. Readmission of air or any other gas permits the renewal of sound transmission.

The nature of the conducting medium is not a matter of indifference, for the speed with which sound is propagated varies with it. The velocity of sound is a function of the density of the medium and its elasticity. As compared with that of light, the propagation of sound is an extremely slow process. For air at 15° C. the rate is 340 m/sec. A convenient figure to keep in mind is the approximate equivalent in the English system, 1100 ft/sec. Sound velocity is about four times as great as this in water and is again approximately quadrupled when

94

such solids as steel, glass, India rubber, and the hardest woods become the medium. It is interesting to note that, whereas the majority of sounds we hear are air-borne over the greater portion of their paths, the final conduction rate we must deal with in audition is that for the liquid filling the inner ear and is thus of the order of about 4500 ft/sec.

When we speak of the velocity of sound it is, of course, the speed of the *wavefront* that is under consideration, for the individual particles of air "conducting" the sound are displaced from their position of rest only slightly and describe to and fro movements of constantly changing acceleration, longitudinal to the direction of propagation.

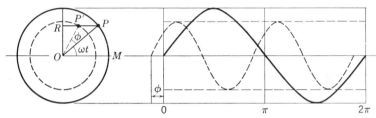

Fig. 35.   Representation of harmonic (sinusoidal) motion in sound propagation. Besides demonstrating that the sine wave is the projection of uniform circular motion, the diagram shows how two such waves may differ in frequency, amplitude, and phase.   From Stevens and Davis, 273.

If a sound generator of the simplest sort, such as a tuning fork, is the driving force the motion will be *harmonic* or *sinusoidal.*   Figure 35 is a representation of such motion, spread out on a time axis; it will be seen to be the projection of uniform circular motion.   The crests of waves represent points of maximal compression (or, more exactly, points of maximal increase over normal atmospheric pressure), while the troughs are regions of greatest rarefaction of air or reduction of pressure.   Sound waves thus consist of successive pressure variations and, in their least complex form, sinusoidal pressure variations.

Frequency, Amplitude, and Phase.   The time required for a complete cycle of changes to occur is called the *period* of the wave, and the distance traveled by the wavefront in one period is its *wavelength.* Since, as we have seen, velocity is a function of a number of variables, it has not become conventional, as it has with light, to characterize sound waves by their length but rather by the number of cycles completed per unit of time, that is to say, by their *frequency.*   Wavelength and frequency are, of course, related reciprocally.

Roughly, the frequencies of importance for human hearing are those between 20 and 20,000~ (cycles) per second.   For the good ear this wide frequency band represents a region of continuous audibility. There are clear evidences that some animals, cats, dogs, bats, and rats among them, can hear tones higher in frequency than 20,000∿ (so-called ultrasonic waves), and frequencies below 20∿ are not without their effect on the human ear, as we shall see.

Another way of designating frequency is by reference to the musical scale. It is comprised of a range of frequencies extending to nearly 5000∿ in discrete steps, the latter selected partly on esthetic and

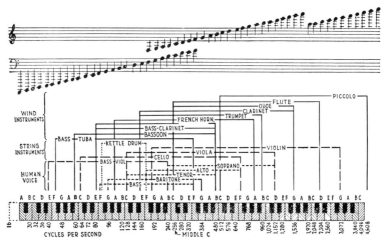

FIG. 36. Tonal frequency and the musical scale. After Henney, *165*.

partly on practical grounds. The ranges of various orchestral instruments and the human voice are shown in Fig. 36. It is interesting to observe that the lowest frequencies used musically, those generated by the largest organ pipes (16∿), extend even below the lower limit of tonal audibility and must make their contribution to musical enjoyment by serving as tactual rather than as auditory stimuli. The largest grand pianos have a range extending from A = 27.4∿ to c′′′′′ = 4214∿ (when pitched to a′ = 439∿). Orchestral tones encompass the lowest note of the contra bassoon (B♭ = 28.8∿) and the b′′′′ of the piccolo (3951∿), but all instruments have *overtones,* some of which are musically effective at least as high as 12,000∿.

Certain positions on the frequency scale have come to be of special significance, just as certain spectral points have value for reference. Insofar as there can be said to be any universally accepted scientific standards of frequency they are 256∿ and 1000∿, the former for its coincidence with "middle C" (the nearest power of 2 to musical c′) and the latter for its obvious convenience within the decimal system.

The musical standard, a′, has a long history of fluctuation, having been subject to the caprice of various artistic and practical demands. Ellis, in his remarkable history of musical pitch (*164*, pp. 493–513) has shown that a′ has varied from 373.1 to 567.3$\sim$, in different times and places and under various influences, the chief of which have been the desire for orchestral "brilliance" (high-pitched a′) and the accommodation of the human voice (lower-pitched a′). Attempts to standardize a′ include that of the Stuttgart Congress of Physicists in 1834 (a′ = 440$\sim$, so-called "Stuttgart pitch") and that involving the "diapason normal" (a′ = 435$\sim$), established by French governmental decree in 1859 and now known as "international pitch." Because that tuning fork which is the prototype of the "diapason normal" has been calculated to have a frequency of 439$\sim$ at the usual room temperature of 68° F., there has been an attempt to standardize a′ at this frequency, despite the numerical inconvenience involved.

Besides differing in wavelength or frequency, sound waves vary in *amplitude*, the amount of displacement of the vibrating particles in either direction from the position of rest. Obviously, amplitude of vibration is related to energy. However, the relation is not a simple, direct one. Energy is proportional to the product of the squares of the amplitude and frequency, or $E = ka^2f^2$. Thus sounds of high frequency possess greater energy than those of equal amplitude but lower frequency.

A third feature of the sound wave is its *phase*, the stage to which vibratory motion has advanced from its starting point or position of rest. Two tuning forks of the same period, struck simultaneously, will move alike at every instant and will be "in phase." If they are struck successively, so as to keep their motions always opposed, they are of "opposite phase." Any other relation is an "out-of-phase" one. Phase differences may be measured in terms of fractions of periods or, more commonly, in phase *angles* (see Fig. 35).

Complex Vibrations. Sounds possessing the simple sinusoidal form of vibration are actually of quite rare occurrence in nature, just as "monochromatic" lights are. Only a few sound generators, such as tuning forks and the best electric receivers driven by well-constructed oscillators, yield "pure" tones. All musical instruments emit tones having considerable complexity of waveform. It is, in fact, on the basis of differences in wave complexity that we are able to distinguish the "quality" or *timbre* of instruments. Fortunately for the science of sound, however, complex vibrations are susceptible of exact analysis into simple components. *Fourier's Theorem,* first devised in 1822 in connection with the analysis of heat, states that "a continuous periodic motion of any form can always be represented as the composite of a series of simple harmonic motions of suitable phases and amplitudes." Such motions have periods related to each other in simple mathematical ratio—1:2:3:4:5, etc. Whereas Fourier did not apply the principle to sound, it turns out that it is sufficiently general to permit

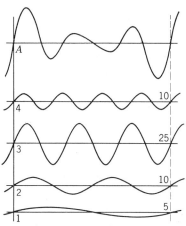

such application, and the analysis holds exactly for even the most complex of sound vibrations. Figure 37 shows four simple harmonic components of a complex wave. The diagram may be viewed either analytically or synthetically, for simple harmonic motions may be added together to produce wave forms of any degree of complexity. But the relation is more valuable in its analytic aspect, for it provides the principle on which are based various kinds of tone analyzers. These analyzers are composed of a series of tuned resonators or, in the case of the electric harmonic analyzer, sharply tuned electric circuits which respond to the individual components of the wave, revealing not only what frequencies are present but the relative contribution of each. It is an interesting feature of the ear's action that

FIG. 37. Analysis of a complex wave. The irregular curve at the top may be analyzed into the four regular ones beneath it, each with the relative amplitude given by the number to the right. Viewed synthetically, the top curve is the resultant of the others acting conjointly. From Beasley, 22. By permission of Harper and Brothers, publishers.

it behaves as though it were such an analyzer, and it is possible for the ear to detect, in a complex tone, many of its harmonic constituents. This fact, that we hear only pendular vibrations as simple and that all degrees of tonal complexity may be resolved into components falling in the Fourier series, is known as *Ohm's Acoustic Law*.

The structure of a complex tone, as revealed by the harmonic analyzer, is illustrated in Fig. 38. Here the record was obtained from a piano playing C = 128∿ (one octave below middle c). The components of the tone, as shown by its *acoustic spectrum*, are seen to extend over a considerable frequency range. The largest contribution is made by the *fundamental* (128∿), and, in general, the higher harmonics (overtones) have smaller and smaller magnitudes as the scale of commensurable frequencies is ascended. However, it is notable that in this instrument the sixth harmonic (fifth overtone, $g'' = 768\sim$) contributes a little more than half the amplitude of the fundamental. Doubtless other keys of the same piano or the same key struck differently would reveal other patterns of harmonics. Almost all other stringed instruments show patterns in which the higher harmonics

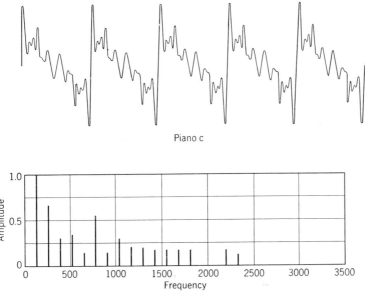

FIG. 38. The elaborate waveform produced by a piano playing $c = 128\sim$. The relative contribution made by each of the components is shown in the lower chart. From *Speech and hearing* (revised ed.), H. Fletcher, Bell Telephone Laboratories, Inc., copyright 1952, D. Van Nostrand Company, Inc.

make relatively greater contributions. Individual instruments vary, and only a small shift of emphasis in the components of the acoustic spectrum may make the difference between a Stradivarius and a run-of-the-mine fiddle.

Tones and Noises: Speech Sounds. Thus far we have been dealing with sustained tones, those having waves repetitive in form and frequency and, for appreciable intervals, unvarying in amplitude. Our ears are also assailed by a variety of other sounds, however—sounds chiefly notable for their lack of sustained frequency and commonly classed as *noise*. A sharp line of demarcation between tones and noises is difficult to draw because noises, like tones, are also comprised of a large series of components and are thus susceptible of similar analysis.

Moreover, most tone generators produce some noise, especially at the moment of being set into operation. Drop a piece of hardwood on a concrete floor, and it may be difficult to judge whether the resulting sound is predominantly noise or tone. It is not entirely facetious to suggest that such a device is, in fact, a musical instrument in embryo—

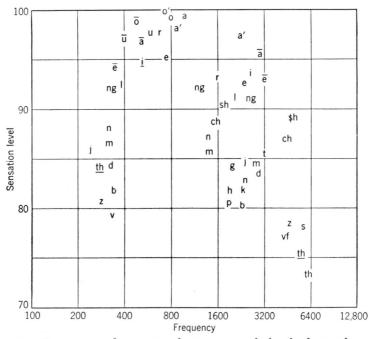

Fig. 39. Frequency and intensity characteristics of the fundamental speech sounds. Those elements having more than one principal component appear in two or three different positions on the chart. From *Speech and hearing* (revised ed.), H. Fletcher, Bell Telephone Laboratories, Inc., copyright 1952, D. Van Nostrand Company, Inc.

witness the xylophone and marimba. In these instruments resonators strengthening the tonal components throw the balance in the direction of sustained patterns of sound. Other percussion instruments similarly have much of the noise character about them.

Not only have noises a greater conglomeration of frequencies in them, but the components are likely to extend over a wider range. Whereas the sound energy represented in the orchestral rendition of a symphony may vary by a ratio of as much as 100,000 to 1, the moment-to-moment variation in the sound of an explosion may be many times this.

Speech sounds partake of the characteristics of both tones and noises, showing relatively sustained patterns at times and transient irregular waves at others. The characteristic powers ("sensation levels," defined below) and fundamental frequencies of various speech sounds are presented graphically in Fig. 39, taken from the Bell Telephone Laboratory studies. It will be noted that certain speech sounds appear at several positions on the chart; these have more than one principal frequency component. If the energy distribution throughout

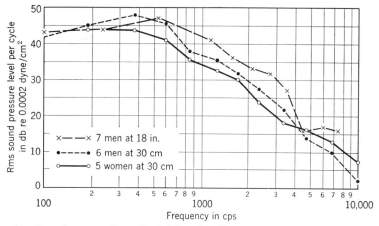

Fig. 40. Speech spectra for male and female talkers. The curves are plotted from averages of somewhat protracted sound pressure measurements and thus obscure the known differences in momentary speech patterns. From Licklider and Miller, *202*.

the range of audibility is measured for some representative samples of continuous speech, and the resulting values are then averaged, there are obtained curves of the kind shown in Fig. 40. The greater part of the speech energy lies in the lower frequencies, below 1000~, whether the speakers are men or women (*202*).

Interference and Reinforcement. Much of what has been said about the behavior of sound waves is true only when the vibrations are traveling in free space. Most laboratory conditions introduce complications in the control of sound. Walls, ceilings, and articles of furniture provide surfaces which may reflect waves. These return to interfere with the outgoing train and tend thus either to cancel or augment them. Smooth walls are excellent reflectors of sound, and even rough ones, if their irregularities are smaller than the length of the sound wave impinging upon them, behave in this respect as if they were perfectly smooth. It does not do to enclose the sound in tubes, for the opportunities for interference are then augmented. A steady tone released in a room sets up quite promptly an intricate pattern of advancing and returning waves which produce local intensifications and diminutions called *standing waves*. In small enclosed spaces these come to be of extreme importance and, as might be expected, are of common occurrence in musical instruments and other tone generators employing vibrating air columns. It is because interference effects are so intricate and incalculable that their makers use almost entirely empirical knowledge in the construction of flutes, organ pipes, and similar instruments, no trustworthy theoretical formulae having been evolved.

The immediate consequence of these considerations is that it does not suffice, for experimental purposes, to measure the characteristics of a sound generator at the source and assume that they will therefore be known at the ear. Through reinforcement a sound several feet in front of a loud speaker may be more intense than at the instrument itself.

Of late years, to be sure, there has been an upsurge in acoustical engineering knowledge, and we appear to have emerged successfully from the age of half-developed ideas when auditoriums were strung with fine wires to "break up" the sound (actually, their effect was negligible) and have begun to use some fairly efficient sound-absorbing materials to reduce reflection. Absorption, changing the rhythmic motions of sound waves into the random motions of heat, is accomplished best by porous materials like sheets of compressed vegetable fiber and acoustical plasters. It appears not to be possible ever to produce complete absorption, and there is little likelihood that rooms will ever be prepared in such a way as to permit their simulating the acoustical properties of free space.

Sound Intensity. There are several ways of specifying sound intensity, just as a number of alternatives present themselves in the measurement of light intensity. The basic concept for sound is that of pressure variation. We have seen that motions of the vibrating particle are the result of alternate increases and decreases of atmospheric pressure. Maximum pressure is realized at the crest of the wave, minimum pressure at the trough. . If we were to take a simple average of all pressures throughout the period of the wave we should, of course, arrive simply at the value for atmospheric pressure and should have no indication that energy is being expended in the wave, since there is as much compression as rarefaction of air in the course of the cycle of changes. The difficulty is obviated by taking a root mean square (r.m.s.) value of the pressure variations. The calculation is made in accordance with the formula:

$$\text{r.m.s. pressure (dynes/cm}^2) = \sqrt{(p - p_0)^2/2}$$

where p_0 is normal atmospheric pressure and p is the pressure at the point of maximum displacement in either direction (crest or trough). A short expression is that, for sinusoidal waves, the r.m.s. pressure is equal to the pressure amplitude divided by $\sqrt{2}$.

It is natural that our fundamental unit of intensity should be one of pressure variation, since most practical intensity-measuring devices, such as microphones, have responses directly proportional to r.m.s. pressure of the waves actuating them. These can be calibrated against standard pressures and used as direct-reading instruments. But current practice, growing out of the more or less complete electrification of sound equipment, has dictated that another way of specifying intensity will be preferred. At the present time a newer unit, the *decibel*, has fairly well usurped the field.

The decibel is defined as $\frac{1}{10}$ the common logarithm of the ratio between two energies, the one being measured and some other standard energy or *reference intensity*. Since pressure and energy are related by the square law, the decibel may also be defined as $\frac{1}{20}$ the common logarithm of the ratio between two pressures. Stated as a formula, where N equals the number of decibels:

$$N = 10 \log E_1/E_2 = 20 \log p_1/p_2$$

E_1 and E_2 are the two energies in question, and p_1 and p_2 the pressures. One reference intensity (E_2 or p_2) frequently used, because it is especially meaningful, is the threshold of hearing—the least energy necessary to produce an auditory sensation. Since this point may be somewhat unstable, another reference intensity has been agreed upon for exact acoustical measurements. This is an intensity represented by a power of 10^{-16} watt/cm^2; it corresponds to a r.m.s. pressure of approximately 0.0002 dyne/cm^2 in a plane progressive sound wave in air. The two commonly used reference intensities are not far apart. The average threshold of hearing for a 1000$\sim$ tone is very close to the physical reference intensity of 0.0002 dyne/cm^2.

The physical intensity of sound may be stated either in terms of *intensity level* or *sensation level*. In both cases the unit of measurement is the decibel. The difference between the two lies in the reference intensity used, intensity level being referable to a "zero" of 0.0002 dyne/cm² and sensation level calling for the absolute threshold as the point of zero decibels. Figure 41 will be of aid in giving concrete meaning to the decibel; the scale shown is one of sensation level, as the definition of zero reveals.

The device most commonly employed in making sound-intensity measurements is a microphone for which a pressure calibration, i.e., the relation between current generated and pressure on the diaphragm, has been obtained for all frequencies to be measured. Since, in the calibration process, the introduction of a microphone to the sound field is likely to distort appreciably the sound waves comprising it (microphones cannot be made infinitely small!), it is necessary to take one additional step. This makes use of a clever device invented by Lord Rayleigh and known as the Rayleigh disc. It consists of a very light plate which will not appreciably alter a sound field in which it is suspended and which will tend to orient itself at right angles to the direction of propagation of the waves flowing past it. The relation between the turning moment of the disc and the velocity of the air particles may be worked out and the device used as a primary standard against which to calibrate a microphone. This so-called

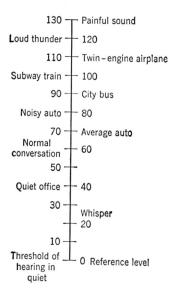

FIG. 41. The decibel scale in terms of some familiar sounds. From Chapanis, Garner, and Morgan, 57.

"field calibration" of the microphone then permits its use as a secondary standard, provided due consideration is given to the direction in which the microphone diaphragm is oriented with respect to the source of an unknown sound to be measured.

However, measurements of the type described in the foregoing paragraphs are concerned with "ultimates." As has been previously suggested, most modern systems for sound production are electrical, and working standards of intensity are likely to be provided within the control networks of oscillators, resistance boxes, and potentiometers which are already calibrated in decibel units. As with illumination measurements, it is rarely necessary to refer to primary standards.

Anatomy of the Ear. The mechanism for hearing is divisible, anatomically, into three parts: the external ear, the middle ear, and the inner ear. Functionally, we may think of the external and middle divisions as a system for collecting and transmitting sounds, by air and bone conduction, to the inner ear where are situated within a fluid medium the sensitive endings of the eighth cranial, or auditory, nerve.

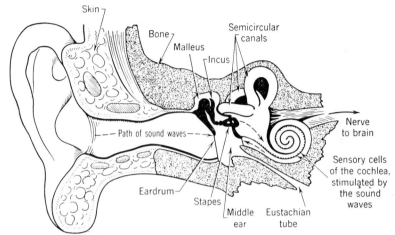

Fig. 42. Gross anatomy of the ear. A semischematic drawing showing the main path of sound. Vibrations entering the external auditory canal first affect the eardrum. Oscillations of the drum are transmitted through the middle ear chiefly by bone conduction over the chain of ossicles: malleus, incus, and stapes. The foot of the stapes carries the vibrations to the fluid of the cochlea, in which the hair-like endings of the auditory nerve are immersed. After Davis, 76. By permission of Rinehart Books, Inc., copyright 1947.

The gross structure of the ear is shown in Fig. 42. The *pinna* serves to funnel sounds striking it into the external auditory canal, a tube 7 mm in diameter and about an inch in length. At the terminus of the canal is the eardrum, or *tympanic membrane.* The latter divides the external from the middle ear. The drum serves very much the same function as does the diaphragm of a microphone, not vibrating with a period of its own but forced into oscillation by any and all frequencies of sound impinging upon it. From this point to the terminations of the auditory nerve, vibrations may be conducted: (1) by air conduction through the cavity of the middle ear to the *round window* in the temporal bone, (2) by bone conduction through the walls of the middle ear cavity to the cochlea, and (3) by direct mechanical transmission through the chain of ossicles (hammer, anvil, and stirrup) to the *oval window*, thence by way of the cochlear fluid to the nerve endings. It is by the last route that conduction is mainly effected. The hammer (*malleus*) is securely attached to the tympanic membrane and vibrates with it. The three ossicles, tied together by ligaments, form a remarkable lever system, reducing the extent of the excursions initiated at the drum but preserving in large measure the "thrust" so that the stirrup (*stapes*), driven back and forth in the oval window, moves with an amplitude somewhat less than that of the drum but exerts a correspondingly increased pressure on the fluid of the cochlea. Since the drum (average area of 66 mm²) is about 20 times larger than the foot of the stapes (area of footplate, 3.2 mm²) and the ossicles are pivoted in such a fashion as to provide a small mechanical advantage, there is concentrated on the oval window a very considerable pressure, per unit of area about 25 to 30 times as great as that found at the drum. Some such "impedance matching" is necessary in going from an air to a hydraulic conduction system if efficiency of transmission is to be preserved.

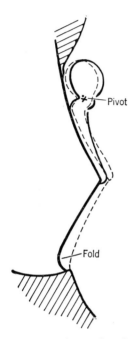

FIG. 43. The eardrum's mode of action. The entire drum moves as a unit at low frequencies of vibration. The pivotal point is at the head of the hammer. A fold at the lower edge of the drum permits this unitary action. From von Békésy and Rosenblith, *30*.

The manner in which the tympanic membrane responds to vibratory pressures imposed on it is revealed by Fig. 43, taken from the ingenious work of von Békésy (*30*). Much of the upper portion of the drum, being attached to the handle of the malleus, vibrates as a unit. The axis of rotation is near the hammer's head. The lower part of the drum has a tissue fold which, like the crimped edge of a loud-speaker cone, permits relatively large excursions to take place. Up to a frequency of about 2400⌒ the drum vibrates as a rigid system, like a plate; above this point on the frequency scale the vibratory pattern gets complicated and the drum responds in segments.

The drum and ossicular chain, together with the attachments that keep them in place, form a physical transmission system which, like all such arrangements, is bound to respond more favorably to some vibration frequencies than to others. The middle ear system, taken as a whole, has a "natural period." This has been determined by cementing a tiny chip of mirror to the malleus, reflecting a light beam from it, and setting the system into momentary action by imparting the sound of a click to the eardrum (30, p. 1084). The natural frequency revealed by such an optical lever turns out to be in the neighborhood of 1300—. The same experiment tells one about the damping characteristics of the middle ear. The system proves to be highly damped, i.e., comes promptly to an equilibrium with the forces acting on it. This permits the middle ear to be a relatively faithful conductor of all manner of tones and noises, however rapidly their wave shapes may change.

Two other features of the middle ear should be noted. The *Eustachian tube*, running from the middle ear cavity to the throat, serves as a pressure-equalizing device. Normally closed, it opens during swallowing and permits air interchanges that keep pressure on the two sides of the tympanic membrane equal. If this were not the case the drum might be painfully bulged or retracted as, indeed, happens when a head cold blocks the Eustachian tube and the drum is subjected to extreme atmospheric pressure variations. Anyone who has traveled by plane under such circumstances is vividly aware of the consequences. The other feature of middle ear anatomy concerns the intra-aural muscles, the *tensor tympani* and the *stapedius*. The former is attached to the malleus and by its contraction places the drum under greater tension, drawing it inward so that its shape is somewhat conical and concave to the external auditory canal. The stapedius, the action of which is opposed to that of the tensor tympani, is attached to the stapes. When contracted it changes the articulation between the foot of the stirrup and the oval window. When both muscles contract together, as they normally do, there result more intimate operation of the ossicles and more favorable response to high tones. There is good reason for believing that the two muscles, acting jointly, have an essentially protective function, by reflex contraction reducing possible damaging effects of loud low-pitched sounds by shifting the response characteristic of the conduction system towards the higher frequencies.

Another protective device, demonstrated by von Békésy (30, pp. 1085–1086), consists in a change in the mode of vibration of the stapes in the presence of a very loud sound. The relation of the footplate of the stirrup to the oval window is such that, normally, the stirrup moves about a vertical axis and, in a somewhat hinge-like action, compresses the fluid of the cochlea. When overdriven, however, its vibratory pattern changes to one in which most of the motion of the footplate takes place around an axis at 90 degrees to the former one and the large amplitudes brought to the stapes by the malleus and incus are harmlessly expended in rotary motion.

The portion of the auditory mechanism constituting the inner ear begins at the oval window (foot of the stapes) and terminates, as a sound transmission system, at the round window. It occupies a complex cavity, appropriately named the *bony labyrinth,* in the temporal bone (see Fig. 44). Whereas there are three major divisions of the labyrinth, the *vestibule,* the *cochlea,* and the *semicircular canals,* the last-named structures need not complicate our thinking at this point, for they are not at all concerned with hearing. At one time it was supposed that they were; it is now known that they are exclusively concerned with another class of events, those involved in the maintenance of body equilibrium. Fitting loosely into the bony cavity of the labyrinth and surrounded by a watery fluid, the *perilymph,* is a series of sacs, collectively called the *membranous labyrinth.* All interconnect and are filled with the same fairly viscous fluid, the *endolymph.* That portion of the membranous labyrinth situated in the bony cochlea and following its spiral form is known as the *cochlear duct.* In it are located all the specialized tissues most intimately concerned with the initiation of impulses in the fibers of the auditory nerve.

Early in embryonic life the cochlea appears as a straight tube, without the coiled "snail-shell" appearance characteristic of full development. About the second month of uterine life the cochlea begins to coil on itself and continues the process until somewhat more than $2\frac{1}{2}$ turns (left to right in the right cochlea and the reverse in the left) have been completed. The cochlea is divided longitudinally by a combination of bony shelf (*spiral osseous lamina*), which extends partway toward the outer wall, and the *basilar membrane,* which completes the division and upon which are situated the highly specialized endings of the auditory nerve. These lie along the inner edge of the basilar membrane and in contact with epithelial hair cells, collectively known as the *organ of Corti.* Movement of these structures is thought to be the device whereby impulses are generated in the fibers of the auditory nerve.

The spiral lamina and basilar membrane effectively divide the cochlea into two main chambers, the *scala vestibuli* above and the *scala tympani* below. Both contain perilymph. The oval window, with stapes hinged in it, lies at the base of the upper chamber; the membrane-covered round window is at the lower termination of the scala tympani. Communication between the two is effected by a tiny

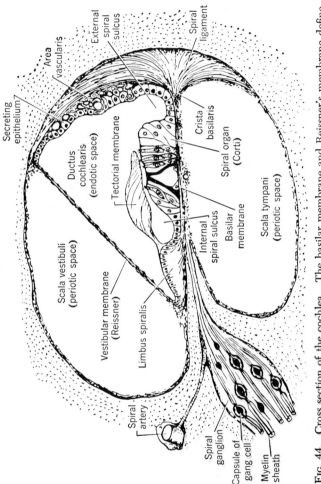

Fig. 44. Cross section of the cochlea. The basilar membrane and Reissner's membrane define the limits of the cochlear duct (scala media), within which is located the organ of Corti. The hair cells of the latter are the receptors for hearing. From Rasmussen, 241. By permission of the William C. Brown Co., publishers, and the author.

opening at the apex of the cochlea, the *helicotrema*. This is scarcely larger than a pinhole, being but 0.25 mm² in area. Of course, pressure communication between the two chambers can also be brought about through the basilar membrane itself since, though it is a tough, fibrous structure, it is a flexible one. A further anatomical subdivision is effected by *Reissner's membrane*, a delicate structure running from the spiral lamina to the outer wall of the cochlea and forming an angle with the basilar membrane. The area thus enclosed is the scala media (*cochlear duct*). Still another membrane is to be found in the cochlear duct, the *tectorial membrane*. It is attached to the bony shelf just below Reissner's membrane but, unlike the latter, does not extend entirely across the cochlear canal. The outer edge apparently floats freely in the endolymph. The function of the tectorial membrane is not known. Some have guessed that it strikes the hair cells during vibratory motions of the basilar membrane and that the essential mode of stimulation of the auditory endings is tactile. The tectorial membrane certainly occupies a position favorable to such an operation.

Whereas the bony cochlea necessarily becomes smaller and smaller in cross-section area as the apex is approached, the basilar membrane, interestingly enough, becomes progressively wider. At the vestibular end it is about 0.16 mm wide; near the helicotrema it has broadened to 0.52 mm. The hair cells, of which there are about 23,500, according to the best counts, also vary in length from base to apex. At the vestibular end they are of the order of 0.05 mm long, while at the apical end they are 0.085 to 0.1 mm in length. They are spaced quite evenly along the basilar membrane, though not in a single row. About 3500 of them are situated quite close to the membrane's point of attachment to the bony shelf (*inner* hair cells); the remainder (*outer* hair cells), several of which appear in a single cross section of the cochlear duct, lie further out on the basilar membrane. All hair cells have tiny cilia, or filaments, which extend into the endolymph of the cochlear duct.

Auditory Nerve Pathways. Nerve fibers, from both the inner and outer hair cells, pass under the spiral lamina and enter the bony central axis of the cochlea, the *modiolus*. Here they assemble to form the *spiral ganglion of Corti*, the beginning of the auditory branch of the eighth cranial nerve. Each of the inner hair cells is supplied with one or two nerve endings, and each nerve fiber connects with one or two hair cells. The outer hair cells are differently innervated. Here a single fiber may connect with many hair cells, and a particular outer hair cell may be supplied by many nerve endings. There are at least

25,000 ganglion cells in the twisting and woven auditory nerve of the modiolus, more at the level of the basal and middle turns than near the apex.

Upon leaving the base of the cochlea the auditory nerve enters the medulla of the brain. This organ lies immediately adjacent; in fact, it is only 5 mm away in the human. Here the majority of fibers con-

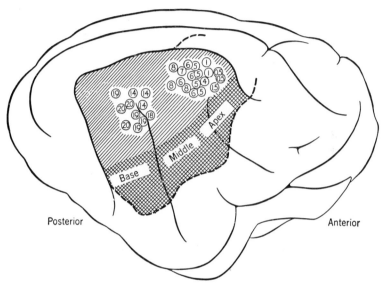

Fig. 45. Cortical loci of electrical responses after cochlear stimulation. The data of Woolsey and Walzl (324) on the cortical projection of auditory fibers in the cat are summarized. The shaded region is the primary projection area, the cross-hatched region the secondary. The numbers in the little circles stand for stimulus locations expressed as distances in millimeters from the basal end of the cochlea.
By permission of the Johns Hopkins Press and the authors.

nect with others which cross to the contralateral side and ascend by way of the lateral lemniscus to the *medial geniculate body* of the thalamus. Radiating fibers from the geniculate body spread, fan-like, to the cortex of the temporal lobe of the cerebrum. A chain of four nerve cells is involved in this devious path from the cochlea to the cortex.

The region of the cortex concerned with final projection of auditory impulses has been located with some precision. Several methods have proved successful. One of the best, that used by Woolsey and Walzl (324), consists in electrically stimulating various local areas on the spiral lamina of the cochlea and recording the resulting potentials created at the surface of the cortex. With a cat under deep enough general anesthesia to suppress the spontaneous brain rhythms normally present, it is still possible to record well-localized cortical wavelets generated by peripheral shocks. Figure 45 shows the loci of the strongest responses, the numbers in the circles revealing stimulus locations in millimeters up from the basal end of the cochlea. The primary projection area (shaded) occupies an extensive portion of the superior temporal convolution. Much of it lies deep in the fissure of Sylvius. There is also a secondary area (cross-hatched), which receives fibers from a separate region of the medial geniculate body.

It is still a moot point as to whether there is preserved any neat geometrical arrangement in the complex pathways leading from the basilar membrane to the auditory cortex, and there are many uncertainties about the mode of operation of some of the relay stations en route. This much is certain, however; each cochlea is represented bilaterally in the brain. There are many evidences, anatomical and physiological, that the "projections" of the two ears become completely intermingled in the higher centers. Removal of one cerebral hemisphere of a dog reduces acuity hardly appreciably (210). Further removal of the nervous connections, by interruption of the fibers ascending the lateral lemniscus, results in a loss in acuity of about 10 decibels, but it is a matter of no consequence whether crossed or uncrossed tracts, i.e., those leading from the contralateral or the homolateral cochlea, are destroyed. The same loss follows either interruption. Apparently the two sets of ascending fibers are of equal value in conducting impulses to the auditory cortex. Recordings of electrical responses, taken from various levels of the auditory tract, also show that each cochlea is represented in both halves of the brain. In fact, somewhat stronger cortical responses result from contralateral than from homolateral cochlear stimulation (287).

The physical characteristics of auditory stimuli and the mechanisms for their reception having now been reviewed, we are in a stronger position to examine the phenomena of hearing. At least we may feel some confidence that our interpretations of the phenomena will be realistic in that they are aligned with the known physical and biological facts.

7

Auditory Phenomena

The Intensitive Threshold. We have already had occasion, in considering the "reference intensity" for sound measurements (Chap. 6), to pay some attention to the absolute intensitive threshold of hearing. It will be recalled that "sensation level" is expressed in decibels above that threshold. It remains to ascertain how the threshold value is determined and upon what variables it depends.

Intensitive thresholds may be measured either in terms of minimum audible pressure on the tympanic membrane or intensity of the minimum audible sound field in which an observer is placed. The values obtained by the two methods characteristically differ, and it becomes necessary, in stating the value of the absolute threshold, to specify by what method the result was derived.

In determining the least pressure on the drum necessary to arouse an auditory sensation a sound generator, typically an earphone, is held tightly to the ear, thus enclosing in the external auditory canal a known volume of air. The excursions of the diaphragm of the phone being determined, either optically or by the known electrical response characteristics of the phone, it is then possible to compute with some accuracy the air pressure exerted on the drum. An alternate device is to make use of a "search tube," an air conductor held very close to the drum, the pressure variations in the end of the tube being regarded as identical with those impinging on the drum. In either case the pressure variations are reduced to the point where the sound becomes just audible (strictly speaking, half of the time just audible, half inaudible), and the pressure is calculated. The ear is so highly sensitive, i.e., it will respond to such small pressure variations, that there is no known method whereby direct physical measurement of minimum audible pressures can be made. It is necessary, therefore, to calibrate the sound generator employed at intensities well above threshold and extrapolate downwards. This may be done if the response characteristics of the generator are intimately known.

113

Auditory Phenomena

In measuring thresholds by the "minimum audible field" method there is established a field of sound in "free space" (no disturbing reflected waves), and the effective pressures at a given point in it are determined. An observer is then introduced to the field, his head is placed in the measured area (conventionally, facing the sound), and the intensity is reduced to threshold level. Stimulation may be either monaural or binaural. In the stimulation of two ears the threshold is likely to be lower than for one, though not all results unequivocally support this statement.

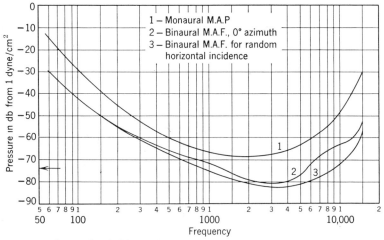

Fig. 46. Auditory threshold as a function of frequency. M.A.P. stands for "minimum audible pressure," M.A.F. for "minimum audible field." After Sivian and White, 260. Courtesy of the editor, *Journal of the Acoustical Society of America.*

Figure 46, which combines the results from several investigations, shows the size of the threshold (both "minimum audible pressure" and "minimum audible field" measurements) as a function of frequency. Threshold pressure values have been reported in decibels below a reference point of 1 dyne/cm². On such a scale the standard "reference intensity" (indicated by the arrow) has a value of −73.8 db. It is seen from the curves that maximum sensitivity is realized in the region of 2000–4000〜 and that thresholds are higher in both directions from this region. Thresholds at frequencies below those represented are higher still, being of the order of −20 db on the same pressure scale for frequencies around 20〜, the lower limit of frequency recognition.

To pressures of the magnitude involved in threshold responses the tympanic membrane responds with extremely small excursions. A direct determination of this has been made by Wilska (*314*), using an ingenious technique. He cemented to the eardrum a light wooden shaft, the other end being attached to a loud-speaker coil. At amplitudes of vibration just arousing tonal sensations the excursions of the rod were measured with a microscope. Whereas such direct measurements could be made only at relatively low frequencies, it was possible to calculate threshold amplitudes for all others in the hearing range. Wilska's data reveal that, for frequencies in the neighborhood of 3000~, the threshold amplitude is of the order of 10^{-9} cm, a value considerably less than that of the wavelength of light. Speculation as to what must be transpiring in the cochlea in response to such slight movements leads to the conclusion (*273*, p. 56) that the basilar membrane must be capable of initiating auditory sensations with movements smaller in extent than 1% of the diameter of a hydrogen molecule!

Audiometry. The measurement of intensitive thresholds throughout the range of audible frequencies provides, of course, a means of assessing auditory sensitivity and of detecting any significant hearing loss. There has therefore been a large development of testing instruments, known as audiometers, which make possible standardized threshold determinations. Most commercial audiometers are of electronic design and consist of audiofrequency oscillators arranged to generate eight or more fixed frequencies, usually the octaves of C from 64~ to 8192~. The output of the oscillator to a phone, which is held against the ear of the examinee, is calibrated in "sensation units" (decibels), the zero of the scale being representative of the average threshold for the "good" ear. The amount, in decibels, which the tone must be increased above zero to render the tone audible is a direct measure of "hearing loss" for that frequency. A graph connecting the threshold values thus derived constitutes the so-called *audiogram*.

In the sample audiogram shown in Fig. 47 the broken line labeled "Total Loss of Serviceable Hearing" is of interest. This line marks the position, throughout the hearing range, of the so-called "threshold of feeling," the point at which tactile receptors in the tissues of the ear (probably chiefly the middle ear) respond with clear sensations. Whenever a tone is made sufficiently intense there is this tactual complication, at low frequencies felt chiefly as a vibratory pressure sensation, at high frequencies experienced as an itching, pricking, or "burning" feeling. For all practical purposes the threshold of feeling may be taken as the upper limit of audibility for, whereas it is probably true that the hearing mechanism could continue to operate with some fidelity at still higher intensities, the risk of tissue damage is too great

Auditory Phenomena

to warrant experimental investigations in these ranges. The area, on the audiogram, between "zero loss" (normal thresholds) and the broken line (feeling thresholds) may be taken as the effective *auditory area*.

A convenient way of expressing hearing losses as percentages is provided by the audiogram, since the proportionate loss at any frequency may be related to "total" loss as defined by the feeling threshold. Thus, in Curve D of Fig. 47, the loss at 1024∿ is only about 7.5% (7.5%

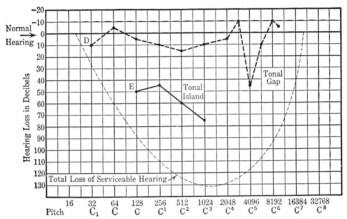

FIG. 47. Two audiograms. Curve D represents a case of normal hearing except for a well-defined *tonal gap* in the region of C^5, 4096∿. Curve E shows a *tonal island* extending over four octaves, 128∿ to 1024∿. From Wever after Guild, Crowe, Bunch, and Polvogt (*134*).

of the distance from the line of normal hearing to the curve of total loss), whereas at 4096∿ it is nearly 40%. The losses at 128∿ and 1024∿, shown on Curve E, are both about 57% by this method of reckoning.

Large-scale audiometric surveys have been made in an effort to establish the picture of normal hearing characteristics in the general population and to ascertain the nature of age and sex differences. In the course of making the National Health Survey, conducted in 1935–1936, there were measured 4662 people all of whom had had a clinical history of normal hearing (*23*). They ranged in age from under 10 to over 60 years. Clear trends were present in the results: (1) In males, advancing age has no deteriorating effect on tonal reception for frequencies below 1000∿. (2) Large and significant losses for high tones occur with increasing age. This is especially the case for the highest tones measured (4096∿ and 8192∿). The average loss for men 60 years and over, for these two frequencies, was 31 db. (3) At all age levels females show somewhat more loss for low-frequency tones (below 2000~) but considerably less for tones of high frequency. The sex difference is a very real one; aged women do not normally suffer partial high-tone deafness to as great a degree as do aged men.

Intensity Discrimination. In vision we confronted the problem of $\Delta I/I$, or differential intensity discrimination, and found the Weber

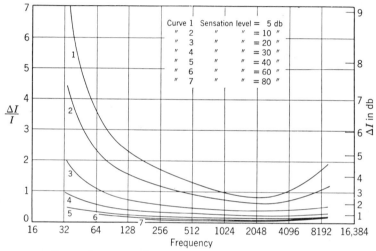

Fig. 48. Differential intensity discrimination. The data of Riesz (247) at seven different intensities, from 5 to 80 db, and for a wide range of frequencies are plotted. Reference to the ordinates on the right gives the magnitude of ΔI to the left ordinates, $\Delta I/I$.

fraction to vary in an interesting way with changes in intensity. In audition we encounter a strictly analogous problem. Given an initial intensity, I, how much must the energy of the stimulus be increased to produce a just noticeable difference, i.e., what is the size of ΔI? A number of determinations have been made, and several variables influencing the magnitude of ΔI have been discovered to exist. It makes a difference whether the starting point is low or high on the intensity scale, at what frequency the measurement is made, whether one or both ears are stimulated, what the durations of the tonal exposures are and whether or not they are separated by a silent interval, whether there is an abrupt or a gradual transition between the two tones to be compared, and whether the observer making the judgments has the exposure sequence under his own control so as to be maximally "set" for change when it occurs. Many of these experimental variables were not encountered in vision. The ear is not essentially a "spatial" organ, as the eye is, and comparison of two intensities simultaneously present is not possible. Successive presentations, which must necessarily be resorted to, introduce complications.

The classic data on $\Delta I/I$ are those of Riesz (247). To avoid the production of "transients," unwanted additional sounds which are inevitably involved in presenting successively two discrete tones, he made his measurements by the "beat" method, two tones 3~ apart being allowed to sound together. This produced alternate intensification and diminutions (3 per second) of what was experienced as a single tone. From the energies present at the threshold of the beating complex he arrived at the values presented in the curves of Fig. 48. The size of ΔI (and of $\Delta I/I$) is seen to be minimal, i.e., differential sensitivity is greatest, in the region of 2500~. Thus it appears that the frequency range in which greatest absolute sensitivity occurs is also that to which the ear responds differentially with the greatest efficiency.

The effect of the other major variable, intensity, may be observed by comparing the relative sizes of ΔI in the seven curves, each representative of a different intensity (sensation level). Far from being a constant, as demanded by Weber's Law, $\Delta I/I$ varies roughly between the limits of $\frac{1}{20}$ (2500~ at 100 db) and 7.5 (35~ at 5 db).

Frequency Recognition. The limits of tonal recognition have already been stated to be 20~ to 20,000~ for the "good" (and young) human ear. These are the approximate limits. Apparently the response system of the ear cannot follow disturbances imposed upon it with frequencies higher than about 20,000~; possibly the mass of the ossicles is too great to be overcome and thus permit threshold energy to be delivered to the cochlea at vibration rates higher than this. The lower limit is not so simply dismissed. If a pure-tone generator is set in operation at the very low frequency of 5~ and is raised progressively in vibration rate there are heard, in succession: (1) a "chugging" sound (discrete noises, having prominent high-frequency components); (2) an intermittent flutter; (3) a "thrusting effect" (resembling "piston slap" but complicated at one point in the cycle by high-frequency sound "very like the escape of steam from a jet"); and (4) a "rumbling" tonal effect. In one of the best controlled experiments designed to analyze these phenomena, that of Wever and Bray (311), the tonal character entered at 20~, for some observers, and was present for all at 25∿ with intensities above 15–20 db. The lower limit of tonal recognition depends upon the intensity of the tonal stimulus. If intensity is kept down to 10 db nothing at all will be heard below 20∿; then noises make their entrance, and a tonal character is not present until a frequency of about 60∿ is reached. Other experiments have placed the lower limit for tone at 18∿ (29, 48), and one of these, that of von Békésy, found "pitch" discrimination to be possible all the way down to 1∿, even though fused tones were no longer present below 18∿. The great difficulty in establishing the point where tone replaces flutter results from the fact that the transmission system of the middle ear and cochlea responds to even pure sinusoidal waves with a complex spectrum of vibrations. Harmonics thus introduced may serve as the basis of frequency recognition and give a misleading result.

The range of vibrations from 20∿ to 20,000∿ is not infrequently interrupted by the presence of a *tonal gap*, a local region of relative insensitivity. Such a gap may show up in an audiometric test; one such occurrence is illustrated in Curve *D* of Fig. 47. Ordinarily a tonal gap is of no practical consequence to its possessor, unless it is the forerunner of an expanding area of deafness, since pure tones of the limited frequencies that would fall in it are encountered only under special testing conditions. For some reason, as yet undetermined, tonal gaps occur much less frequently among women than among men. It will be recalled that audiometric data reveal other clear sex differences.

There also occurs, though quite infrequently, another restriction of the range of frequency recognition. This is the *tonal island*, which, as the name implies, consists in the preservation of a reduced range of audible frequencies with deafness for tones higher and lower on the scale. Curve *E* in Fig. 47 illustrates this anomaly. In this particular instance the tones retained have also undergone reduction of sensitivity.

Differential Frequency Discrimination. If we begin at the lowest frequency audible as a tone and ascend the frequency scale it is possible to measure the size of successive Δf's and, from such measurements, to determine the differential frequency discrimination of the auditory apparatus, $\Delta f/f$. As with $\Delta I/I$, certain difficulties present themselves. If discrete, successive tones are compared there is encountered the annoying problem of transients, additional harmonics and noises that accompany any abrupt initiation, termination, or change in tone production. If a gradual transition from one fre-

Auditory Phenomena

quency to another is resorted to there may be an artificial augmentation of Δf, for it has long been known that continuous changes are less noticeable than abrupt ones. The lesser of the two evils would seem to be to keep the stimuli relatively pure by employing a "sliding" tone. This was done in the classic experiment of Shower and Biddulph (259). They found that optimal judgments were made when the two frequencies to be compared were alternated at the rate of two per second, and this comparison frequency was used throughout the range of tones from 31∽ to 11,700∽ and for a range of intensities (sensation levels) from 5 db to the maximum the subjects could "take."

The magnitude of Δf is a function of the absolute frequency at which the measurement is made. It is also a function of intensity. The size of $\Delta f/f$, for each of several frequencies and intensities, may be read from Table 2. It may be seen that $\Delta f/f$ is roughly constant for

TABLE 2. THE VALUES OF $\Delta f/f$ FOR A WIDE RANGE OF INTENSITIES (SENSATION LEVELS) AND FREQUENCIES

The data are those of Shower and Biddulph (259) and represent the performance of five subjects between 20 and 30 years of age. From Stevens and Davis, 273. Reproduced by permission of Bell Telephone Laboratories, Inc.

Sensation Level	5	10	15	20	30	40	50	60	70	80	90
Frequency											
31	.1290	.0873	.0702	.0563	.0438	.0406					
62	.0975	.0678	.0546	.0491	.0461	.0426	.0351	.0346			
125	.0608	.0421	.0331	.0300	.0266	.0247	.0270	.0269			
250	.0355	.0212	.0158	.0130	.0109	.0103	.0099	.0098	.0100	.0107	
500	.0163	.0110	.0081	.0067	.0055	.0052	.0042	.0035	.0042		
1,000	.0094	.0061	.0044	.0039	.0036	.0036	.0036	.0034	.0031	.0030	.0026
2,000	.0079	.0036	.0029	.0021	.0019	.0019	.0019	.0018	.0017	.0018	
4,000	.0060	.0044	.0038	.0031	.0027	.0023	.0023	.0020			
8,000	.0063	.0051	.0045	.0038	.0036	.0029	.0025				
11,700	.0069	.0058	.0042	.0038	.0036	.0035	.0030				

the higher frequencies (for a given intensity). For the lower frequencies (below 500∽) Δf by itself is roughly constant, though this generality does not pertain to the lowest tones measured.

If the results of Shower and Biddulph may be taken at face value it would appear that there are, between the lowest and the highest audible tones, about 1500 j.n.d.'s. This result contrasts sharply with the older data of Luft (204), which, for many years, were responsible for the common textbook statement that there are 11,000 discriminable frequencies. Boring (44), reviewing the experiments performed on Δf and weighing the many experimental variables that enter into its determination, has concluded, "The 1500 discriminable frequencies given by the results of Shower and Biddulph are thus probably too few to express maximal sensitivity, but the 11,000 tones from Luft's data must be too many—very much too many."

Pitch and Loudness. Thus far, in dealing with auditory responses, care has been taken to speak always of discriminable features of *physical stimuli.* The sensations aroused by them have dimensions of their own, however, and these are describable from direct observation. *Pitch* and *loudness* are two such dimensions.

Pitch, as a dimension of tonal sensation, is the name given to the highness or lowness of tones. Because low frequencies yield low-pitched tones and high frequencies high-pitched ones it is natural to think of pitch as a simple, direct correlate of frequency. However, pitch is not uniquely determined by frequency, as we shall see.

Loudness is a second dimension, in general determined by the physical intensity of sound, but here again there is no one-to-one relation between the intensity of the sound and the loudness observable in its presence. Loudness is quite complexly related to intensity; also, intensity is by no means the sole determinant of loudness.

The important thing to note, at this point, is that pitch and loudness are names for separate aspects of auditory sensation and that they are not to be identified in our thinking with frequency and intensity of auditory stimuli. The former concepts are psychological, the latter physical. We shall subsequently discover still other psychological dimensions of auditory sensation to exist. It does not follow that, because there are only two dimensions of sound waves, frequency and intensity, there are therefore only two dimensions of the sensations they arouse. The sensation is the final step in a complex chain of events. Modes of variation, arising in the ear and its nervous attachments, may introduce discernible new dimensions.

Pitch as a Function of Intensity. A phenomenon reminiscent of the Bezold-Brücke effect in vision occurs in audition. It will be recalled that increasing or decreasing the intensity of most spectral lights will produce shifts in hue. Only certain "invariable points" are exempt. Similarly, the auditory apparatus responds to changes in intensity by effecting shifts in pitch. Low tones, when increased in intensity, become lower, whereas high tones are raised in pitch when intensified. There is likewise an "invariable point"; it appears on the frequency scale in the region of maximal auditory sensitivity.

The experiment demonstrating pitch shifts with change of intensity is performed by presenting, in succession, two tones of slightly different frequency. The intensity of one of the tones is adjusted by the observer until the two tones appear to be of identical pitch. On the basis of results from such an experiment Stevens (270) has derived curves showing the correspondences which must obtain between frequency and intensity to preserve constant pitch. Figure 49 presents a family of "equal pitch contours" from his work.

This phenomenon of shifting pitch as an accompaniment of intensity changes is an important one for auditory theory. Accordingly, it has prompted a fair amount of experimental work and no little speculation (309, pp. 340–346). Even though the shift is a relatively small one, it is definite and measurable. One would like to know what characteristics of the auditory system permit its occurrence. The available evidence suggests that the explanation is to be found in the mechanics of neither the middle ear nor the cochlea. Some crucial experiments performed by Thurlow (279) demonstrate that the same pitch changes occur—lowering of low tones and raising of high ones—when the initial tone is presented to one ear and the "loudening" occurs exclusively through the introduction of a second tone to the other ear. While the effect is most prominent if the second tone is identical in frequency to the first, this is not a necessary condition. Any frequency, higher or lower, produces the effect.

One would suppose that pitch changes induced by intensive variations would play havoc with music. After all, the pitch shifts are appreciable ones, amounting in some instances to a whole musical tone. However, it is found that pitch variations of the type under discussion occur noticeably only with relatively pure tones. Musical instruments, with their complex timbres, produce tones which are perceived as of very stable pitch, and this occurs whether the instrument is played loudly or softly—happily for music! The explanation of this difference between the behavior of pure tones and that of complex ones is at present far from complete. It may be that musical tones, which characteristically have many and prominent harmonics in the region of maximal sensitivity (2000∼ to 4000∼), are "anchored" by overtones falling in the invariable region. Or it may be that complex patterns of stimulation, once being set up in the central nervous system, are not easily altered by energy changes.

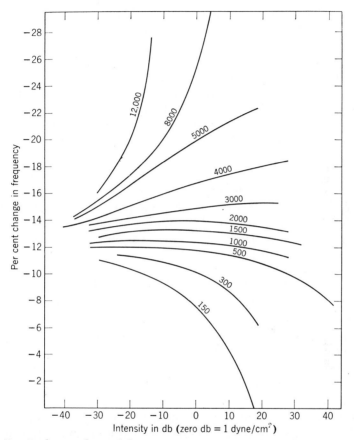

FIG. 49. Pitch as influenced by intensity. Contours of equal pitch from the experimental results obtained by Stevens (270). There is plotted the percentage change in frequency needed to keep the pitch of a tone constant as its intensity is changed. "The ordinate scale was arbitrarily chosen so that a contour with a positive slope shows that pitch increases with intensity" (273, p. 71). Courtesy of the editor, *Journal of the Acoustical Society of America.*

Makeup of the Auditory Area. Having seen something of the nature of Δf and of ΔI it is now pertinent to ask what the result would be of integrating all the just noticeable differences of both frequency and intensity throughout the entire auditory area. How many separate tones are distinguishable in the region bounded by the intensive threshold, the threshold of feeling, and the upper and lower frequency limits? The calculation has been performed by Stevens and Davis (273, p. 153) on the basis of the Riesz data for ΔI and those of Shower and Biddulph for Δf. The result shows that approximately 340,000 discriminable tones are contained in the auditory area. This figure may be a conservative one; it will be recalled that the Δf results possibly err in the direction of containing too few steps.

Other Dimensions of Auditory Sensation. Pitch and loudness we have already seen to be two separately discriminable aspects of auditory experience. Both are dependent on frequency and intensity, but they are quite different functions of the same two variables. Observation shows that there are two other dimensions of auditory sensation, *volume* and *density* (45, p. 375 ff.).

"Volume" is a word of several meanings. Because it has been used so freely in everyday speech as a synonym for "intensity" ("volume controls" on radios, e.g.) we do well to inquire carefully into its technical meaning when applied to auditory sensations. Tones appear to be big or little, massive or small; they vary with respect to volume. Typically, low-pitched tones are large tones; they seem to pervade space. High-pitched tones are tiny; they seem not to take up much room. If it is difficult to think of the shrill tones of a fife or piccolo as "massive" it is equally difficult to picture the pedal notes of a pipe organ as "pointed" or "minute." Perhaps it is entirely a matter of "picturing" it that way. Perhaps volume is a pseudodimension coming out of the common association of low tones with the large instruments that produce them and of high tones with the small ones from which they come. However, the case for volume as a sheer association is defeated by the experimental approach. Several researches have been directed at the measurement of "volumic limens." The variables of frequency and intensity may be manipulated to produce a just noticeable increase or decrease in observed volume. It is found that there is better than fair agreement among observers; in fact, it is possible to state with some accuracy the functional dependence of volume on intensity and frequency (278). Figure 50 shows the relation by way of presenting an "isophonic contour" of volume (as well as contours for other dimensions). The reduced volume consequent upon raising frequency may be compensated by an increase in intensity.

The same figure reveals the nature of the remaining dimension, density. Tones vary with respect to their "compactness" or "thinness." High-pitched tones are typically "hard," "compact," "beady"; low tones are "loose," "rare," "thin." But, within limits, intensive changes may make up for the densitive shifts brought about by frequency, as the isophonic contour for density demonstrates. The same compactness present in a high tone may be induced in a lower tone by raising its intensity.

The minor dependence of pitch on intensity and that of loudness on frequency, with which we are already familiar, are also shown in the remaining curves of Fig. 50.

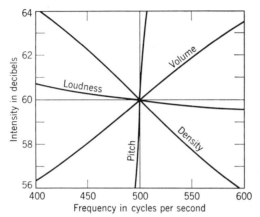

FIG. 50. Isophonic contours for loudness, volume, density, and pitch. Each line represents a set of coincidences between tonal intensity and frequency which will yield the same observed loudness, volume, etc. Thus a tone of 450~ and 58 db and one of 550~ and nearly 62 db are judged to be of equal volume. From Stevens, *269*. Courtesy of the National Academy of Sciences.

Other "dimensions" have been suggested from time to time, and certain of them have enjoyed brief careers of scientific acceptance. Thus *brightness, tonality,* and *vocality* have all had their day. We should have some familiarity with the concepts, for there is no doubt that the words refer to *something* discernible in auditory experience. The pitch scale may be thought of as a scale of "brightness." High tones are "bright," while low tones are "dull." However, two independently variable dimensions, pitch and brightness, are not found, nor are the differential thresholds for the two significantly different (*245*). Moreover, it is found that tones may be "brightened" by permitting high-frequency transients to enter into their production (*46*). "Tonality" refers to the intimacy of the octave relation. High c sounds more like low C than any tone between the two. In fact, we say in music that these are the *same* tone an octave apart. The confusion of octaves is the easiest error to make in identifying tones. But such confusions do not make tonality a dimension. The current judgment, influenced by the failure to discover experimentally the quantitative relations a dimension should yield, would seem to be that tonality is simply a name for the fact that octaves are confused more readily than are other tonal intervals. "Vocality" has made a more determined bid for recognition as a separate dimension of tonal sensation. By "vocality" is meant "vowel similarity." Tones are vowel-like or possess "vowel quality" in the sense that an observer, instructed to listen to simple tones and state which of the vowel sounds it most "resembles" will, after some preliminary training, make his reports with a fair degree of assurance and with surprisingly good consistency.

The classic experiment is that of Köhler (187), who, in 1910, used a series of tuning forks for low frequencies, and a variable-pitched whistle (the so-called Galton whistle) for high frequencies, and attempted to ascertain the frequencies that most nearly resembled selected vowel sounds. His results are of interest, quite apart from the question of their bearing on a separate vocalic dimension. The *u* sound (tr*u*e) was most intimately connected with a tone of 263~; *o* (r*o*ll) gave 525~; *a* (f*a*ther), 1053~; *e* (t*e*n), 2100~; *i* (mach*i*ne), 4200~. The successive vowels: *u, o, a, e, i* were thus spaced approximately an octave apart. In addition to the vowel sounds the nasal *m* was linked with a frequency of 132~ and the sibilant *s* with 8400~, thus adding an octave to either end of the vowel range. The current status of vocality as a dimension is not unlike that of tonality. Indeed, some have identified the two. On the other hand, Rich's repetition of Köhler's experiment (245) tended to equate vocality to volume, since the sizes of the differential thresholds for the two aspects of tonal sensation did not clearly warrant their separation.

Aural Harmonics. It is unlikely that anyone has ever heard a loud pure tone. The ear's response to a sinusoidal wave, at least one of large amplitude, is one which fails to preserve the simplicity inherent in the stimulus. The hearing mechanism, in common with many sound-transmission systems, distorts sound waves impinging upon it. The distortion takes the form of the introduction of harmonics, overtones of the fundamental frequency received. Thus, even though one is careful to present to the ear a pure tone from a properly activated phone or a carefully struck tuning fork of good construction, the moment the auditory mechanism goes into action it responds by making of the pure tone a clang of some degree of complexity. At low intensities, say below 40 db, the distortion effects may be imperceptible. As intensity is increased above this point the "richness" of the tone becomes increasingly apparent, and at high intensities the distortion effects are considerable. The overtones thus injected into the situation, because they are due to the ear's own operation, are called *aural harmonics*.

The distorting action of the ear was brought under measurement for the first time in the 1920's, when the Bell Telephone Laboratories undertook a systematic investigation of it by an ingenious technique (*94*, p. 175 ff.). Noting, in experiments dealing with "masking" (later to be discussed), that frequencies corresponding to the higher harmonics of a pure tone behaved in a curious fashion, the Bell Laboratories investigators isolated the phenomenon and studied it. In the presence of a continuous pure tone of high intensity a second "exploring" tone, variable in frequency and intensity, was introduced. Whenever the variable tone came into a region corresponding to one of the overtones of the steady stimulus, audible beats were produced. On the reasonable assumption that the intensity of the exploring tone which gave the most prominent beats was a measure of the magnitude of the aural harmonics present (beats are most readily detectable when the tones producing them are equally strong) there were charted the frequencies and intensities of several of the aural harmonics. Their frequencies are, of course, exact multiples of the tones producing them. Their strengths depend both upon the fundamental frequency of the inducing tone and its intensity. Thus, for a pure tone of 60∼, all the first four overtones have made their entrance as detectable aural harmonics before a sensation level of 25 db has been reached. For pure tones in the region of 1500∼ no overtones are noticed until a 50-db sensation level is reached, where the first overtone is just detectable, and an intensity of 86 db is necessary to render the fourth overtone audible.

Aural harmonics may be studied by a more direct method, though chiefly in the ears of animals as yet. Whenever the cochlea goes into operation there are generated within it electrical disturbances, the so-called "cochlear response" or *cochlear microphonic*. These waves are found to be exact counterparts of the sounds being led into the ear with, however, the important difference that they contain also the aural harmonics generated within the ear itself. Electrodes contacting the round window or some accessible inner ear structure may be attached to an amplifier and wave analyzer and the full structure of the sound spectrum present in the cochlea may be determined. Such an analysis should tell one quite exactly what is going on at the site of stimulation of the organ of Corti. By this means Wever and Bray (*312*) have measured the amount of distortion present in the ear of a cat when stimulated by a 1000∼ tone. There were found, as well as the 1000~ fundamental, a large group of harmonics, as many as 16 being identifiable in some experiments. At high intensities of stimulation the aural harmonics were so prominent in the wave analysis as to make a total contribution over half that of the fundamental. At very low intensities no components other than the fundamental were present; the cochlear response was "pure."

In general, when stimulation is of moderate intensity and distortion is not great, the harmonics appear in descending order of magnitude, e.g., the first overtone is more prominent than the second, the second larger than the third, etc. However, at high intensities, when the transmission system of the ear is being "pushed," another phenomenon appears, viz., certain harmonics (3rd, 5th, 7th, etc.) become proportionately greater at the expense of the remainder (2nd, 4th, 6th, etc.). This fact goes far to identify the characteristics of the ear as a sound receiver. Sound-conducting systems may be broadly classified as linear or nonlinear, and as symmetrical or asymmetrical. Under forced vibration a nonlinear but symmetrical system will generate only odd-numbered harmonics. An asymmetrical system yields even-numbered harmonics. It is apparent, from the manner in which aural harmonics behave, that the ear's distortion is both nonlinear and asymmetrical when the system is forced into vibration by sinusoidal waves of moderate amplitude. At larger amplitudes the departure from linearity is the major feature of its response.

Multiple Stimulation: Combination Tones and Beats. We have seen what happens through aural distortion when a single loud pure tone is led to the ear. What will be the result of stimulating with two such tones simultaneously? The nature of the response will depend upon the nature of the two tones. If they are of quite different frequencies there will be set up, in addition to the aural harmonics of each stimulus, some new products of interaction called *combination tones*. If the frequencies are quite close together there will result the phenomenon of *beats*.

Combination tones may be studied by either of the techniques used to identify aural harmonics. Certain of them are directly observable in the presence of the two interacting fundamentals, and additional ones may be located by the "exploring-tone" technique. Also, wave analysis of the electrical response of the cat's or guinea pig's cochlea yields a large number of combination tones.

There are two varieties of combination tones: *difference tones* and *summation tones*. The former have been known since the early eighteenth century and were discovered by the celebrated Italian violinist, Tartini. He observed the presence of a third tone in double-stopping and came to use it as a check in tuning his strings. Difference tones are still sometimes called "Tartini's tones." The discovery of summation tones awaited the systematic researches of Helmholtz in 1856. As the name implies, a difference tone has a pitch determined by the difference between the frequencies of two other tones; a summation tone's pitch results from the addition of frequencies. Thus the first difference tone, D_1, which is easily detectable when two properly selected generating tones are used, has a pitch number coming from a simple subtraction of one frequency from the other; e.g., if the higher tone (h) has a frequency of 1000∼ and the lower one (l) is 700∼, $D_1 = h - l = 300$∼. The first summation tone, S_1, would come from the summing of the fundamentals; $S_1 = h + l = 1700$∼. There are two "second-order" difference tones: $2h - l$ and $h - 2l$; three of the third order: $3h - l$, $2h - 2l$, $3l - h$; four of the fourth order: $4h - l$, $3h - 2l$, $2h - 3l$, $4l - h$; etc. The general formula is: Order $= m + n - 1$, where m and n are all possible integers. A similar series exists, of course, for summation tones. The pitch number for any particular combination tone is therefore given by the expression: $N = mh \pm nl$.

Obviously a very large number of combination tones is obtainable, though from direct observation few appear. The reason is that combination tones lying at or near the location of either of the fundamentals or any of the prominent overtones of either fundamental may be masked to the point of inaudibility. Strong fundamentals are necessary to produce the distortion pattern to which the combination tones owe their existence; this situation also produces powerful masking. Analysis of the electrical potentials in the guinea pig's cochlea, under strong stimulation by tones of 700∼ and 1200∼ has, however, revealed the existence of 64 combination tones simultaneously present (222). Another similar experiment (313) found difference tones of the 20th order from fundamentals of 10,000∼ and 100∼ ($h - 20l$, a tone of 8000∼).

Now, what of the case where the two interacting fundamentals do not differ sufficiently in pitch number to generate combination tones? As has been stated, beats result when the two tones have frequencies quite near each other. If two tone generators are only very slightly mistuned, say 1∼ apart, a very slow beat will result. Once each second there will be a regular loudening and softening of the heard tone. Similarly, two tones 30∼ apart will produce 30 beats per second, etc. The rule is that the number of beats occurring each second tells one the frequency difference, in cycles per second, separating two tone generators. As has been seen, this fact may be put to use in the identification of unknown tones. Also, the fact that two perfectly tuned generators will not beat with each other is a convenient one; piano tuners make use of it constantly to bring two or more strings to the same pitch.

Beats may be detected when the mistuning of the primaries creating them is only very slight. The waxing and waning of loudness, which constitutes the "beat" under these conditions, may occur as infrequently as once in 2 minutes and still be noticeable. The exact lower limit for the detection of beats cannot be stated generally, since it is dependent upon the absolute as well as the relative intensities of the beating components. The problem is clearly that of determining how gradually ΔI may be introduced and still remain ΔI.

In the middle pitch range, when the frequencies are such that not more than four or five beats per second are created, the periodic surging is readily observed as a smooth rise and fall of loudness, commonly judged to be pleasant in character and effectively used in music. Beyond this point, with further separation of the generating frequencies, the smooth surging gives way to an intermittence which, if the tones are sufficiently intense, may be quite unpleasant. The intermittent effect consists of individual pulses separated by brief silences. With larger frequency differences, say 25–30~, intermittence goes over into a roughness which continues so long as beats are observable. The point at which roughness appears and the further point at which it fades out, leaving only two clearly separate tones, are dependent upon the absolute frequencies involved. If the frequencies are high and of sufficient intensity tones may be heard to beat even though they are separated by as much as 250~.

The apparent pitch of a beating complex is a matter of some interest. Beats are easily heard, but what is it that beats? Most investigators agree that, when the two primaries are close together, the heard pitch lies between them; the beat comes from an *intertone*. When the frequency difference is made larger the intertone remains and "carries" the beat, but the two fundamentals make their entrance on either side of it. Finally, the intertone drops out, only the roughness remaining along with the primaries to signal the presence of tonal interference.

The occurrence of beats is a testimonial to the fact that the ear is far from a perfect analyzer of sound. If analysis were complete, if Ohm's Acoustic Law held exactly, two tones differing by a few cycles would not beat with each other but each would be heard separately and distinctly, as they are when the tones are sufficiently separated to produce a resolution of the conflict.

Although both beats and combination tones arise from multiple tonal stimulation, care should be taken not to confuse them with respect to their probable physiological bases. Because the pitch number of the first difference tone is mathematically equivalent to the number of beats produced between the two fundamentals, many have been misled into regarding difference tones as "beat tones." Actually, beats and combination tones have nothing to do with each other. Combination tones, as we have seen, depend upon the ear's distorting action, much of it doubtless being due to non-linearity contributed by the ligaments holding the ossicular chain together. If the response of the auditory mechanism were completely linear and symmetrical, which it is not, we should still hear beats, though combination tones would never occur.

Consonance and Dissonance. When two or more tones are sounded together, the various possible combinations differ very markedly with respect to their capacity to produce pleasing or displeasing effects. This is, of course, a matter of basic concern in music. Those tones which "fuse" well, when presented simultaneously, produce *consonant* intervals; those which have a "jarring" and generally unpleasant effect, which do not fuse intimately, are said to be *dissonant*. Though it has not always been a matter of universal agreement among musicians— musical styles, like others, change—those intervals, falling within the compass of an octave, generally regarded as consonant are: the octave itself (frequency ratio of 2:1), the major fifth (3:2), the fourth (4:3), the major sixth (5:3), the major third (5:4), the minor third (6:5), and the minor sixth (8:5). The last four have sometimes been called "imperfect" consonances, and, indeed, the various intervals differ, from person to person and in different ages of music, with respect to their relative "perfection" of consonance. One may, through repetitive hearing of a pair of tones, become so habituated to an interval as to change radically his judgment of its pleasantness or unpleasantness. The intervals commonly regarded as dissonant are: the minor second (16:15), the major second (9:8), the major seventh (15:8), the tritone (F–B, 32:45), and nearly all the intervals in which one term of the ratio is 7 (7:5, 7:6, 8:7, etc.), though some find the minor seventh (7:4) not unpleasant, especially as a transitional chord.

The language of music is an ancient one, and men in all ages have speculated about possible bases for consonance and dissonance. Galileo, in his *Dialogues* (1638?), addresses himself to the "splendid subject" of music and says, ". . . we may possibly explain why certain pairs of notes, differing in pitch produce a pleasing sensation, others a less pleasant effect, and still others a disagreeable sensation. Such an explanation would be tantamount to an explanation of the more or less perfect consonances and dissonances. The unpleasant sensation produced by the latter arises, I think, from the discordant vibrations of two different tones which strike the ear out of time. . . . Agreeable consonances are pairs of tones which strike the ear with a certain regularity; this regularity consists in the fact that the pulses delivered by the two tones, in the same interval of time, shall be commensurable in number, so as not to keep the ear drum in perpetual torment, bending in two different directions in order to yield to the ever-discordant impulses. . . ." (*104*, pp. 99–100)

This perspicacious explanation does not sound too strange to the modern ear. In fact, the theory of consonance most favored at the present time, that of Helmholtz, is not very different in basic conception. It was Helmholtz' belief that relative consonance occurs when the upper partials of the tones producing the interval are coincident and that the "roughness" accompanying dissonance results from the beating of partials separated by too small frequency differences to give unique impressions. Thus, the octave is the most consonant interval because all the even-numbered partials of the two coincide and reinforce each other. A dissonant interval such as the minor second not only produces beats between the fundamentals but also between a multitude of combinations of higher harmonics.

This view of Helmholtz' has not always met with ready acceptance. There have been many competing theories of tonal fusion (*224*, Chap. 6). However, the chief objection raised against Helmholtz, that consonances and dissonances remain when entirely pure tones are used in producing the intervals creating them, necessarily had to subside with the discovery of the aural harmonics. The ear provides the mechanism for beating upper partials if the stimuli do not.

Masking. Several effects of multiple tonal stimulation have now been considered: difference and summation tones, beats, and consonance-dissonance. There remains another, the phenomenon of *masking*.

If two tones of different frequency, one of high and the other of low intensity, are simultaneously led to the same ear it is likely that the weaker one will not be heard at all. It is said to be "masked" by the stronger. To reach audibility, to "cut through" the masking tone, the weaker one has to be intensified considerably. The amount by which the threshold of a tone (or noise) is raised by virtue of the presence of a second one may be taken as a direct measure of the masking strength of the latter.

This suppressive influence is non-specific in the sense that it extends great distances throughout the frequency range, though the masking effect is greatest on closely adjacent frequencies. Another generality is that masking is greater in the high-frequency direction, viz., a tone will mask another of considerably higher frequency more readily than

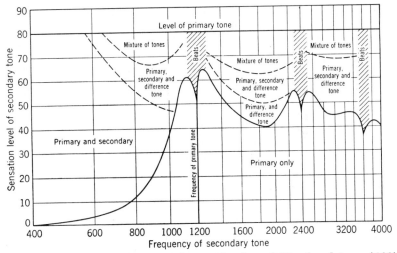

Fig. 51. Tonal interrelations in masking. The data of Wegel and Lane (302), revealing the complex phenomena produced by a steady "masking" tone of 1200~ and 80 db (sensation level) as a secondary tone of variable frequency and intensity, are introduced.

one of much lower frequency. This comes about, of course, as a result of the presence of aural harmonics, each of which may serve as a masking influence if sufficiently intense.

Quantitative determinations of masking have been carried out systematically by Bell Telephone Laboratories, and the data obtained there by Wegel and Lane (302) are classic for this phenomenon. Figure 51 provides a picture of: (1) the degree of masking produced by a steady (primary) tone of 1200~ and 80 db (sensation level); (2) the complex phenomena occurring once the masking level is exceeded by the masked (secondary) tone; (3) the occurrence of beats in those regions where the secondary tone lies close to the fundamental or overtones of the primary. The continuous, irregular curve (the "masking audiogram") is the locus of thresholds of all frequencies of the secondary tone in the presence of the primary, masking one. Obviously, for all points under the curve the masking tone only will be heard. Above it, in those places where the intensity of the secondary tone is relatively low (roughly, less than 40 db), both tones will be detected. In certain regions, e.g., at 1800~ and 45 db, the primary and the first difference tone are perceived; the secondary tone has emerged above threshold but makes it presence felt only through the generation of a difference tone. At higher levels the secondary tone enters the complex as a separately perceived component, and, at still higher intensities, the mixture of tones becomes elaborate as a result of the addition of prominent aural harmonics.

The interesting question whether the masking phenomenon is essentially cochlear or central in origin may be answered by delivering the primary tone to one ear and the secondary to the other. Under these conditions some masking occurs, but only a fraction of that produced in monaural stimulation. Moreover, binaural masking is most effective at high-intensity levels, and the result can then be attributed in large measure to direct stimulation by the masking tone of the contralateral cochlea, the tone having arrived there by way of conduction through the bones of the head. It is clear that masking is primarily a cochlear matter.

During World War II the problem of auditory masking came to be of considerable military importance, since efforts to upset radio communications frequently took the form of "jamming" with interfering tones and noises. Accordingly much valuable data on audibility, especially word intelligibility, has come from systematic investigations of masking by sounds complex in composition.

Auditory Fatigue. It is not an uncommon textbook statement that the ear, unlike the eye, does not undergo adaptation. Actually such statements perpetuate a myth. Auditory "fatigue," manifesting itself in a reduction in responsiveness of the auditory mechanism as a direct result of stimulation, is a real phenomenon and has been investigated experimentally a number of times (252). It has been shown that steady stimulation both reduces the apparent loudness of a tone and raises the intensive threshold for immediately subsequent stimulation.

A direct frontal attack on the problem, the result of which provides a partial picture of the fatigue phenomenon, was made by Wood (318). Using a fatiguing tone of 1000~ at moderate intensity, he charted the course of sensitivity reduction as a function of time. The procedure was entirely analogous to that followed in measuring light adaptation by the comparison field method (Chap. 3). A fatiguing tone was led from an oscillator and attenuator system to one phone of a headset.

After steady stimulation of one ear for intervals ranging from 5 sec to 2 min the fatiguing tone was cut off, and a comparison tone was delivered immediately to the other, previously unstimulated ear. In successive trials the intensity of the comparison tone was systematically changed, and the intensity providing a match with the loudness last heard from the fatiguing tone was determined. Wood's results, summarized in Fig. 52, are expressed in relative values of the comparison

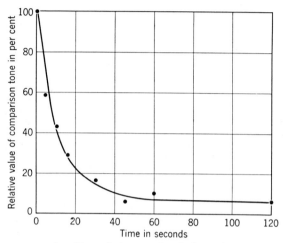

FIG. 52. The course of auditory fatigue. The decline of apparent loudness of a steadily exposed tone of 1000∼. Percentages of the initial intensity required to produce a loudness match in the unfatigued ear are plotted on the ordinate. From the unpublished work of Wood (318).

tone (as percentages of the initial intensity) required to effect a match. The results are surprisingly similar to those obtained in retinal adaptation studies.

The correctness of Wood's measures depends upon the essential independence of the two ears. We have seen, from a consideration of the neural anatomy of the auditory pathways, that the two cochleas presumably do not have separate cortical projection areas. Moreover, it is known that the physical stimulus does not confine itself to one cochlea but is carried, by bone conduction through the head, to the opposite one. However, if the locus of the fatigue process is peripheral rather than central and if, at the intensities used in this experiment, the energy conducted to the "matching" ear is not appreciable (as presumably it was not), the fatigue curves may not be too far in error. In any case the mere fact that, after a period of continuous stimulation of one ear, a lower intensity delivered to the other will produce

apparently equal loudnesses reveals either the existence of a reduced
sensitivity in the first (auditory fatigue) or a sensitization of one ear
through prolonged stimulation of the other.   The latter possibility
should not be dismissed too lightly.   A study by Egan (86) has demonstrated that speech sounds received in one ear may be made louder
by the introduction of a continuous noise in the other or, conversely,

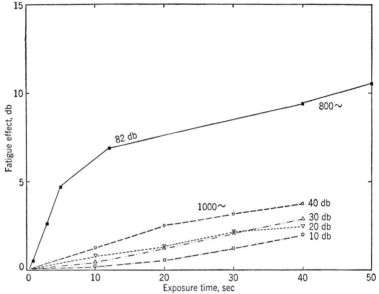

FIG. 53.   Elevation of thresholds through fatigue at different intensities.   The
curves for 1000~ show the raising of the threshold for tones of low and moderate
intensity.   The results for the high-intensity 800~ tone reveal more clearly the
curvilinear nature of the function connecting fatigue effect and time.   From
Wever, 309.

the removal of the steady noise weakens the speech sounds heard in
the contralateral ear.

Results having much the same import as those of the Wood experiment come out of auditory fatigue studies in which altered sensitivity
is indicated by the heightening of thresholds, rather than by reduced
loudness, at the conclusion of the adaptation period.   Figure 53 presents Wever's combining of the results of two different but comparable
experiments (309, p. 320), both conducted by the threshold method.
Low and moderate intensities of fatiguing tone (10 to 40 db) lead to
a simple exponential loss of sensitivity (the "fatigue effect" is plotted
in decibels), while a strong tone (82 db) produces an initial rapid
drop which is followed by a more gentle decline.

The whole problem of auditory fatigue requires more research. There needs to be worked out, in a systematic fashion, a clear set of functional dependencies relating the extent of auditory fatigue to various stimulus durations, intensities, and frequencies. Comprehensively obtained results connecting these three variables would not only be of considerable intrinsic value but would have important consequences for auditory theory. The course of recovery, analogous to visual dark adaptation, similarly needs to be charted.

"Persistence," "Flutter," and After-Effects of Stimulation. Does there occur in audition anything analogous to "flicker"? It will be recalled that the flicker phenomenon provides a valuable tool for the investigation of visual processes. Repetitive flashes of light, fusing to give a steady, uninterrupted impression, yield evidence that excitation outlasts the stimulus; i.e., visual impressions "persist."

It has been claimed that persistence is also a characteristic of auditory excitation and that the "flutter" experiment is proof of it. The best-known work here is that of Weinberg and Allen (303). They attempted to produce alternate periods of sound and silence by rotating a disc, having four symmetrically disposed holes cut out of it, in front of an orifice conducting sound to the ear. What they actually succeeded in doing, of course, was to produce periodic fluctuations of intensity, as Wingfield (315), who repeated their experiment with better control, has adequately demonstrated. "Flutter" is produced under these circumstances, but a "critical fusion point" is never reached so long as the tonal cutoff is really effective. If as much as one j.n.d. of intensity separates the uninterrupted and (partially) interrupted phases flutter will result; if less than one j.n.d., a continuous tone will be heard. The latter, however, is in no sense the "fused" continuity of the kind found in vision above the critical frequency of flicker. The parallel between the two is not even a remote one. Experiments on "flutter," as classically performed, have no bearing whatever on the question of persistence.

However, it would not be surprising if the effects of auditory stimulation did briefly outlast the stimulus. The transmission system of the ear is highly, but not critically, damped. Observation of the movements of the ossicles in response to sharp clicks reveals rapidly damped oscillations following cessation of the click, as we noted when we were examining the middle ear's mode of operation. Also, the electrical response of the cochlea displays an "off-effect," a short series of rapid discharges, at the moment of termination of the stimulus. Other elaborations of the basic response are conceivably possible in the complex series of catenary events leading to final cortical excitation. The great difficulty in ascertaining the facts lies in the complications introduced when brief impulsive stimuli are used. We have encountered it before —the production of multi-frequency transients whenever tones are abruptly cut on or off.

A curious after-effect of relatively prolonged stimulation has been discovered in the Harvard Psychoacoustic Laboratory (*201*, p. 1013). After listening for a half-minute, say, to a continuous series of strong, sharp pulses, which appear as a steady, intense buzz, new sounds presented to the ear take on a peculiar "metallic" or "rasping" quality temporarily. The noise of a typewriter in action, of two pieces of sandpaper being rubbed together, or of any other familiar sound pattern, especially if it is discontinuous and complex in harmonic content, takes on this ringing or jangling timbre immediately following the conditioning exposure. The after-effect lasts only a short time, from 1 or 2 sec up to 10 or 12, depending on exposure time, stimulus strength, constitution of the pulse train, and probably the character of the test stimulus. Attempts to discover the optimal conditions for the effect (*253*) reveal that: (1) A certain kind of stimulating pattern is necessary. Random noise, whether continuous or interrupted, is ineffective. (2) A square-wave pattern produces the effect but not nearly as vividly as rectangular pulses of the same peak intensity; (3) prominent high-frequency components must be present in the acoustic pattern for the best after-effect to result; (4) duration and intensity of exposure may be substituted for each other to a certain extent; i.e., brief strong stimuli and long weak ones operate in an equivalent manner; and (5) a relatively narrow range of pulse frequencies (30 to 200 per second, with a maximum slightly above 100) may be used effectively. The after-effect displays itself only in the presence of a test sound. It does not assert itself against a background of silence. For this reason it is best to characterize the phenomenon as an *after-effect* of stimulation, not as an auditory "afterimage," as its co-discoverers have unhappily called it.

8

Electrophysiology
and Auditory Theory

The Microphonic Action of the Cochlea. Electrical potentials recorded from the region of the round window can serve as a revealing index of events transpiring within the cochlea. The story of the discovery of the cochlear potential is one of the most dramatic in modern psychophysiology. In 1930 Wever and Bray, working in the Princeton Psychological Laboratory, attempted to study action potentials in the auditory nerve of a cat by hooking a pair of electrodes to the short extent of nerve leading into the medulla, amplifying, and reproducing the electrical changes in a loud speaker. They were successful in picking up electrical waves accompanying tonal and vocal stimulation of the cat's ear. The waves proved to be faithful reproductions of the stimuli, so faithful that an observer listening at the receiver could identify, by the quality of his voice, the person speaking into the cat's ear! It appeared that the cat's auditory nerve was serving as one part of a telephone system and was reproducing with considerable fidelity all the complex waves delivered to the ear, even those of relatively high frequency.

The phenomenon reported by Wever and Bray naturally aroused considerable scientific interest, and several repetitions of the experiment were undertaken almost immediately. Not only did the "Wever-Bray effect," as it came shortly to be called, seem to be crucial for auditory theory, but the finding that high frequencies of nerve impulses could apparently be conducted by the auditory nerve seemed in a fair way to revolutionize modern neurology. Hitherto it had been thought that the maximum frequency any nerve could conduct was of the order of 1000 per second, being limited to this value by the "absolutely refractory period," known to be about 1 msec in duration. The Princeton investigators had reproduced tones of 5000~ over their cat-telephone, and this would call for a refractory period lasting no longer than $\frac{1}{5}$ msec.

The work stimulated by the Wever-Bray experiment was extensive and valuable. More solid facts were added to auditory psychophysiology in the next ten years than in any other similar period of research in this field. It turned out that the first interpretation—that the counterpart of the stimulus was being carried over the auditory nerve—was incorrect. The Wever-Bray effect proved to be compounded of two phenomena: auditory nerve action potentials and aural microphonics, the latter generated not in the nerve but in the cochlea. Since the two may be picked up simultaneously from the auditory nerve close to the cochlea—and will be, unless special steps are taken to isolate one or the other—it is not greatly to be wondered at that they were intermingled in the initial Wever-Bray study.

The two effects have important points of difference, however, and it is possible to separate them analytically, even though their physical separation is not simple. Let us examine briefly some of the differentiating features. Whereas, in experimental animals, both the nerve response and the electrical response of the cochlea are adversely affected by cold, reduction of blood supply, anesthetics, or death of the animal, the cochlear response is considerably more resistant to such changes. The waveforms of the two are also different. The cochlear microphonic follows the waveform of the stimulus (except for the addition of aural harmonics, as we have seen); the nerve response displays "spikes" characteristic of action potentials in other nerve preparations. The temporal characteristics of the two responses also differ. The time lag of the cochlear microphonic is almost inappreciable; its onset follows the introduction of the stimulus by only about 0.0001 sec or less. The nerve response always shows a considerably longer delay. The cochlear microphonic has no "threshold" in the same sense that the nerve has one. The lower limiting value for the former is that of the instruments used to record it; the nerve response requires considerably more energy to set it off. Perhaps the outstanding difference, however, has to do with the frequencies displayed by each. Action potentials never have the extremely high-frequency components found in aural microphonics. The latter presumably go at least as high as the upper-frequency limit of hearing (16,000~ waves have been recorded), while 4000~ seems to be the maximum frequency yet found in the auditory nerve, and this is not well synchronized with the stimulus. The high frequencies in the Wever-Bray experiment were a part of the cochlear microphonic.

In sum, then, the cochlear microphonic has no refractory period or any of the other "all-or-nothing" features connected with nervous action. This indicates that the two phenomena, nerve response and cochlear potential, probably have quite different origins. How is the cochlear potential generated? A final answer is not possible as yet, but there are some promising hypotheses. One of these places the origin of the electrical effect in Reissner's membrane. This is supposed to be electrically polarized by virtue of the fact that it lies between two fluids, the endolymph and the perilymph, which may have quite different ionic concentrations, since they arise from different sources. Mechanical movements of Reissner's membrane, forced by waves ascending and descending the cochlea, might under these circumstances generate electrical currents. Another, and more generally accepted, hypothesis of the origin of the electrical response of the cochlea regards the hair cells of the organ of Corti as being the generating elements. This view relies heavily on the evidence from albino animals, though this is not the sole support. In cats, dogs, and "waltzing" guinea pigs having deficiencies of the cochlea it has been demonstrated a number of times that electrical responses cannot be elicited at all; post-mortem examination has revealed an absence of hair cells, though other cochlear structures may be intact. The evidence thus far is not entirely crucial, but the hair-cell theory, which has been worked out to a nicety by Stevens and Davis (273, Chap. 14) seems capable of subsuming all the major known facts.

Responses of the Auditory Nerve. Certain characteristics of the nerve response, differentiating it from the cochlear microphonic, have already been considered. Other features are disclosed by studies of action potentials originating in the auditory nerve bundle. The most intimate picture thus far obtained has come from experiments in which the responses of individual nerve components have been isolated by the use of tiny pipette electrodes, only about 0.005 mm in diameter, inserted in favorable locations in the eighth nerve of the cat (102, 75). When Galambos and Davis, who performed the experiments, made their initial analysis they believed their electrodes to have been contacting axons of fibers whose dendrites originate at the base of the hair cells of the organ of Corti and whose cell bodies lie in the spiral ganglion. Subsequently, from detailed microscopic study of similar segments of the cat's eighth cranial nerve, it could be deduced that the original records must have come mainly from cell bodies of the cochlear nucleus (103). Second-order, rather than first-order, neurons had been involved. Nevertheless, the second nerve cell in the chain of four from the cochlea to the cortex presumably carries much the same information as does the first one; probably the two do not differ radically from each other in mode of operation. As Wever has said (*309*, p. 184), "The cochlear fibers must perform at least as well as the second-order neurons; they may do better in their representation of the stimulus, but they cannot do worse." Since the second-order nerve cells behave in a quite elaborate and revealing fashion, it is of interest to see what phenomena they displayed in response to external stimuli.

When tones of low intensity were delivered to the cat's ear it was found that individual elements responded in a quite specific fashion. At threshold intensity a particular element might show potentials only in response to tones of a very limited frequency range, e.g., 690∼ to 710∼. To all other tones it would be entirely unresponsive. Other units had, at threshold, similar specificities. If the stimulus intensity were increased, however, a wide band of frequencies became effective in bringing about discharge. The spread of response as the energy of the stimulus was raised was an asymmetrical one favoring the lower frequencies. Figure 54 shows the roughly triangular "response areas" for four different units. The behavior of the "2000∼ element" (the one responding at threshold only to tones in the immediate vicinity of 2000∼) may be taken as typical. When stimulated with high-intensity tones, at a level corresponding to about 90 db human sensation level (10 db below 2 volts, on the chart), this unit has become so non-specific in its response that tones from 250∼ to 2500∼ will excite it. In other words, an element "tuned" to respond at threshold only to a very small range of frequencies will, if stimulated intensely, respond to tones three octaves below and one-half octave above its "characteristic" frequency. Cells having characteristic frequencies as low as 200∼ and as high as 50,000∼ were found in the cat. The "low-pitched" neurons were rare.

Except for the feature of specialized frequency reception the individual auditory nerve components behave very much as do fibers belonging to the other senses. They show characteristic random discharges ("spontaneous" activity) in the absence of external stimuli. They may display a brief period of no response, a "silent period," on cessation of prolonged stimulation and also "after-discharge," an accelerated rate of firing after the silent period. They give evidence of "equilibration" (a rapid decline in discharge rate in the presence of a continuous stimulus). Their refractory periods are not found to be unusually short (as was suspected in the days of the "Wever-Bray effect"). They also respond, individually, to intensity increases by discharging with greater rapidity, though there is a limit to which this occurs; most units show a maximum discharge rate of about 450 per second, and this level is reached at only 30–40 db above threshold.

Frequency of discharge in the auditory nerve is thus determined by two variables, stimulus frequency and intensity.

The question may be raised, as it was for the cochlear response, as to how the nerve discharge is initiated. Once more we have to appeal to hypothesis to some extent, for the facts are far from being all at hand. One view is that the genesis is mechanical; vibratory distortion of the hair cells of the basilar membrane produces both the nerve im-

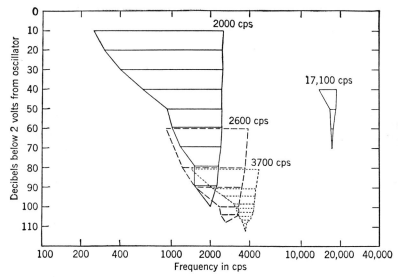

Fig. 54. The "response areas" of four neurones in the cat's cochlear nucleus. At threshold only a single narrow range of frequencies is effective. The higher the intensity, the less critically "tuned" is the responding element. From Davis (75) after Galambos and Davis (102). By permission of the publishers and the authors.

pulse and the cochlear response, the latter as a by-product. Another hypothesis is that the auditory nerve, like other nerves in which such a mechanism has been pretty well demonstrated, has to be discharged by a chemical mediator. Recent researches on acetylcholine as the initiator of nervous impulses lend credence to this idea. In the transmission of impulses from nerve to muscle the role played by acetylcholine is beyond dispute. Perhaps the final step in the excitation of all nerves is the same. At any rate, the appreciable time delay in the arousal of auditory nerve action potentials demands some such explanation and the facts fit the chemical mediation theory well.

A third hypothesis has been that the cochlear potential, the aural microphonic, is itself the initiating agent, that the nerve is stimulated electrically by the currents generated in the cochlea. This view is an attractive one because nerve impulses can, of course, be set off by direct electrical excitation, and the cochlear potential is known to be a large one, appropriately located and possessed of some of the other requisite properties for service as a nerve excitant. However, it does not have all of them, and this fact has led to the search for some intermediary process, some set of events standing in more immediate relation to the discharge of the nerve twigs at the base of the hair cells. Cleverly designed experiments by Davis and his associates (77), characterized by the use of high-frequency stimulation and suitably placed multiple electrodes in the guinea pig's cochlea, have led to the detection of a third set of electrical waves. This ·component of the ear's electrical response, termed the "summating potential" because of its capacity to add the effects of two or more sound waves if they recur rapidly enough, has a separate existence from that of the cochlear microphonic and also from that of the conventionally recorded nerve action potential. It is distinguishable from the microphonic in several ways, lagging behind it in time by about 100 μsec, being separable from it by operative injury or other adverse conditions, reacting differently to a polarizing current, and, especially, outlasting the mechanical motion of the basilar membrane that presumably creates it. It may be distinguished from the nerve action potential, which, as we have seen, is probably generated in the cell bodies of the spiral ganglion, by lacking the "all-or-nothing" properties of nervous functioning, such as the occurrence of the refractory period. Moreover, its electrical behavior is such as to locate its origin at the organ of Corti, close to the point of generation of the aural microphonic.

The discovery that there is a local excitatory potential does not, of course, necessarily invalidate the mechanical and chemical hypotheses. All three could be right. The mechanical motion is certainly there, and it is still a mystery as to how mechanical distortion or changing tension can initiate a nervous discharge. Moreover, the chemical hypothesis is not incompatible with the mechanical and electrical ones. Biochemical processes may be triggered by mechanical deformations; they also usually have electrical manifestations. The mechanical, chemical, and electrical accounts may simply provide three different but related pictures of the same set of basic events. At any rate, until we have a more intimate knowledge of the ways in which receptor cells act as energy transducers we shall not be in a position to reject any of the current guesses concerning initiation of nerve impulses.

Responses of Nervous Centers. Electrical signs of nervous activity appear at higher levels of the nervous system as well as in the auditory nerve. Electrodes contacting various parts of the ascending tracts from the auditory nerve to the cortex reveal, up to a point on the frequency scale, potentials which reproduce stimulus frequencies and, beyond that, electrical responses of an asynchronous variety. Thus, at the cochlear nucleus of the medulla there may be found all the complex phenomena occurring in the nerve itself, as we have seen. With some electrode placements the amplitude of the potentials may actually be much greater than those found in the nerve, presumably because "gray matter" (aggregates of many cell bodies and synaptic tissue) is making the electrical contribution. At the trapezoid body there begins to be a limitation on the upper frequency of synchronized impulses which will come through. Kemp and his collaborators (*181*) found 2500∽ to be the maximum stimulus frequency that would reproduce itself at this neural level, though tones as high as 4000∽ produced an asynchronous discharge. Higher in the auditory tract, at the lateral lemniscus, the top frequency was 1000∽. At still higher centers it is possible to get responses, but they show a further frequency restriction, and, if an attempt is made to record from the highest of all, the temporal cortex, tonal stimuli show no synchronized responses whatever. At the cortical level it is possible to reproduce a series of discrete clicks; the potentials will follow the succession of sounds up to a frequency of 100 per second. Beyond this the synchronized response breaks down.

There are good reasons why the higher nervous centers seem not to record faithfully the regular tonal sequences reproduced so accurately by the peripheral mechanism. In part it is a matter of experimental techniques, viz., anesthetics and electrodes. A general anesthetic always influences the highest centers first and extends its influence progressively downward, neurologically speaking. It is not easy to find the fine balance that will keep an experimental animal "under" and yet allow the cortex to function sufficiently well for the purpose at hand. As to electrodes, those of the type used to obtain the "click-response" data, just described, are relatively gross affairs as compared with those in the investigation of second-order neurons of the eighth nerve. If glass micropipette electrodes are substituted for the larger ones somewhat different results are obtained, at least at certain of the intermediate relay stations on the way to the cortex. At the inferior colliculus, e.g., recording with microelectrodes no larger than 0.005 mm in diameter at the tip has led to the finding that the same kind of frequency specificity discovered in the cells of the cochlear nucleus also obtains here (*280*). Triangular "response areas" of the type shown in Fig. 54 may be plotted for the colliculus, the width of the band of effective frequencies being determined by stimulus intensity. A still higher center, the medial geniculate body, displays precisely the same phenomenon (*133*). These two regions of the central nervous system thus add their testimony to a growing collection of evidence that there is a good deal of localization of neural response on the basis of frequency differentiation.

A clear-cut set of facts has been adduced concerning the time relations involved at the several nervous levels between the cochlea and the brain (*181*). If the time is measured between the reception of a strong click, signalled by the aural microphonic, and the appearance of the first action potentials in the auditory nerve (first-order neuron), at the trapezoid body (second-order neuron), and at the lateral lemniscus (third-order neuron), there are found to be some significant delays. The wave appears in the auditory nerve approximately 1.0 msec after the onset of the cochlear response. It has reached the second-order neuron in another 1.3 msec. By the time third-order neurons respond a total of at least 3.5 msec has elapsed. Due allowance being made for conduction time in the nerve fibers it appears that the delays are mainly those at synaptic junctions. From these measurements it is found that the time lost at each of the synapses must be 0.8 msec, a value which accords well with calculations made on other comparable synaptic junctions in the central nervous system.

As with investigations of higher nervous pathways in vision, we are yet at the threshold of much solid information concerning the manifold and complex relations existing in the auditory tract. Part of the failure to make more prompt discoveries is, of course, to be attributed to the intrinsic complexity and relative inaccessibility of the structures concerned; part is due to the technical difficulty that the anesthetics used to make such experiments possible also operate to diminish or destroy the very phenomena being investigated.

Theories of Hearing. The chief facts of hearing are now before us. Into what sort of framework shall we put them? Are there available for our use any embracing conceptions which will permit us to arrange our facts in more meaningful patterns and, looking past them, enable us to foretell where new facts are to be found? This is the service good theories perform.

More than a score of auditory theories exist, but there are few which, over the years, have prompted research leading to significant discoveries. If this is made a criterion we are reduced to two major theories and three minor ones. The "resonance" theory of Helmholtz and the "telephone" theory of Rutherford and Wrightson fall into the category of major theories; the minor ones are Ewald's "sound-pattern" theory, Meyer's "hydraulic" theory, and a "frequency-resonance" theory due to Troland. We shall consider each in turn, though devoting more attention to the first than to the others, for Helmholtz' theory, now nearly a century old, has stood well the test of time and continues to prove its worth as a stimulator of new investigations.

The Helmholtz resonance theory is sometimes called the "harp" or "piano" theory, since the central idea is one which pictures the transverse fibers of the basilar membrane as acting very much like harp or piano strings. Everyone is familiar with the fact that, if the sustaining pedal of a piano is held down and a tone is sung near by, the strings corresponding to the vocal frequencies will vibrate sympathetically, i.e., will resonate to the sounds striking them. The fibers of the basilar membrane, varying as they do with respect to length (long at the apex of the cochlea and short at the base) and perhaps variable also in tension and "loading," seem admirably suited for service as a series of graded resonators. Here is a mechanism which, because it can respond selectively to different frequencies, may be an adequate tone analyzer and thus meet the requirements of Ohm's Acoustic Law. A given "place" (a particular fiber or group of them) on the basilar membrane is responsible for a particular pitch; overtones stimulate a series of fibers spaced down the membrane. Tones so close together as to affect overlapping portions of the membrane produce local interference and hence the beat phenomenon. Consonance and dissonance yield no disturbing facts; as we have seen, the beating of upper partials may be responsible for creating dissonant intervals.

The theory, as left by Helmholtz, had little to say about loudness. Intense tones produced vigorous movements of the membrane and strong impulses in the nerve fibers attached to the hair cells. It was not until much later that anyone questioned this aspect of the theory. Meanwhile, some objections had been raised concerning the basic notion that the transverse fibers could vibrate independently of each other. They are, after all, closely connected with each other in the tough, tendinous tissue of the basilar membrane, and sharp tuning would not be expected of such a structure. The objection was formally met by A. A. Gray, in 1900, though the principle he employed was inherent in Helmholtz' own statement of the theory (*309*, Chap. 5). Gray pictured the basilar membrane's response to a pure tone as involving, as well as the "in-tune" fiber, other fibers adjacent to it. The extent to which neighboring fibers will be called in depends upon the intensity of the stimulus. However, the "in-tune" resonator reacts with the greatest vigor and gives its pitch to the complex response; those flanking it have progressively diminishing amplitudes the further situated they are from the center of the responding group. Gray called this the "principle of maximum stimulation," and this amendment to Helmholtz' original theory is commonly called "Gray's modification."

The first real difficulty encountered by the resonance theory came in 1912 with the discovery of the "all-or-nothing" principle of nerve discharge. It was clearly demonstrated by Lucas and Adrian that nerve fibers normally respond by discharging "at full strength." Either a nerve discharges completely or it does not discharge at all; except under special circumstances there are no graded responses within the individual nerve fiber. What of the correlate for loudness in the Helmholtz theory? Amplitude of sympathetic vibration was supposed to be translated into strength of nerve discharge to take care of the intensity-loudness correlation.

At first the discovery that there are no graded "strengths" of nerve discharge seemed to present an insuperable difficulty. Then, in 1915, there came a new theoretical formulation of sensory intensity. Forbes and Gregg surmised that varying intensity of stimulus might be reflected in variable frequency of discharge within a single fiber. Whereas, in conformity with the all-or-nothing principle, a fiber must always discharge with its full capacity to do so, it may fire only a few times a second or may deliver very rapidly successive discharges, depending upon the amount of energy acting upon it. Immediately following discharge there occurs a brief period, of the order of a millisecond, in which the fiber is "absolutely refractory"; no amount of stimulation can affect it. Following this there occurs a "relatively refractory period," in which the original sensitive state is being rebuilt and in which the fiber can again respond. A weak stimulus must wait until quite late in the rebuilding period to effect discharge, and the fiber's response will thus be infrequent. A strong stimulus, by invading the relatively refractory period early, will produce more frequent responses. In this way stimulus frequency comes to be translated into discharge frequency. The demonstration that single nerve fibers actually behave in this manner did not come for another dozen years. The Forbes-Gregg hypothesis, meanwhile, rescued the Helmholtz theory from the temporary embarrassment into which the all-or-nothing discovery had plunged it.

There is another way in which intensity may be mediated. A strong stimulus may call into action a large number of fibers in a nerve bundle, while a weak one will involve only relatively few. This principle is commonly employed to account for graded muscular responses and may be used to explain variations in sensory intensity as well. However, as applied to the auditory nerve, it would seem to introduce complications for the Helmholtz theory. To bring into play any large number of fibers is to involve somewhat remotely situated nerve endings and these, being at other "places," would generate a conglomeration of pitches. Loud tones should be "muddy" tones. There is a question as to how far Gray's modification can be relied on to preserve tonal purity. The matter of aural harmonics is not concerned here. Harmonics have, of course, pitch numbers demanding wide spacing on the basilar membrane.

What are the evidences for the "pitch-place" correlation, the very heart of the Helmholtz theory? Unless it can be shown that tones have individual loci of reception in different portions of the basilar membrane, that low-frequency tones are analyzed out by fibers terminating near the apex of the cochlea, and that high-frequency tones are mediated by those in the basal turns, the whole theory falls to the ground. The chief relevant facts are those concerning (1) localization of the microphonic effect within the cochlea, (2) pathological findings in partial deafness, and (3) results of "stimulation-deafness" experiments.

That the aural microphonic arises in different portions of the cochlea, depending upon the stimulating frequency, seems certain. Electrodes situated at the base of the cochlea show high-frequency responses to be favored; records from the apex reveal low-frequency waves to have the greater magnitude (*141, 274*). The most convincing evidence of a fairly specific localization comes from the work of Culler (*67, 68*) and a confirming experiment by Kemp and Johnson (*182*). Culler explored the external surface of the guinea pig's cochlea, determining at each of 23 points the frequency requiring the least intensity to produce a small, constant electrical response. The presumption was that the most effective frequency, at any given point, must be generated in the immediate vicinity. A schematic representation of the results is shown in Fig. 55. Even though an elaborate mathematics and set of corrections were required to establish the individual points there would seem to be little doubt that low frequencies of the aural microphonic are generated in the apical turns; high frequencies have their origin near the base.

The evidence from pathology, as is so often the case, is not without internal contradictions. However, the clearest results support a general "place" differentiation for pitch. In cases of high-tone deafness, whether characterized by gradual losses toward the higher frequencies or more abrupt ones, post-mortem examination of the cochlear structure most commonly shows partial atrophy of nerve fibers and other degenerative changes in the basal turn (65). These findings, while not crucial, are at least consistent with the "place" theory.

Considerable work has been devoted to "stimulation deafness," the production of lowered or abolished sensitivity in experimental ani-

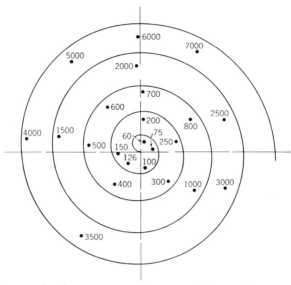

Fig. 55. Topographical variations in the size of the cochlear potential. The guinea pig's cochlea is represented schematically, apex at the center. There are shown optimal positions for obtaining the cochlear potential at each of the stimulus frequencies indicated, according to the reports of Culler and his associates (67, 68). By permission of the editor, *Annals of Otology, Rhinology, and Laryngology.*

mals by exposing them to intense tones for a matter of days or weeks. The early experiments connecting local degeneration with tonal gaps seemed decisive and were frequently cited in support of the Helmholtz theory. However, by now there have been more than a score of such experiments and the conclusions seem far less certain (180). There is little doubt that cochlear lesions can be produced in this way, providing the stimulating tones are sufficiently intense and prolonged, but the losses as well as the lesions are likely to be quite general, and, in the better-controlled experiments, the zone of greatest loss (as determined by diminished electrical response) has not always coincided with the "place" one would expect the "deafening" tone to occupy. Post-mortem inspection of the cochlear alterations is likely to show degeneration to have occurred in the region theoretically belonging to frequencies in the range 1000–2000∿, i.e., in the region of greatest sensitivity. Like the pathological findings in human deafness, the results of stimulation-deafness experiments thus far fail to provide critical evidence for the Helmholtz theory. While, in general, they are not incompatible with it, they do not clearly prove its correctness.

In arriving at a tentative evaluation of the Helmholtz theory it must be said that its "place" feature is not the least of its virtues. In addition to the evidences just cited there are some other facts that are accommodated well by the assumption that there is a systematic pitch localization along the length of the basilar membrane. The way in which various frequencies contribute to total loudness and to speech intelligibility, and the operation of critical frequency bands in the production of masking, find most ready interpretation in the light of the pitch-place assumption.

On the other hand, the resonance feature of the original Helmholtz theory must be said to have appeared more and more improbable as the evidence on cochlear mechanics has accumulated. There is little doubt that a kind of "resonance" occurs. The relative amplitudes of vibration of different parts of the basilar membrane and its attachments change in a regular manner as stimulus frequency is changed, the point of greatest displacement moving towards the base of the cochlea as frequency is raised, but a large portion of the membrane is in operation for all frequencies. This is especially the case for low tones. Moreover, the phase differences existing between widely separated parts of the vibrating system clearly prove that we are dealing with a traveling wave rather than with a simple resonance of the "harp-string" variety. The basilar membrane, it turns out, is not a series of stretched transverse fibers. The membrane is not even under tension. This is demonstrated by making fine cuts in it, either longitudinally or transversely. The cut edges do not pull apart; they should, of course, in an elastic tissue under tension. As one estimate has it (30, p. 1094), "Had the theory of hearing not started with the notion of a vibrating piano string, the basilar membrane might never have been regarded as under lasting tension at all."

The place idea, then, we do well to preserve, while rejecting the crude notion of "resonance through sympathetic vibration." Withal, the modern form of the Helmholtz theory seems capable of embracing the major facts of hearing, and with its fruitfulness in pointing to new discoveries there can be little dissatisfaction.

The "telephone" or "frequency" theory of hearing, first devised by Rutherford in 1886 and given more elaborateness of detail by Wrightson in 1918, also deserves serious consideration. Its assumptions are quite different from those of the Helmholtz theory; in fact, in a sense, the two are diametrically opposed. This opposition has, more than once, served to provide the impetus and the setting for an experimental problem. Thus the frequency theory, like the resonance theory, has proved its value as a guide to research.

The basic tenet of the frequency theory is that the basilar membrane vibrates as a whole and thus behaves very much as does the diaphragm of a telephone or a microphone. Whatever complexities are present in the vibrations transmitted by the foot of the stapes are also present in the movements of the basilar membrane and hair cells. The latter, perhaps by striking the tectorial membrane in the upward phase of their excursion, discharge their attached nerve fibers, and the entire pattern of stimulation is reproduced in the response of the auditory nerve. Loudness is accounted for by the assumption that a vigorous response on the part of the basilar membrane, arising from energetic motions of the transmission system, will bring into play a large number of fibers, while a weak stimulus will involve relatively few. Thus the correlation between intensity and number of fibers, not readily accommodated by the Helmholtz theory, is the naturally acceptable one to adherents of the telephone theory.

It is to be noted that the whole matter of tonal analysis is shifted, under the frequency theory of hearing, to the brain. The central nervous system must perform the dissection of the complex wave demanded by the Fourier analysis and Ohm's Acoustic Law, for the pictured mechanism is one which makes of the cochlea simply a device for detecting and faithfully transmitting to higher nervous centers the complex waveforms falling on the ear.

An objection that may be fairly urged against the telephone theory in its unmodified form is that it calls for the transmission of impulses over the auditory nerve at rates of repetition which are probably impossible of realization. If the nerve is to report to higher centers precisely the frequencies present in the basilar membrane's movements, and the latter are in step with those of the eardrum, it follows that the highest audible frequencies must be represented by nerve discharges of 20,000 per second. This requires a refractory period as short as 0.05 msec, and the weight of experimental evidence places the shortest refractory period at about 1.0 msec, perhaps slightly less.

It was this circumstance that led Wever and Bray to propose a modification of the frequency theory which they called the "volley" theory. They supposed that, up to a point established by the absolutely refractory period, individual fibers will yield increasingly frequent responses as the stimulus intensity is raised. All responses are synchronized with the stimulus because it is only at a particular phase of the sound wave's action that the hair cells are stimulated. It is further assumed that not all fibers are identical in their response characteristics. Some have short refractory periods, others long. For a low-frequency tone it may be possible for all fibers to "keep up with"

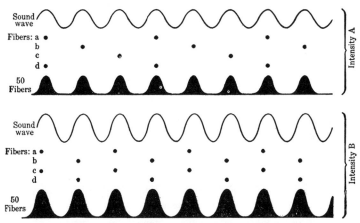

Fig. 56. The operation of the volley principle. At Intensity A (low) all fibers represented are responding to every third wave. At Intensity B (high) each fiber responds to every other wave. In both cases synchronism with the stimulus is preserved. The sum of responses of many fibers is represented by the black hillocks. These reproduce both the frequency and intensity of the stimulus. After Wever and Bray, 310. By permission of the Psychological Review and the American Psychological Association.

the stimulus and thus respond to every wave. Meanwhile other fibers, having other refractory periods, are responding to waves skipped by the first. At the highest frequencies it may not be possible for even the most sensitive of fibers to respond more frequently than to every tenth wave; however, its neighbors will be responding at their own pace to the missed waves. The "regiment" of fibers thus fires by "platoons," and the net result is a high frequency of response on the part of the bundle of nerves but only relatively infrequent discharge on the part of the individual components. Figure 56 illustrates the operation of the volley principle. For Intensity A, each of the fibers is discharging only to every third wave, but the refractory periods of a, b, c, and d are so chosen that no period of the sound wave is without its discharge. For the higher Intensity B, each of the fibers is responding to every other wave (more frequently, in accordance with the Forbes-Gregg principle), and the integrated response for a large number of fibers shows a larger (louder) response. The frequency of the stimulus is also preserved, as demanded by the telephone theory, through synchronization of the impulses with the sound wave. Thus, by way of addition of the volley principle, the frequency theory again becomes plausible and acceptable as an explanatory framework for the chief factors that must be handled by auditory theory, pitch and loudness.

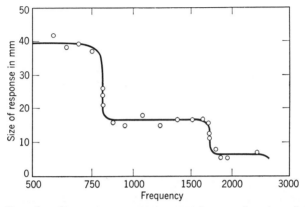

Fɪɢ. 57.   Size of auditory nerve action potentials as a function of frequency. There has been plotted the magnitude of the initial response to strong stimulation at each of a large number of frequencies.   The sudden drops in the curve are explained by the failure of individual fibers to follow stimulus frequency, and the consequent synchronization with submultiples of it.   From Stevens and Davis, 272.   Courtesy of the editor, *Journal of the Acoustical Society of America.*

A nice confirmation of the correctness of the volley principle comes from an experiment in which there was measured the initial size of the action potential in the auditory nerve of a cat, when maximal stimulation was delivered throughout a wide range of stimulus frequencies (272). In Fig. 57, which summarizes the findings, the size of the response (amplitude of action potential on the screen of an oscilloscope) is seen to undergo sharp reductions at two critical frequencies, 850∽ and 1700∽. At low frequencies all fibers can follow the stimulus, discharging with every cycle of pressure changes. Then, at 850∽, the absolutely refractory period is apparently encountered and the discharge amplitude drops to about half its former value; presumably half the fibers are firing in one cycle, the other half in the next, the first group again in the third, etc. When twice the frequency is reached, at 1700∽, there is a further abrupt drop to one-half the previous amplitude of response, and three "platoons" are now sharing the burden.   Above 3000~ the response becomes asynchronous and random; individual fibers are firing "at will."

The remaining theories need not detain us long.   While containing some interesting ideas they do not offer the possibility of accommodating any large assortment of hearing facts, at least in a manner suggestive of crucial experiments.

The "sound-pattern" theory of Ewald gets its inspiration from the phenomena displayed by vibrating plates and diaphragms.   If a metal plate on which sand has been sprinkled is set into vibration by striikng or bowing the edge there are created elaborate patterns in the sand, these reflecting the complex motions of the plate.   Each tone, indeed each variation in intensity, has its own pattern.   Ewald, experimenting with diaphragms and photographing the patterns formed on them by standing waves, became convinced that the basilar membrane must behave in a similar manner.   His theory of hearing therefore supposes that each combination of frequency and intensity must have its unique pattern, what Ewald called its "acoustic image."   The sound pattern of a complex tone, replete with overtones, must be very elaborate indeed.   Analysis of tones, recognition of voices and musical instruments, and discrimination of the nuances of musical passages must place a very heavy burden on the brain.   The scientific judgment of the sound-pattern theory has been that there is no need to admit so much complexity for the reception of even a simple tone until forced to do so by the failure of more parsimonious principles.

The hydraulic or "displacement" theory of Max Meyer (*211, 212*) is essentially a "frequency" theory but one which denies resonance to the basilar membrane or any of its components.   In fact, it holds that the basilar membrane is not an especially elastic tissue and that it behaves as one might expect a stiff piece of leather to act.   When pushed into one position by the pressure of the cochlear fluids it remains there until pushed into another.   Meyer's theory has been dubbed the "leather chair-seat" theory for this reason.   The foot of the stapes, on its inward excursion, communicates pressure to the basilar membrane, which is depressed progressively along its length just so long as a positive pressure continues.   As much of the membrane ("phragma," as Meyer persists in calling it) is pushed out of position as is required to make room for the fluid displaced by the stirrup's motion.   When the stapes comes to a stop and describes a return movement the basilar membrane bulges in the opposite direction, again beginning at the base.   A length of the membrane will reproduce the motions of the stapes and thus preserve synchronism with the stimulus, even though the waveform be an intricate one.   The extent of the membrane involved will determine loudness. A weak stimulus will jerk the membrane out of position for only a short distance before the disturbance dies out; a strong one may involve the entire membrane up to the apex. Unlike other adherents of frequency theories, who have left analysis to be cared for by the brain, Meyer has worked out a mechanical analysis within the cochlea. This involves differential action by successive sections of the membrane and accounts peripherally for Ohm's Law and combination tones. The analysis, rather than being based on the Fourier series, is essentially a geometrical one.

The displacement theory possesses all the virtues of any frequency theory and certainly provides a unique picture of cochlear mechanics. It does this, moreover, without bringing in the concept of resonance. It has not been a popular theory, however. Perhaps this is because it is inherently a difficult theory to understand, as Wever has pointed out (309, p. 88). Perhaps it is because, until only quite recently, no one has been able to demonstrate the plausibility of some of the mechanisms hypothesized by the hydraulic theory. At any rate, it can safely be said that over the years it has not provided a great impetus to research and discovery. Perhaps it may yet come to do so.

A theory which is essentially eclectic in spirit, in that it borrows both from the resonance theory and the frequency theory, is one devised by Troland in 1929. A not too dissimilar one was outlined by Fletcher in 1930 (95). As much of the Helmholtz theory as assigned different pitches to separate locations on the basilar membrane is preserved in order to make of analysis a peripheral event. However, pitch is determined by the frequency of impulses in the nerve, regardless of the point of origin of the discharging fibers. As in other frequency theories, synchronism between the stimulus and the neural pattern of discharge is assumed. This use of resonance for analysis and frequency for pitch demonstrates that the central conceptions of the two most successful of the auditory theories are not necessarily incompatible. Troland's theory and Fletcher's theory are notable in another respect—they anticipated (somewhat in advance of the "Wever-Bray effect") the volley theory by correlating loudness with "the total number of impulses passing a fixed cross-section, per second, in a group of cooperating fibers" (285). Thus, by a division of labor, there was avoided the refractory phase difficulty encountered by earlier frequency theories.

Other combinations of principles contributed by the classic theories are possible. There is no reason to assume, because history would seem to have it that way, that either the place theory or the frequency

theory is generally applicable to all auditory phenomena. The current
state of our knowledge would seem to prejudice us toward a place
theory for high tones and a frequency theory for low ones. Some-
where in the middle range of tonal frequencies one principle may give
way to the other, the two thus complementing each other. This is the
view championed by Wever in his modern statement of the volley theory
(309). Of course, there is always the possibility that there will eventually emerge an idea of a higher order, a "master principle," capable
of subsuming under it all known auditory phenomena. Our current
auditory theories have, after all, attained a riper age than most good
scientific theories ever achieve.

9

The Skin and Its Stimuli

The Classification of the Senses. Two avenues of sense, vision and audition, having already been dealt with in the foregoing chapters, it may seem odd that only now is there being raised the question of how, in general, the senses are to be classified. The reason becomes clear when it is learned that there are five senses, or more than a score of them, or some intermediate number, depending upon what decision is made concerning sensations originating in the skin and internal organs of the body. Classically, there are five special senses: vision, audition, smell, taste, and "touch" or "feeling." Aristotle had it that way (though even he expressed some doubt about "touch" as a single sense), and his fivefold classification of the senses has upon it the sanction of the centuries.

Current popular usage is, of course, completely in the Aristotelian tradition. At various times, however, and especially of relatively recent years, the list has been expanded. Always the "extra" senses have come out of the sense of feeling by a process of subdivision; whenever the number has shrunk back to five the additional senses have gone back into "feeling" again. Boring (43, p. 34), listing the "sense-qualities" of feeling for which some fair claim to independent status had been made by 1915, includes: pressure, contact, deep pressure, prick pain, quick pain, deep pain, warmth, cold, heat, muscular pressure, articular pressure, tendinous strain, ampullar sensation or dizziness, vestibular sensation or sense of translation, appetite, hunger, thirst, nausea, sex, cardiac sensation, and pulmonary sensation. Others, including itch, tickle, vibration, suffocation, satiety, and repletion, at one time or another have been raised to independent status.

In the intricate history of the classification of the senses there have been, in general, three logically distinct approaches. Sensations may be grouped together (1) *qualitatively,* on the basis of their observational similarity, (2) *stimulus-wise,* with respect to the objects or forms

158

of physical energy that typically set them off, or (3) *anatomically,* in accordance with the system of sense organs or tissues initiating them. The last of these seems to provide the best organizational principle, and, wherever knowledge about the bodily structures responsible for originating sensation has been sufficiently complete, the anatomical basis of classification has been preferred. We could talk about the "sense of green" and the "sense of gray," but since we know the production of these qualities to be the work of a single anatomical unit, the eye, we are accustomed to grouping the two classes of sensation together as "visual." Similarly, we might appeal to stimuli and, in hearing, speak of the "sense of tone" and the "sense of noise," but both kinds of sensation are mediated by the ear and hence are classed as "auditory." In the cases of smell and taste the anatomical reference is natural. Olfactory sensations are "nostril sensations"; those of taste belong to the tongue and palate.

When we come to consider the sensations aroused in the skin and internal organs of the body there is some indefiniteness of classification, mainly because we do not have entirely certain knowledge of the anatomical mechanisms involved. Indeed, the question of what nerve endings in the skin and deeper-lying tissues respond to common touches and pressures is still far from settled. As to the detailed manner in which they operate to elicit sensations we can as yet only make shrewd guesses. Despite the fact that the skin is, from the evolutionary standpoint, the oldest of the sensitive tissues of the body, it has yielded up its secrets reluctantly. It houses a multitude of variously constituted and differently disposed structures, and the opportunities for variation in their performance are many. Perhaps it is not surprising, therefore, that its phenomena are complex and hard to master. Perhaps, too, it is not greatly to be wondered at that its sensations are difficult to bring under simple classificatory concepts. If, under one set of prejudices, the cutaneous and internally aroused sensations all seem to belong together and thus indicate the existence of a single sense of "feeling" and, under another bias, seem to bespeak a veritable plethora of separate and distinct "senses," this is but a reflection of our current ignorance of the basic facts and uncertainty as to the interpretation of those we have. For several reasons, which will later become apparent, we shall think of the skin as housing three systems of sensitivity, one for pressure reception, one for pain, and one responsive to temperature changes. Those belonging to the deeper tissues, muscles, and visceral organs, as well as the receptor system located in the non-auditory labyrinth of the inner ear, will be thought of as constituting the "internal senses."

The Skin and Its Sensitivities. The first thing to be noted about the skin is that it is not uniformly sensitive. If a pencil point is moved gently across the back of the hand there are aroused at some places sensations of touch or pressure, at others cold sensations may flash out, and there may be felt tickling or even itching at others. Moreover, if the stimulus is changed to a sharper or duller object, or if the mode of attack is varied to involve direct pressure into the skin, or if warmed or cooled metal points are used, a considerable range of sensations may be brought forth. This suggests that the skin's potentiality for yielding a great diversity of sensations can be gauged only by exploring sample areas in a systematic manner, controlling the many variables that must enter to produce such widely differing phenomena.

To make systematic exploration possible it is obviously necessary to resort to some kind of mapping procedure so that the same local skin area may be readily found again, either to investigate its constancy of response when uniformly and repeatedly stimulated or to isolate it for systematic variation of the stimulus in successive trials. The common laboratory technique is to utilize a rubber stamp prepared in the form of a square grid, 20 mm on a side and thus containing 400 mm^2 squares. An ink impression of such a grid is stamped on the skin area to be explored, and the center of each tiny square becomes the locus of stimulation. Since there is nothing permanent about such marking (perspiration and accidental rubbing of clothing readily smear or even obliterate it), a technique making the grid lines reproducible has been devised by Dallenbach (72). This consists of injecting into the skin with a finely drawn-out glass tube or a hypodermic needle, at the four corners of the grid marking, a small "dot" of India ink. The corners of the grid pattern, thus being permanently tattooed into the skin, make possible exact placement of the grid in successive stampings. With the aid of such "anchor points" the author has been able to stamp the skin and relocate spots especially sensitive to cold and pressure a dozen years after they were first found.

If a somewhat more intimate map of a skin area is desired, a free-hand sketch of the surface as seen through a low-power ($10\times$ to $30\times$) binocular microscope may be made. Better still is a microphotograph of the area. With judicious lighting, furrows and ridges, hair stumps, and other distinguishing marks may be brought out and used as orientation signs to assist in stimulus placement. An ingenious method to provide a somewhat temporary but perfectly reproducible set of marks is to make use of the method of electro-osmotic staining (119). A solution of methylene blue or other dye is used to saturate a piece of filter paper, which is then placed over the skin region to be marked.

A positive electrode of appropriate shape and size is then pressed firmly on the filter paper, the negative electrode being attached to the body at some indifferent point. A direct current of 1–2 ma, at 20–40 v, is allowed to flow through the circuit for 5 min or more at the termination of which the dye has been carried into the skin by way of the sweat duct openings. A few days after such a dyeing operation the individual sweat duct openings are clearly marked and remain so for long periods of time, perspiration depositing particles of dye in tiny "craters" at the skin surface.

With the aid of any of these marking methods the skin's sensitivities may be explored. The system of sensitivity called into action will, of course, be a function of the type of stimulus used in the exploration. Here the possibilities are many, for the skin proves to be responsive to a wide range of stimuli: *mechanical, thermal, electrical,* and *chemical.* For the arousal of "touch," "contact," and "pressure" any thermally indifferent solid or liquid will, of course, suffice, and even air blasts have been used in some experiments. For these sensations the technique of exploration developed by von Frey, at the end of the last century, has become standard procedure. This involves the use of hairs, both human and animal, of various lengths and diameters, attached at right angles to the end of a match stick or other wooden holder. Following von Frey's lead, most investigators of touch and pressure sensations have made point-by-point serial explorations of skin samples with hairs varying from 0.05 mm to 0.2 mm in diameter. The end of the hair is placed over the spot to be stimulated, and the holder is then depressed in such a way as to make of the hair a long cylindrical column with its force exerted perpendicularly to the skin surface. Fair constancy of stimulation is assured by reason of the fact that the greatest force of which a given hair is capable must be expended in each stimulation; "loading" is maximal at the pressure at which the hair bends as the holder is moved downwards. Moreover, its force is exerted practically instantaneously. The intensity of the stimulus depends, of course, both on the stiffness and length of the hair. Because stiffness may be expected to alter with changes of humidity some investigators have substituted glass wool filaments. In either case calibration may be effected by determining, with a sensitive balance, the heaviest weight that can just barely be raised in one scale pan by the hair, pressed down to the point of bending, in the other.

To elicit warm and cold sensations any device which will conduct heat to or away from the skin will serve. Immersion of an area of skin in previously warmed or cooled water is one readily available

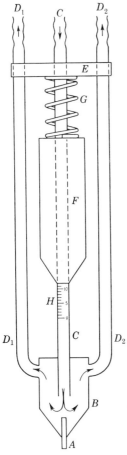

FIG. 58. The Dallenbach temperature stimulator. Either warm or cold water enters the instrument through C and is exhausted through D_1 and D_2. A sufficiently rapid flow keeps the chamber, B, and thus the 1-mm stimulus point, A, at constant temperature. The handle, F, is lowered to a given point on the scale, H, after A has contacted the skin, partially relieving the spring, G, and controlling mechanical pressure. After Dallenbach, 70.

procedure. For the rapid raising of skin temperature the delivery of radiant heat to an exposed skin area from an electrically heated coil or thermocautery is convenient. "Infra-red" lamps of the type now generally available may be used effectively for this purpose. To produce cooling of the skin convection currents from evaporating "dry ice" may be directed against a general skin area.

Such "macroscopic" stimuli fail, of course, to reveal the great local variations in thermal sensitivity of the skin, and a point-by-point exploration is needed to bring them out, as in the case of pressure sensations. Several different devices have been designed to accomplish local thermal stimulation. The Dallenbach temperature stimulator (Fig. 58) is well known. This instrument has its contacting point limited to an area 1 mm in diameter. In addition to the feature that circulating water keeps the stimulus point at a constant predetermined temperature, it possesses the advantage that concomitant pressure on the skin can be controlled. To explore cold sensitivity in a truly punctiform manner von Frey and his students have employed tiny copper and brass cylinders constructed of bits of wire, the stimulating ends of which have been fused into small knobs. In these heat conductivity is a function of the composition and dimensions of the wires, and a graded series can be easily prepared by manipulation of these factors. The common laboratory instrument for the mapping of warm and cold sensitivity is the "temperature cylinder" (Fig. 59). A series of such cylinders, preheated or precooled, may be used successively, each one serving until its temperature has changed significantly. The cylinders, being solid and thus having considerable heat capacity, may be used continuously for several minutes at a time without returning them to their water bath. At least, this is the case for temperatures not greatly divergent from that of the surrounding air.

For "prick," "pain," and allied sensations any strong stimulation will suffice, though typically needles or other sharp-pointed devices which will actually penetrate the skin surface or produce a steep declivity in it have been used. Thistles, attached to the ends of von Frey hairs to

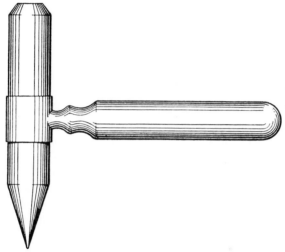

Fig. 59. A temperature cylinder. Adapted from Boring, Langfeld, and Weld, *A manual of psychological experiments*. John Wiley & Sons, 1937.

permit pressure control, have been used commonly, for punctiform exploration. For the pain associated with extreme thermal stimulation extensions of any of the procedures outlined for temperature sensations may, of course, be used. Chemical stimuli have been worked with in the arousal of pain, though not entirely in a systematic fashion. Chemicals and drugs have been, in general, of more interest for their possibilities in allaying pain and have been studied chiefly for their anesthetic properties. However, some facts of stimulation are known.

Water-soluble materials have little effect upon the horny surface of the skin and to stimulate receptors must be injected hypodermically, driven into the tissues electro-osmotically, or introduced into injured surface areas. Whereas generalities concerning the differential effects of the various classes of chemical stimuli are difficult to arrive at, it appears that the hydrogen ion is particularly effective in the arousal of pain. Solutions varying in hydrogen-ion concentration (pH values of

5.8 to 8.0), when injected into the skin, have been shown invariably to produce pain at pH values below 7.2, the intensity of pain increasing progressively with degree of acidity. At pH 5.8 the pain is unbearable. The introduction of alkalis of pH values above 7.2 produces an immediate quelling of pain. Of the inorganic salts only those yielding excess potassium ions seem capable of arousing pain. However, a number of organic compounds, including a large class of "irritant poisons," are effective. Temperature sensations may also be initiated by a considerable range of chemicals, by creating rapid interchanges between the skin and the surrounding air, by altering the circulation of blood and thus disturbing the heat equilibrium of the skin tissues, or by direct action on nerve endings.

Electrical stimulation of the skin seems capable of arousing all systems of sensitivity contained within it. Whether this comes about through intermediation of receptor organs or by directly affecting their attached nerve fibers is not as yet known. Physically, the possibilities for both would seem to be present. Exploration of an area with electrodes delivering either discrete shocks or steady alternating current will evoke reports indicating tremendous local variations in sensitivity. One of the best of the methods of electrical exploration is that devised by Bishop (36). It involves the creation of high-voltage potentials which are allowed to spark across from the exploring electrode to the skin, the discharge taking place at very low amperage. Single or multiple shocks may be delivered to any desired point. One of the chief advantages of this technique is that it provides uniform stimulation devoid of any accompanying mechanical distortion of the skin surface. With its aid it is possible to arouse, at different points, the full range of basic cutaneous sensations: touch, pressure, pain, warmth, and cold in all their intensitive variations.

Structure of the Skin. Some of the conditions for the experimental investigation of cutaneous sensations now having been set forth, it will be well for us to inquire into the makeup of the tissues concerned.

Considered from its external and superficial aspect, the skin presents a highly variegated structure. Of relatively smooth appearance in some parts of the body, it is deeply creased and furrowed in others; in some parts hairless and in others richly endowed with hairy appendages; in some places, especially over bony protuberances, stretched to the point of tautness and in others highly mobile and even flabby; in some regions thickened, horny, and tough but in others thin, pliable, and vulnerable to injury; in some portions dry and scaly but moist and flexible in others. If widely differing reactions to uniform stimulation are found to accompany these differences 'of composition it should not be surprising. Owing largely to the manner in which underlying structures are disposed, areas in different parts of the body display radically different properties. The larger part of the skin surface presents many small furrows which intersect in such a manner as to enclose rectangular, triangular, and polygonal spaces. On the palms of the hands and soles of the feet the furrows run in close parallel rows separated by slender ridges, and the eminences contain the openings of sweat ducts with which these regions are liberally supplied. Contrasted with this high degree of structural organization are the smooth and relatively undifferentiated surfaces of the calf of the leg and the area of the upper arm over the biceps. Something of the variations in surface consistency may be judged from the photographs of Fig. 60. Were it not for some fundamental similarities of subsurface structure one might even suppose that different parts of the skin surface ought to be regarded as a collection of quite separate organs. However, there are uniformities, and we should see of what they consist.

Though classification of the successive layers of the skin is somewhat arbitrary, it is conventional to mark off three major groupings: the *epidermis* or cuticle, the *corium* or true dermis, and *subcutaneous tissue*. The epidermis (see Fig. 61) consists of two chief layers: the horny, most superficial tissue, called the *corneum;* and a deeper *germinative* layer (stratum germinativum or Malpighian layer) from which the cells of the corneum arise. The transition from the germinative layer to the corneum is, in some parts of the body, quite abrupt. In the process of growth and replacement the cells of the lower layer move up toward the surface of the epidermis, become closely packed and flattened, lose their nuclei, and acquire a horny consistency. The surface structure, only a few cells thick in most areas, is constantly being sloughed off and renewed from beneath. Two additional states of transition may be marked off in some regions. In the process of cornification there may be distinguished a layer just above the germinative layer. This, because of the appearance in it of coarse granules in the cell material, is called the *stratum granulosum*. The cells here are in process of losing their nuclei and are becoming flattened and angular. The granule cells quite abruptly acquire a shiny, translucent appearance and thus give rise to the differentiation of a fourth epidermal layer, the *stratum lucidum*. In some tissue preparations the latter, usually only two cells thick, is indistinguishable from other parts of the cornified surface tissue but, because it is deeply colored by several stains commonly used by the histologist, may serve as a distinct ribbon-like lower boundary of the corneum.

As is seen in Fig. 61, the separation between the epidermis and corium is a highly irregular one, the uppermost layer of the corium

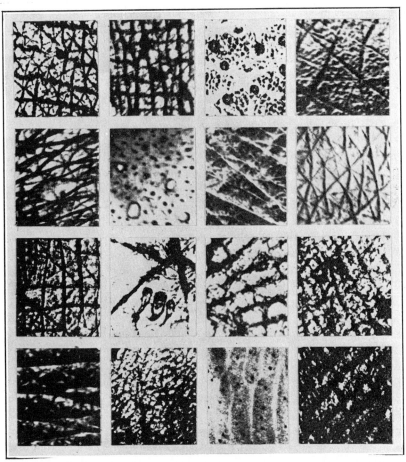

Fig. 60.   Skin samples from different parts of the body.   Photographs from von Skramlik, *261*.

(papillary layer) consisting of conical mounds of connective tissue, *papillae,* projecting into the floor of the epidermis and almost completely surrounded by the basal cylindrical cells of the Malpighian layer.   The papillae are made up of finely interwoven fibers and house the greater portion of the smallest blood vessels and nerves of the skin.   Some of the papillae contain capillary loops and are hence classed as vascular; in others are found specialized nerve endings, the *corpuscles of Meissner*, and are thus of the nervous or tactile type. The papillae vary greatly in length, some of those found in the sole of the foot projecting into the germinative layer as much as 0.2 mm, those

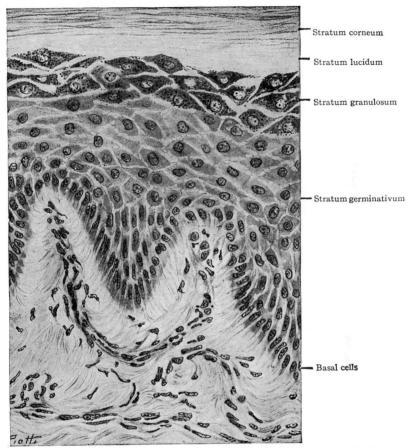

Fig. 61. Detail of the structure of the epidermis. From Bremer and Weatherford, *49*. By permission of the Blakiston Company, Philadelphia.

in the facial region being but 0.035 to 0.040 mm long. It is the regular and fixed lineal disposition of the papillae that gives to the fingers and toes the orderly arrangements that make fingerprint and toeprint classification possible. Below the papillary layer of the corium is the *reticulated dermis*. This has a looser texture and consists of interlacing bundles of connective tissue. It is almost devoid of capillaries and nerve endings but contains many larger blood vessels, small nerve

The Skin and Its Stimuli

trunks, the tortuously coiled ducts of the sweat glands, the smaller hair
follicles, and a considerable amount of elastic tissue that forms a bond
with the lowermost layers of the skin.

The subcutaneous tissue consists chiefly of fibrous bundles which
extend down to the muscles and bones. In some parts they are loosely

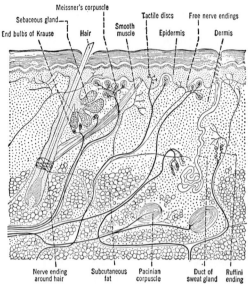

Fɪɢ. 62. Composite diagram of the skin in cross section. The chief layers, epidermis, dermis, and subcutaneous tissue, are shown, as are also a hair follicle,
the smooth muscle which erects the hair, and several kinds of nerve endings. In
the epidermis are to be found tactile discs and free nerve endings; in the dermis
are Meissner corpuscles, Krause end bulbs, Ruffini endings, and (around the base
of the hair) free terminations. The subcutaneous tissue is chiefly fatty and vascular but contains Pacinian corpuscles, the largest of the specialized endings.
From Gardner (105) after Woollard, Weddell, and Harpman, 321. By permission of W. B. Saunders Company, Philadelphia.

meshed, and the spaces between them are occupied by fatty lobules;
in others they are more tightly interlaced and give a firmer texture to
the whole skin mass. In general, the more nearly parallel to the skin
surface the connective tissue bundles are disposed, the greater is the
skin's mobility. In the subcutaneous tissue are also to be found most
of the larger blood vessels, nerve trunks, sweat glands, and hair follicles of the skin. The sebaceous (oily) glands have their secreting
tissues here. Several types of encapsulated nerve endings, with which
we shall later become acquainted, are found in subcutaneous tissue.
Figure 62, which is a composite diagram with emphasis placed on the

nervous connections and terminations of the skin, will serve to provide an overall view of the skin's structure, the relative depths of the various layers, and the disposition of many of the tissues that have been described. It should be apparent, from what has been said of local variations in skin structure, that no single section of skin will reveal all the features of importance to us, nor can any such single representative be thought of as "typical."

Nerve Endings in the Skin. A considerable variety of nerve terminations is to be found in the skin layers. They range in size from that of the deep-lying Pacinian corpuscles, large enough to be seen with the unaided eye, to that of the finest naked fibrils in the epidermis. The latter terminations, so-called *free nerve endings,* are the most numerous. In histological skin sections they are found to terminate at all levels, in the epidermis, corium, and subcutaneous tissue. When they enter the epidermis, as they frequently do, they are observed to penetrate as far as the granular layer. A great many endings may derive from a single nerve fiber, so that an appreciable area may contribute to the discharge of a particular nerve cell. Free nerve endings are best studied in the cornea of the eye, where no other type of termination can be discovered. It has been shown (283) that free terminations covering as much as an entire quadrant of the cornea belong to a single sensory fiber. Moreover, other fibers supplying the same general area have endings which maximally overlap and ramify into each other's fields, though functional independence of each network seems to be preserved despite the close anatomical proximity of endings. The supposition is that in the skin generally a single fiber may, through successive branchings, have a great number of separate terminations, covering in some instances areas of several square millimeters or even centimeters, but that a single fiber does not alone "possess" the region. Interlocking and proliferating endings, forming an intricate network and arising from other fibers, also lay claim to the region and participate in its response.

If one regards the free nerve ending as the prototype of all cutaneous nerve terminations the remaining "types" of endings found in the skin may be regarded simply as elaborations of or developments from this fundamental form. Indeed, many histologists believe that if a completely systematic examination of all representative tissues were made there would be found an unbroken continuum of nerve endings in which the free terminations, at one end of the series, would be found to have been transformed, at the other, into the most elaborately formed of corpuscular endings. The first step towards anatomical complication would seem to have been taken by certain of the skin endings on the tips of which appear tiny knob-like swellings. Others, the so-called *Merkel discs* found in the epidermis of the finger tip, mouth, and lips, represent perhaps an additional step; minute flattened plates, scarcely larger than the knob endings, appear on these and constitute the specialized nerve endings. Still others, known as *hederi-*

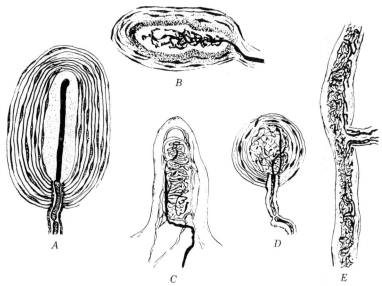

Fig. 63. Encapsulated nerve endings of the skin. *A*, a Vater-Pacini corpuscle; *B*, a Golgi-Mazzoni corpuscle; *C*, a Meissner corpuscle; *D*, a Krause end bulb; *E*, a Ruffini cylinder. Drawn from descriptions and photomicrographs of Boeke (*40*), Ramón y Cajal (*239*), and Ruffini (*200*).

form ("ivy-like") *endings*, have been observed in the lower generative layer of the epidermis, between the papillae projecting upward from the corium.

All other forms of endings have acquired sufficient structural complication to be classed as *encapsulated endings*. Several varieties have been described and named (see Fig. 63). *Meissner corpuscles*, found in the papillae of hairless skin regions, vary from 40 to 150 μ in length and 20 to 60 μ in width. There may be as many as 20 or 30 of them packed into a square millimeter. One to five sensory fibers enter the lower end of each, lose their protective sheaths, and coil into the corpuscular ending. *Krause end bulbs*, somewhat smaller on the average than Meissner corpuscles, are also found in the dermal layers. They have been observed in the eye, near the margin of the cornea, and also in the tissues of the external genitals and of the tongue. They are believed to be quite generally distributed throughout the corium. *Cylinders of Ruffini,* also known as terminal cylinders and arboriform terminations, occur in the dermis near the junction of the subcutaneous layers and have also been found in deeper tissues. Most of them have their nerve entrances at the side, as shown in Fig. 63, though some have been observed with connections at the end. A single dividing nerve fiber is occasionally found to connect with several Ruffini cylinders. The largest and in some respects the most elaborate of the encapsulated endings are the *Pacinian corpuscles* (Vater-Pacini) or lamellar corpuscles. These are 0.5 to 4.5 mm long and 1.0 to 2.0 mm wide. They occur deep in the corium and subcutaneous tissue and are abundant in the hand and foot regions. They are found also in the tissues of the joints, ligaments of the leg and forearm, in the external genitals, in the coverings of bones, in the connective tissue of the abdominal cavity, and near the walls of large blood vessels. Pacinian corpuscles have a thick coat composed of 10 to 50 successive layers of connective tissue arranged concentrically around a central granular core in which the nerve fibrils terminate. Minute blood vessels enter the basal pole, and the capillary network may be found between the onion-like layers. Apparently closely related to the Pacinian corpuscles are the similarly complex *Golgi-Mazzoni corpuscles.* These also have a somewhat general distribution, though they penetrate to higher levels of the corium and, in deeper-lying tissue, are especially noted in the junctions of tendinous and muscular tissues. Golgi-Mazzoni endings have fewer lamellations and a relatively larger soft granular core than do Pacini corpuscles. The nerve tips proliferate more complexly in the core also. Near the bases of their follicles, deep in the corium or in subcutaneous tissue, are commonly found complicated aggregates of fibrils which, because they appear to form an intricate, generally cup-shaped receptacle for the hair bulb, are called *basket endings.* Many of the fibrils terminate in platelets, and the structure is therefore thought by some to consist of Merkel discs. In any case these nerve terminations would seem to be optimally disposed to receive stimulation from movement of hairs.

From time to time variants of the basic forms described above have been noted by histologists, and the naming of new and "special" nerve terminations goes on apace. Thus what is apparently a highly developed Krause end bulb, a large round or oval corpuscle found in the glans penis and clitoris, has been called the "genital" corpuscle. Several variants of Pacinian corpuscles have been named. Such multiplication of "types" is, of course, to be encouraged in the hope that a sufficiently complete cataloguing of the anatomical possibilities will lead eventually to some certain generalizations about the cutaneous endings which, at the present time, are in no more than the stage of belief. Histological techniques have been vastly improved in recent years, and we may confidently expect more cogent descriptions to come from their use. Meanwhile, we only know that a great range of sizes, forms, and dispositions of possible receptor organs is to be found in the skin layers, and we must do our best to identify their functions in mediating sensations.

Central Pathways for the Cutaneous Senses. There exists such a multiplicity of end organs and sensory fibers in the skin and underlying tissues as to lead one to suppose that their attached nerve trunks in the spinal cord must be hopelessly confused. Fortunately, however, it is possible to see some order in the constitution of the central pathways. In fact, far from being haphazardly and chaotically combined, nerves from the periphery become organized progressively in the direction of functional simplicity once they enter the central nervous system.

If any of the sensory nerves traveling through subcutaneous tissue were to be traced out to individual fiber terminations it would be found that the bundle contains components serving all types of endings. Some of the fibers constituting the nerve would be relatively large (15 μ or more in diameter) and a great many would average about 8 μ, while fully half of them would be quite small (2 μ or less) and would lack myelin sheaths. The picture, then, of a cutaneous sensory nerve is one of anatomical complexity. Apparently the bundle is a conduit carrying fibers from a fairly definite skin area but serving several different kinds of sensation. It follows that injury to such a nerve will result indiscriminately in loss of sensations of touch, warmth, cold, and pain in the area supplied by the nerve. There is no way in which the various modalities can be sorted out at the peripheral level. This is also the case just before entrance to the spinal cord. All cutaneous impulses are carried to the cord by way of 30 of the 31 pairs of spinal nerves—the first cervical pair has no sensory roots—and 4 of the cranial nerves (V, VII, IX, X). Up to the point of entrance to the central nervous system these nerves are still serving as functionally undifferentiated conductors, and it therefore follows that interruption of a spinal nerve will abolish all systems of sensitivity in the area housing its terminations.

The region of skin supplied by a particular spinal nerve is called the *dermatome* of that nerve. Since there is considerable overlapping,

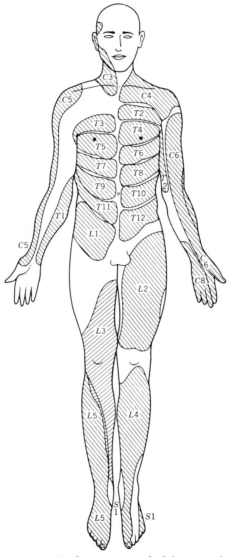

Fig. 64. The dermatomes. Each area is supplied by a single posterior root of the spinal cord. Half the dermatomes are shown on one side of the figure, half on the other side. Extensive overlap is the rule; a single local region of the skin may be innervated by two or even three roots. From Lewis, *199*. By permission of The Macmillan Company.

with branches of two or more spinal nerves typically invading a given skin area, it follows that peripheral exploration will not establish the extent of the dermatomes. However, there are ways of mapping them. One of the best is to make use of Sherrington's method of "remaining sensibility," a procedure involving the sectioning, in animals, of three dorsal spinal roots above and three below the one to be studied. This eliminates overlapping nerve supplies in the skin region belonging to the now isolated spinal root, and there is left at the skin "an island of sensitivity in a sea of anesthesia." By systematic sectioning there have been mapped the dermatomes corresponding to spinal nerves at all levels. They are depicted in Fig. 64. Another way to explore the dermatomes is to inject strychnine into a dorsal root zone. This elicits sensations localized in the corresponding peripheral region, and the licking, biting, and scratching of an animal so injected reveal the extent of the skin area affected. In humans comparable data may be obtained by noting the distribution of skin eruptions in "shingles" (herpes zoster), a virus infection of posterior root ganglia. The pattern of eruptions coincides with the dermatomes.

Once inside the spinal cord a regrouping of impulses occurs in such a way as to bring together all those of a particular modality. Henceforth, as they ascend the cord to the brain, they travel in their own paths. Impulses subserving touch and pressure, upon entering the cord over the dorsal roots, ascend in the posterior tract for a few spinal segments, then terminate in the gray matter of the cord. Here connecting fibers cross over to the opposite side and continue the ascent in the *ventral spinothalamic tract* (see Fig. 65). Collateral fibers also pass up as far as the medulla on the side of entrance to the cord, the net result being that pressure impulses arrive at the medulla from both sides of the body, regardless of which side initiated them. By the time the thalamus is reached, however, a crossing to the contralateral side has been effected. A chain of at least three neurones is involved in this conduction system. The impulses originating in the pain and temperature systems travel in closely adjacent tracts in the cord, and the neurones involved have connections somewhat different from those serving touch. After passing into the cord by way of a dorsal root there is a prompt termination in the gray matter. A connecting fiber crosses to the contralateral side immediately and ascends the cord in the *lateral spinothalamic tract*. There are no collateral fibers, and the pathway to the thalamus is a direct one, no crossing occurring at the medulla. Three neurones are similarly involved. This functional separation in the cord, with pressure impulses traveling up both the posterior tract and the ventral spinothalamic tract while pain and temperature impulses ascend in the lateral spinothalamic tract, makes possible separations of the systems of sensitivity. Thus in *syringomyelia*, a disease of the cord which widens its central canal and affects the lateral tracts, there is brought about a loss of pain and temperature sensitivity but full preservation of pressure sensations in the affected area. The arrangement of the conduction paths also makes possible a surgical operation for persistent and intractable pain. Cut-

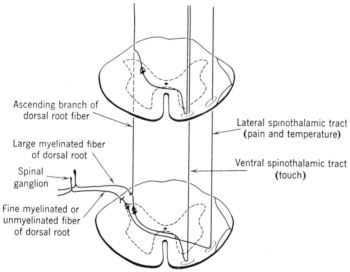

FIG. 65. Ascending pathways for cutaneous sensation in the spinal cord. From Ranson, *240*. By permission of the W. B. Saunders Company, Philadelphia.

ting through the lateral tract at a suitable level will abolish the pain (and sometimes thermal sensations) but does not interfere with pressure sensitivity nor does it, of course, affect motor responses in the region concerned.

The final relay station of the central pathways is at the level of the thalamus; ascending fibers there form synapses with those radiating into the cerebrum. The latter terminate mainly in the cortex of the parietal lobes, and the chief projection is upon the so-called *postcentral gyrus*, the eminence just back of the fissure of Rolando. The various systems of sensitivity having been sorted out in the cord, it may seem surprising that there is, at the central level, any remnant of the topography present in the skin. However, several good lines of evidence agree to show that the body surface is rather nicely represented in the cortex. Indeed, what seems to be missing at the highest level is any geometrical preservation of the cutaneous modalities, as such.

Perhaps the best method for establishing the topographical correspondences between the skin and the cortex is to record from the lat-

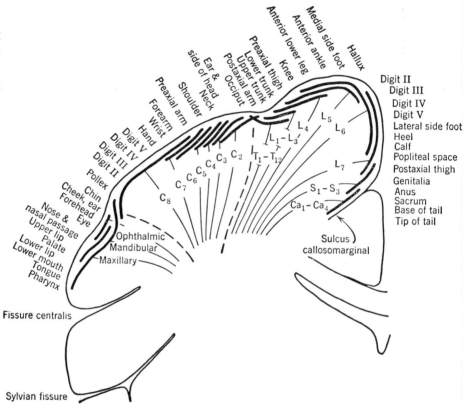

FIG. 66. Projection of the body surface on the central gyrus of the cortex. The left cerebral hemisphere of the monkey is shown in cross section. Correspondences between cortical loci and specific body areas were established by the evoked potential method. After Woolsey, Marshall, and Bard, 322. By permission of the Johns Hopkins Press and the authors.

ter, point by point, the electrical potentials created by stimulation of the skin. By noting, in the monkey and chimpanzee, the optimal skin position for the production of a given electrocortigram Woolsey, Marshall, and Bard (322, 323) have arrived at the chart shown in Fig. 66. Several features of the map are of interest: (1) There is a remarkably faithful projection of the dermatomes on the cortex, each spinal cord segment below the cervical roots preserving its appropriate position in the series. (2) The cervical segments appear to be reversed as a group but to retain their proper internal sequence. The reversal must take place at a fairly high neural level because it has been demonstrated (in the cat) that the cervical segments fall into their expected (unreversed) position at the thalamus (216). Moreover, as Professor Woolsey has pointed out (in personal correspondence), "The reversal actually is of the sort which may be illustrated by raising one's arm above the head. If, in addition, the face is detached and supported by the thumb, the general arrangement seen in the cortex would thereby be illustrated." (3) Those areas which have great density of nerve supply occupy relatively large portions of the cortex, but those sparsely innervated are compressed in a narrow region. Thus the twelve thoracic segments, which innervate the trunk region, are represented by a strip only 2.5 mm wide, whereas the sixth lumbar dermatome, involving the foot region (a highly discriminative and richly supplied area in the monkey serving as subject in this experiment), claims a very considerable cortical projection area. These studies also confirm the general plan deduced from the arrangement of fibers in the cord and brain tracts; except for the face region, where the cranial nerves mediate sensation, there is found to be no bilateral representation. Cortical excitations in one hemisphere are produced by stimulation of the opposite side of the body.

10

Pressure and Pain

Pressure Sensitivity. A variety of names has been applied to the sensations falling under the general rubric, "pressure." Not all pressures have the same "feel." "Contact" designates a bright, lively sensation as contrasted with the dull and heavy feeling of "deep pressure." Some pressures are "dense" and "pointed," some feel "granular," while others are "diffuse." Some have a superficial localization; others seem to have originated in deeper tissues. It has been contended that pressure sensations vary along a continuous scale of "brightness-dullness." Differences in the characteristic manner of arousal are also observable. Some pressures rise to peak in an abrupt fashion, while others develop slowly; others are discontinuous or vacillating. Careful observation leads to the conclusion that no cutaneous sensation is entirely simple in its composition. All have temporal, intensive, and spatial aspects. Each pressure feeling constitutes a "pattern" having these and perhaps other separately variable dimensions. Certain patterns, occurring frequently and familiarly, we come to endow with names: "touch," "contact," "tickle," "vibration," "dull pressure," etc.; others, their particular combinations of attributes coming only occasionally to observation, go unnamed or are indefinitely dubbed simply "pressure."

The usual stimulus for the arousal of pressure is, of course, mechanical deformation of the skin tissue. It can be shown that an essential feature of the deformation, in order to be effective, is the production of a "gradient" of sufficient magnitude. The mere application of mechanical pressure to a skin region does not guarantee that pressure sensations will result. Thus, if a finger is dipped into a jar of mercury only the "ring" at the surface of the liquid is felt. Considerable pressure is being exerted on the immersed part of the finger, but the pressure is evenly distributed, and one local area of tissue is not deformed with respect to its neighbor except at the region of transition from mercury to air. Whenever a sufficiently steep gradient is formed the necessary mechanical condition for the arousal of pres-

178

sure sensations is present. The intensity of stimulation is also to be related to the steepness of the gradient, sharp gradients arousing more intense sensations. It is of no consequence whether the gradient is formed inwardly or outwardly with respect to the skin surface. Traction applied to a thread glued to the skin provides an effective pressure stimulus and demonstrates that the only necessary condition is tissue distortion.

In the final analysis it is, of course, tension within the cutaneous tissues that constitute the physical stimulus for pressure sensations. Deformation is effective only because it invariably creates such tensions. Using a series of small stimulus hairs von Frey and Kiesow (99) were able to demonstrate that pressure thresholds were reached at an approximately constant level of tension (about 0.85 gm/mm). Thus a force of 17 mgm operating through a stimulus hair of 0.02 mm radius and one of 85 mgm imposed on a hair of 0.1 mm radius are both just capable of eliciting pressure. It is neither force *per se* (grams) nor hydrostatic pressure (grams per square millimeter) but tension, expressed in terms of force per linear extent of skin surface contacted, that constitutes the significant variable. The relationship, obtaining uniformly for tiny skin areas, breaks down for larger stimuli and forces.

If, with a von Frey hair or a needle, a gradient of constant moderate magnitude is maintained while exploring, point by point in a systematic manner, a sample area of skin on the underside of the forearm, a map of pressure-sensitive "spots," such as that illustrated in Fig. 67, will be obtained. Some points stimulated will respond with clear sensations of touch, contact, or pressure. Others will yield these qualities but with diminished intensity. Many points stimulated with the same gradient will produce no sensation whatever. Obviously there are great sensitivity differences even within a relatively circumscribed area. It is notable that a close correlation exists between the location of sensitive spots and that of hairs, in the great majority of instances the point of high sensitivity being located on the "windward" side of the hair (the side from which the wind appears to be "blowing" the hair). This peculiar distribution is very suggestive and points either to an intimacy of anatomical relation between pressure receptors and hair follicles or to participation of the hair in the process of effecting tissue distortion. Of course, both could be the case. The former possibility should be considered seriously in view of the profuse network of nerve fibers surrounding hair follicles. That the portion of the hair embedded in the skin serves to facilitate transmission of distorting forces applied to the skin surface can hardly be doubted. Obliquely disposed relative to the skin surface, the hair provides a relatively massive, solid, and unyielding column which could account for tissue displacements at all points along its length. Whereas "pressure points" are found, even with moderately weak stimuli, at other spots than over hair follicles, it is these areas that display the greatest constancy of response as measured by reproducibility of results in successive tests of the same sample skin area.

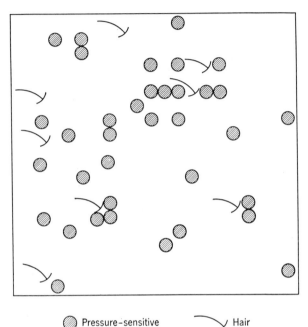

Pressure-sensitive   Hair

Fig. 67. Distribution of pressure-sensitive "spots" on a sample skin area located on the underside of the forearm. Each dot represents the locus of stimulation evoking a report of "pressure" when a constant, moderate gradient was applied systematically 400 times in the area. From unpublished data of the author.

Something more of the skin's provision for pressure reception may be learned by using a graded series of stimulus hairs and making a number of successive explorations. As the intensity of the stimulus is increased there are found more and more sensitive "spots," and eventually, if a sufficiently stiff hair is used, it will evoke a positive response wherever it is applied. Guilford and Lovewell (135) have performed an experiment demonstrating this, with results as shown in Fig. 68. The stimuli ranged from 0.01 to 1.60 gm, in nine steps, and each was set down on 200 equally spaced loci in a 1 cm² patch on the shaved back of the hand. As is shown by the curve connecting stimulus intensity with proportion of points responding, the weakest in-

tensity evoked sensations in less than 1% of the trials, while the strongest did so 100% of the time. The shape of the function is interesting,
being of sigmoid form, and suggests that any given "unit area" of the
skin's surface has a statistical probability of responding to a stimulus
of a given intensity.

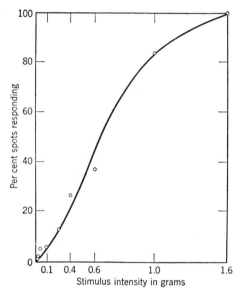

FIG. 68. Pressure sensitivity as determined by intensity of stimulation. Proportion of spots responding in a 1 cm² area as hair stimuli of graduated strength are
used. From the data of Guilford and Lovewell, *135*. By permission of the
Journal Press.

Absolute and Differential Pressure Sensitivity. The intensitive
threshold for pressure sensation has been seen to depend primarily
upon the locus of stimulation. Assuming, however, that the most sensitive local region is selected for measurement, an important question
remains. We have raised it before for visual and auditory sensations.
What is the order of magnitude of the absolute threshold for pressure?
How much physical energy must be expended to arouse a just detectable pressure sensation? Several investigations have been directed
at this point. If a von Frey hair is used one answer will be forthcoming. If a gentler gradient is created by the use of a larger mechanical
contactor the threshold value will be found to be higher. In the hairy
portions of the skin one can take advantage of the fact that a hair
itself serves as a lever of the second class (i.e., with its follicle more
or less firmly anchored below the skin surface) to create disturbances

in the superficial skin layers. Moving the distal end of the hair ever so slightly is likely to arouse lively sensations of touch. It has been found by von Frey (98) that a minimal energy of 0.04 erg, applied to the end of a hair 1.0 cm long, was sufficient to exceed the threshold of sensation. Other determinations by Wolf (316; 261, pp. 134–138), with the aid of an ingenious apparatus making possible the delivery of carefully measured tiny impacts to the skin, yielded the following representative values: 0.026 erg, on the ball of the thumb; 0.037 to 1.090 ergs, on the tips and balls of other fingers; 0.032 to 0.113 erg, at various positions on the underside of the forearm. These values seem small indeed but, compared with the energies needed to excite the retina or the cochlea, they are of tremendous magnitude. Direct comparisons of absolute intensitive thresholds in the visual, auditory, and tactual realms show that the skin absorbs from 100 million to 10 billion times the energy required by the eye or ear in getting into minimal action.

The question of the differential threshold exists for pressure sensitivity, as for vision and hearing. If we begin with a threshold sensation and add energy until a just perceptibly stronger pressure is felt, what will be the size of the needed increment? What is the magnitude of ΔI for pressure sensitivity, and what of the relation between ΔI and I, i.e., what is the size of the Weber fraction, $\Delta I/I$? Is it constant, as Weber's Law requires, or does it vary in some systematic fashion?

The available answers are not as clear-cut as we might wish, despite a considerable amount of experimentation over the years. The major variable is, of course, locus of stimulation. In general, those parts of the body surface displaying high absolute sensitivity show small values of ΔI, while the reverse is true for relatively insensitive regions. Thus ΔI has a large value on the abdomen and thighs; it is small at the lips, finger tips, and on the soles of the feet (261, p. 142). Other variables have been shown to affect the measured size of ΔI. The period for which the initial intensity has been effective, before the addition of the increment, is important, as is the rapidity with which the additonal pressure is applied. Moreover, if ΔI is computed as a decrement, i.e., from unloading rather than loading experiments, its value appears to be approximately doubled (131, 132). If both stimuli (I and $I + \Delta I$) are kept brief the time interval between the two makes a difference, short intervals yielding larger values of ΔI (188). The size of the skin area contacted is important in both absolute and relative measures of sensitivity.

The question of the constancy of the Weber fraction, $\Delta I/I$, can be answered in very much the same fashion as it was for vision and hearing. It is not constant throughout the entire intensity scale, $\Delta I/I$ showing relatively large values at low intensities and smaller (and roughly constant) ones throughout the middle range of intensities. Perhaps the clearest data are those of Gatti and Dodge (*106*) and those of Schriever (*261*, pp. 138–144). Figure 69 reproduces the former set. The Weber fraction, at least for a single pressure-sensitive "spot," appears to pass through a definite minimum in the middle reaches of the scale of effective stimuli.

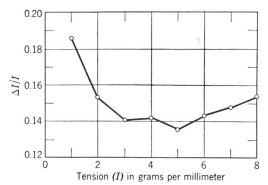

Fig. 69. Differential pressure sensitivity as a function of intensity level. The Weber fraction, $\Delta I/I$, varies with the absolute intensity (tension in grams per millimeter) of the base stimulus. The data were obtained by Gatti and Dodge (*106*) on an isolated pressure spot. After Boring, *45*. By permission of the copyright owners, Appleton-Century-Crofts, New York.

Pressure Adaptation. A decline in sensitivity with continuing action of a stimulus is a very general phenomenon in sensory psychophysiology and one which intervenes significantly in nearly all experimental situations. Pressure is no exception. Let a pressure stimulus, whether areal or punctiform, be applied steadily to the skin, and the sensation will fade, eventually to the point of disappearance. The rate of decline and the total time required for complete obliteration ("adaptation time") depend on several variables. Bodily locus is doubtless one, though it has never been investigated systematically. Intensity of stimulus and area over which it operates are known variables. Adaptation time is longer in the case of intense stimuli and briefer with large cutaneous areas (*327*).

In considering the light and dark adaptation processes in vision we commonly think of them as mediated by reversible photochemical reactions, i.e., as due to altered states of sensitivity of the receptors. The temptation is great to extend such thinking to the cutaneous realm and to picture altered chemical equilibrium states in or near end organs as responsible for adaptation. That the essential process may be of quite a different nature is indicated by some interesting results of Nafe and Wagoner (220). They arranged a carefully controlled apparatus to permit weights varying between 8.75 and 70.0 gm to be placed gently on the leg just above the knee. The progress of the weight as it "sank" into the skin and compressed underlying tissue was followed with a sensitive recording system. Their results show that a weight, once placed on the skin surface, does not rest there but continues to move downward for a surprisingly long time. Pressure is felt just so long as a supraliminal rate of movement is maintained. When tissue resistance reduces motion to an undetectable level the sensation fades out. The end point of "adaptation" has been reached. The conclusion is obvious: "complete adaptation" represents stimulus failure. The stimulus for felt pressure is tension set up within the pliable cutaneous tissues, and the intensity of the sensation presumably is correlated with the degree of tension produced. Another interesting consequence of this view is that removal of a weight from the skin, once adaptation is complete, should result in the rearousal of pressure sensations, since tissue elasticity will cause new tensions to be created in the return to the original equilibrium state. The evidence is in line with expectations. So-called "after-sensations" of pressure are of regular occurrence under such circumstances. "Stimulation" is produced in the absence of any external stimulus.

Temporal Pressure Patterns: Vibration. It has been seen that each feeling of pressure, far from being simple, is organized in a pattern having intensive, spatial, and temporal aspects. Certain of them are mainly notable for their temporal features. Chief among these are the feeling patterns commonly called "tickle" and "vibration."

That tickle falls in the family of pressure patterns is fairly obvious from direct observation. To and fro movement of a hair brings it out, as does light brushing of the lips or other sensitive hairless regions. It is less clear that the vibratory pattern is based on the operation of pressure receptors. Indeed, until relatively recently, when full proof became available, much doubt existed concerning the essential connection between vibration and pressure. A very considerable controversy, elsewhere reviewed by the author (112), continued for a half century between those who viewed vibratory sensations as "pressure in movement" and those who held that there existed a separate "vibratory sense" with its own special receptors and nerve supply. We cannot go into all the arguments. Suffice it to say that the controversy may now be said to have been resolved in favor of the conclusion that the vibratory pattern is in fact "pressure in movement." It is only necessary to know something of the skin mechanics involved in vibration to come to an understanding of the phenomena that led to the mistaken postulation of a special "vibratory sense."

Let the base of a tuning fork or other vibration generator be placed on the skin, and there is felt an intermittent "whirring," somewhat indefinite in localization especially if bony tissue lies directly under the point of application of the fork. Vagueness of localization, a misleading cue in that it seems not to suggest mediation by the somewhat precise pressure sense, can be shown to arise from the fact that vibratory motions impressed on the skin travel great distances, with very little loss, through cutaneous and subcutaneous tissues. Bones are especially good conductors. Widespread transmission of the vibratory disturbances, in all directions from the generator, prohibits the possibility of confining the stimulus to a local region. A very extensive feeling pattern, poorly localized, is set up as a result. From such gross experiments one gets little hint that the mechanism responsible for pressure reception is actually involved.

However, it is possible to design an experiment in such a way as to show the basic identity of the two sensitivities. If, instead of a broad contacting surface, one uses a small, very weakly vibrating needle or hair and makes a systematic exploration of a given skin area, one finds the kind of local variations in sensitivity so characteristic of pressure. Vibration, like pressure, is distributed in a punctiform manner. If, now, within such an area there are isolated for study two populations of "spots," one highly sensitive to pressure and the other having very low sensitivity (requiring gentle and steep gradients, respectively, to elicit pressure sensations from them), one can ascertain with some precision their responsiveness to vibration. It is necessary only to set the exploring needle in motion, at some preselected frequency, and determine the minimal amplitude that will bring out a just detectable "whirring" sensation. If this is done one finds pressure-sensitive spots to have very low and consistent vibratory thresholds, while those showing poor pressure reception require large amplitudes, varying greatly from spot to spot, to produce feelings of vibration (113, 115, 304). The results of one such experiment, involving extensive measurements on ten pressure-sensitive and ten pressure-insensitive spots lying within an area of 2 cm² on the volar side of the forearm, are presented in Fig. 70. Five test frequencies, from 64∼ to 1024∼ in octaves, were used. On the average, pressure-sensitive spots in this region require about 0.025 mm excursions of the needle point, apparently irrespective of the rate of repetition, to call forth the discontinuous, vibratory sensation. Insensitive spots need many times this amount, some of them requiring amplitudes of the order of half a millimeter. The presumption is strong, from such experiments, that pressure sensitivity and vibratory sensitivity go hand in hand, the activity of identical receptors being involved in both.

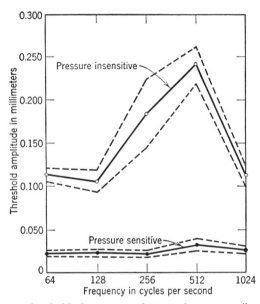

FIG. 70. Vibratory thresholds for two populations of cutaneous "spots," one highly sensitive to pressure, the other highly insensitive. The loci previously determined to be pressure-sensitive have low thresholds to vibratory motion at all frequencies. Pressure-insensitive spots are relatively insensitive to vibration. The dotted lines show variability of measurement. From Geldard, *114.*

Whereas, in the lower curve of Fig. 70, frequency of stimulation seems not to be a determining variable, this conclusion cannot be generalized for all skin areas under all conditions. On the contrary, vibratory sensitivity has been shown under certain circumstances to be a function of frequency. If, instead of delivering the vibrating stimulus to a highly sensitive pressure point situated in a region having a somewhat sparse distribution of receptors, one applies a relatively large contactor to the finger tip, say, it will be found that the vibration frequency selected is a matter of some importance. Several well-controlled experiments are in virtual agreement as to the shape of the frequency function. Figure 71 combines the results of four such experiments, all using the finger tip as the stimulated area, and shows that there is an optimal frequency in the neighborhood of 250∽. There can be little doubt that, for areal stimulation in a highly sensitive region, thresholds will in part be a function of the frequency with which impacts are repeated. The difference between the shapes of the curves in Figs. 70 and 71 has never been satisfactorily accounted for, and further research along these lines is certainly indicated.

Another question poorly answered as yet concerns the upper and lower frequency limits for vibratory sensation. What, in cutaneous

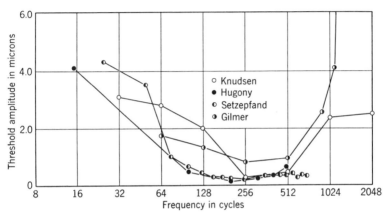

FIG. 71. The frequency-intensity function for vibration at the finger tip. The results of four investigators have been combined in a single plot. All used relatively large contactors applied to the tip of the index finger. Compare Fig. 70 for needle-point stimulation at the wrist. From Geldard, *114*.

vibration, corresponds to the 20 to 20,000∽ range in hearing? The problem of the vibratory upper limit is complicated, as it is to a lesser degree in hearing, by the necessity of producing very high-frequency oscillations of a mechanical contactor at relatively large amplitudes of movement. Driving a phonograph "cutting head" at frequencies of the order of 10,000∽ and with a 50-watt amplifier, the author has succeeded in getting, at the finger tip, fleeting but definite "bursts" of vibratory sensation. That the tissue is actually conducting forced vibrations of this frequency and that the phenomenon is thus not artifactual is attested by the fact that the stimulus frequency, and no other, may be detected by a crystal "pickup" several millimeters distant on the skin surface from the stimulus needle. The upper limit may be even higher than this; thus far instrumentation has not been entirely adequate to a correct solution.

The lower limit is also in doubt, though the failure to provide a definite answer here is not the result of inadequate apparatus. The

observational difficulties are similar, in most respects, to those confronted in establishing the lower limit of tonal perception. As frequency is raised, at what point does the appreciation of discrete impacts pass over into "vibration"? Some experiments have placed it
as low as 10 per second; others would have it as high as 80. Knudsen
(186), taking as a criterion the entrance of a "tingling" sensation, as
opposed to the feeling of separate shocks, got an average lower limit
of 15.3∽. It is probable that, were the facts fully known, the lower
limit would be found to be dependent upon the energy of the vibrator,
as is the case in hearing. The matter needs study.

Vibration, Pressure, and Skin Temperature. If the facts concerning
adaptation point to a mechanical rather than a chemical interpretation
of the operation of the pressure sense, those coming out of vibratory

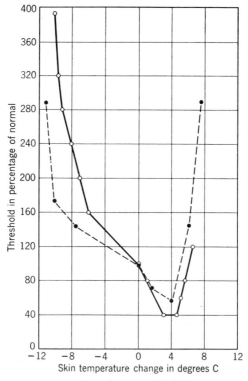

FIG. 72. Vibratory sensitivity as a function of skin temperature. There is an
optimal point, about 4° C. above normal skin temperature, for the arousal of vibratory feelings. The two curves are for different regions of the skin. From Weitz,
305. By permission of the *Journal of Experimental Psychology* and the American
Psychological Association.

studies speak otherwise. Vibratory sensitivity is known to be a function of skin temperature. Precise measures of the effect of warming and cooling the skin on thresholds of vibration have been obtained by Weitz (305). Figure 72 reproduces the threshold-temperature function for two separate loci at the wrist. Threshold amplitude at normal skin temperature is taken as unity, and percentage changes in amplitude of excursion necessary just to elicit the vibratory feeling are plotted against decreases and increases in surface temperature of the skin region in which the stimulated point lay. The complexity of the function—marked reduction in sensitivity (raised thresholds) with initial cooling, enhancement of sensitivity with mild warming, and subsequent sharp decline with continued heating—seems to call for interpretation in other than mechanical terms. Some form of chemical hypothesis, perhaps one which entails the operation of a catalyst and its destruction at high temperatures, seems more congenial to the facts. Incidentally, if further proof were needed, the correspondence between vibratory and pressure sensitivities is made even more certain by the fact that pressure receptors show a similar dependence on temperature, pressure thresholds being related to skin temperature by a concave function with maximal sensitivity between 36° and 38° C. (8), just as with vibration.

Other Pressure Patterns: "Touch Blends." If we forsake, for the moment, the approach to the study of cutaneous sensitivity by way of carefully controlled experiments and pay some attention to the role of the skin in its daily task of gathering information about external objects and situations, we are led to view it as a remarkably discriminative organ of sense. We commonly make entirely correct judgments, on the basis of "feel" alone, concerning hardness or softness, roughness or smoothness, wetness or dryness, stickiness, oiliness, and a host of other object qualities. Even with auditory cues excluded, tapping with a finger nail is often sufficient to determine whether an object is made of wood, metal, or plastic. In nearly all such discriminations movement of the skin relative to the object is a necessary condition; a spatial-temporal pattern of cutaneous excitation is involved. Let the finger tip rest gently on an unfamiliar surface, and, whereas something of its hardness or softness may be estimated, nothing will be learned of its roughness or smoothness. Movement of some degree is essential to the latter judgment. The amount of relative motion can be very slight and still yield a correct impression. A brief tap, lasting no more than $\frac{1}{300}$ sec, has been found in some experiments to be enough for complete identification of the material touched (178). The "threshold for roughness," if sufficient movement of the exploring finger tips is allowed, is also surprisingly small. A lightly etched piece of glass having eminences no higher than 0.001 mm can be successfully discriminated from an entirely smooth one. Assuming a little familiarity with the characteristic "feel" of materials one can make very nice discriminations of roughness and smoothness; "cloth feelers" are able to make their living at it. Since movement is the cue, there is little mystery about the essential mechanism responsible. Slight disturbances imparted to a sensitive skin area send vibratory "shock waves," relatively unimpeded, to large numbers of pressure receptors. Coating the fingers with a thin layer of collodion or interposing an unyielding stick between the material to be "felt" and the fingers makes very little difference in accuracy, as might be expected. The important thing is that the shocks be transmitted to the sensitive receptors, there to set up the complex spatial-temporal excitation pattern characteristic of "roughness."

Pressure sensations enter into a number of other complex cutaneous patterns or "touch blends." The pressure component can be analyzed out by painstaking observation and, once identified, can sometimes be artificially recombined with the other constituents of the blend to produce, synthetically, the original complex. As in chemistry, the test of analysis is synthesis. Thus "wetness" seems always to have a pressure component and one of cold. Is moisture also necessary in the stimulus? The analysis and subsequent synthesis were originally performed about a half-century ago by Bentley (32). He demonstrated that a cold pressure, uniformly distributed over the stimulated area, would produce the feeling of "wetness." Moisture is quite unnecessary. Dip into cold water a finger kept dry with lycopodium powder or with a thin rubber membrane, and the feeling will be quite as "wet" as without such protection.

Other synthetic experiments have been performed with more or less success (45, p. 509 ff.). Thus "oiliness" reduces to weak pressure accompanied by warmth, with movement enhancing its reality. "Hardness" is an even, cold pressure with a good boundary, while "softness" requires an uneven, warm pressure of poor boundary. "Stickiness" takes a variable and moving pressure, while "clamminess" is essentially "a cold softness perceived with movement and supplemented by unpleasant imagery." Complications of a still higher order are possible, of course. Indeed, it is held by one school of theorists that felt emotions are made up in just this way and that a thoroughgoing analysis of anxiety, love, or disgust would reveal them to be compounded of simple qualities belonging to the cutaneous and internal senses.

The Search for Pressure Receptors. The widely accepted current belief is that pressure sensations and their variants are mediated by two sets of cutaneous receptors, (1) free endings of nerves proliferating around hair follicles, in hairy regions of the skin, and (2) Meissner corpuscles, in hairless parts of the body. It should be said straightway that this is a matter of belief; it is far from being one of incontrovertible fact. The argument for these two structures as *the* pressure receptors rests almost exclusively on the known facts of distribution. The common occurrence of high points of pressure sensitivity "to the windward of hairs" is, of course, very suggestive. As has been seen, histological examination of skin sections reveals hair bulbs to be well supplied with sensory terminations, the masses of bare nerve endings proliferating so freely around the bases of hairs as to have earned for them the name "basket endings." These, then, are probable pressure receptors. What about the hairless regions of the skin? Pressure receptivity and discriminability are very high in the lips and parts of the hands and feet where there are no hairs. The guess has been that Meissner corpuscles, conveniently situated in the papillae of the corium in these regions, have the proper location and distribution to serve as pressure receptors. Indeed, histologists have designated the papillae housing Meissner corpuscles as "tactile" papillae out of deference to this belief in their function. Vital staining with methylene blue of a finger about to be amputated has successfully revealed, in subsequent sectioning of the skin, the distribution of Meissner corpuscles and their innervation (299). It appears that Meissner corpuscles occur in groups of two or three, rarely singly, and that ten such groups may be found in an area as small as 1 mm². The nerve fibers leading to corpuscles approach the cluster from various directions, suggesting that considerable overlap from disparate sensory fibers may be the rule of innervation.

Over against this conventional view are several strong bits of evidence which can only be interpreted as indicating that still other structures participate in the pressure response. Slicing down the epidermis at the finger tip with a sharp scalpel arouses only sensations of pressure and, so long as any of the epidermal layers are left, pressure sensations can be elicited. Cutting further, into the corium, produces pain. Since the only known structures to penetrate the epidermis are free nerve endings, these are naturally suspect as pressure receptors. Moreover, microscopical analysis of the parings reveals endings of fine nerve fibers terminating in "loops and figures" (298). Supporting evidence for the free nerve ending as a pressure receptor comes also from comparative studies. Action potentials recorded from single nerve fibers in the dorsal cutaneous nerve of the frog (4) show characteristic high-speed discharges when the corresponding skin area is stimulated. If the epidermis is scraped away the "tactile" response pattern is obliterated, and in its place there appears a continuous discharge of slow impulses indistinguishable from the effect typically produced by the "pain" of acid on the skin.

Attempts to identify the receptors by mapping the skin carefully for pressure sensitivity, excising the underlying tissue, and making a thoroughgoing histological examination of it have been, in general, quite disappointing. There is ordinarily no dearth of free nerve endings in the stained tissue, but the expected specialized structures, such as Meissner corpuscles, are mainly notable for their absence. One promising exception is on record in the study performed by Gilmer and Haythorn (121, 120). Excising tissue centering on known spots of high pressure and vibratory sensitivity, they found only one neural structure, the glomus body, recurring sufficiently often to suggest its possible candidacy for inclusion among the specialized pressure receptors. The glomus, a typically coiled and ball-like junction between tiny arterioles and venules, has a rich nerve supply. Its function has generally been assumed to be a vasomotor one, concerned with the regulation of peripheral circulation, but if it eventually proves to be sensory the distribution would be "right" for pressure reception, especially in the hairless regions of the body. More evidence is needed for a decision.

If much uncertainty exists about the end organs responsible for pressure, there is less concerning the nature of the nerves conducting pressure impulses. Any nerve leading away from the skin will show considerable size variation in its constituent fibers. The speed with which impulses are conducted along individual fibers is known to be a function of their size; the larger the fiber, the greater its conduction velocity. The rule is: speed, in meters per second, is six times diameter, in thousandths of millimeters. Now, when sensory nerves in animal preparations are put out of operation by infusion of a narcotic, such as cocaine, not all fibers drop out simultaneously. The smallest fibers are narcotized first, then larger ones, and finally those of greatest diameter. In humans it is found that similar narcotization results in a progressively selective loss of sensitivity; temperature sensations and pain disappear before pressure sensations, which are most resistant. In the anesthesia brought about by pressure block on nerve (such as when the foot "goes to sleep") there is also a differential order of disappearance of dermal sensations, though in this asphyxia situation the order is not the same. Pressure and cold disappear first, then warmth and pain. It can be shown by suitable experiments on animals that it is the large-diameter fibers that first fail of conduction in compression blocks. Entirely consistent results also come from observations on the return of sensitivity following experimental anesthesia. Whereas the differential rates of loss and recovery are not sufficiently clear-cut to permit the complete sorting out of all forms of cutaneous sensitivity by this technique, one conclusion seems inescapable: pressure sensitivity must be mainly mediated by fibers of relatively large diameter, the so-called "A group" of fibers ranging from 1 to 20 μ in cross section (chiefly 8 to 12 μ) and having conduction rates of 6 to 120 m per second. The great question is how these fibers are selectively discharged in the first place.

Cutaneous Pain. Pain may be brought forth by a great range of stimuli, in fact by agents belonging to all classes of stimuli capable of arousing the skin to sensory activity: mechanical, thermal, electrical, and chemical. As a consequence, pain has a great many modes of appearance. The following terms descriptive of pain, demonstrating the richness of our language in this respect, have been catalogued by Dallenbach (74, p. 614): achy, beating, biting, boring, bright, burning, clear, cutting, dark, digging, dragging, drawing, dull, fluttering, gnawing, hard, heavy, itchy, nipping, palpitating, penetrating, piercing, pinching, pressing, pricking, quick, quivering, radiating, raking, savage, sharp, smarting, squeezing, stabbing, sticking, stinging, tearing, thrilling, throbbing, thrusting, tugging, twitching, ugly, vicious. It is clear that some of these terms characterize the temporal aspect of the feeling pattern, others it spatial dimension, others the blend with pressure or temperature, while some appear to have reference to associated forms of emotional response. Pains are patterned so variously, in fact, that it is difficult to find a common principle holding them all together.

The independent status of pain as a separate cutaneous sense remained in doubt for a long time. Indeed, some scientists currently defend the position that pain is not a distinct unitary form of sensibility but that it always results from overstimulation of one or another of the other senses. Throughout the ages pain has been considered, in various philosophical systems, as very general and pervading in its nature and has, in consequence, been juxtaposed to pleasure as a form of emotion. For both Plato and Aristotle pain was a "passion of the soul," and this traditional view was a long time with us. Only comparatively recently, on the basis of compelling experimental findings, has pain come to be thought of as an independent member of the family of cutaneous senses.

Pain then, like other cutaneous sensations, comes patterned. It seems possible to distinguish two radically different sorts of pains on the basis of typical "feel" and localization and, since the histological discoveries of Weddell and his associates (*300, 301, 90*), on the presumed anatomical bases for them. In general, pain from the superficial layers of the skin is "bright" in quality, ordinarily is relatively sharply localized, and tends quite uniformly to elicit prompt withdrawal reactions. It does not matter which of several methods of stimulation are used. Pain resulting from a light, quick touch with a heated wire, a brief pulse of electric current, a quick tug of a hair, or a jab with a fine needle all feel exactly alike to a subject if care is taken to keep away from him supplementary information concerning the stimuli employed or if their nature is masked by a neutral accompanying stimulus. All pains induced by these means are brief ones; they are all uniformly reported by the subject as "pricking" pain. Similarly, if any of these stimuli is allowed to function in a more prolonged manner the uniform report will be that of "burning" pain. Sir Thomas Lewis (*199*, p. 39) has said, "The difference between 'pricking' and 'burning' pain is not one of quality or tone, it is purely one of duration." There is some doubt that the difference is "purely" one of duration. When later we come to consider the debated question of the "double pain response," we shall see that there are other possible differentia of pricking and burning pain.

Pain sensations originating in deeply disposed tissues are quite unlike skin pains. Deep pains have a dull, aching, much more unpleasant character, and lead more commonly to immobilization of the affected part. They are ordinarily far more difficult of exact localization; in fact, gross errors of localization are the rule. If intense, they have widespread reflex accompaniments—slowing of the heartbeat, a fall in blood pressure, nausea, and sweating. These organic complications are never accompaniments of superficial cutaneous pain.

Intensive and Differential Thresholds for Pain. Whereas pain can be aroused in a great variety of ways, it is not easy to find a stimulating device which will permit quantification of painful effects. Mechanical stimulators must either impair tissue or produce radical deformations in it if they are to arouse pain. Both electrical and chemical stimuli are practically impossible to control in that they cannot be spatially confined. Thermal arousal of pain is somewhat more controllable, but the physical and physiological events intervening between the application or withdrawal of heat and the discharge of sensory impulses must be a very complicated affair in a system having as a prominent feature a self-regulatory temperature mechanism. However, the production of pain by thermal stimuli currently offers the best possibility of experimental control for measurement purposes, as we shall see.

Classic techniques employed in attempts to measure pain thresholds have involved a considerable variety of "algesiometers," for the most part weighted needles, stiff hairs or hairs to which thistle spines have been attached, glass fibers, and similar graded mechanical contrivances. In the hands of von Frey remarkable consistency of measurement was achieved with calibrated hairs. He was able to demonstrate that the pain threshold for a given skin area is constant and is proportional to the hydrostatic pressure (grams per square millimeter) exerted on the tissue. A nice confirmation of these old experiments has resulted from the recent work of Bishop (38). He prepared stimulators consisting of tiny balls of solder impaled on and cemented to needle tips and arranged a graded series of them. With such stimuli and over the range 0.2 mm to 1.5 mm diameter, the threshold of pain is reached, irrespective of stimulus diameter, when the lower hemispherical surface of the ball tip has just been pressed into complete contact with the skin surface. The formula covering all cases is, as it was for von Frey's 1896 experiments, $gm/r^2 = K$. It may be inferred from this general relation that the constant factor in pain arousal is lateral stretch of cutaneous tissue. Bishop goes further and believes that "lengthwise stretch of nerve terminals appears to be the effective stimulus for pain endings in mechanical distortion of the skin." There are several known facts of pain sensitivity that make this supposition credible. Unless inflammation has intervened to complicate the situation, any sharp cut through the epithelium will prove painful when the skin encompassing it is stretched. However, under the same general circumstances relative immobilization of the tissue with collodion will prevent the appearance of pain. It is a well-known surgical phenomenon that pain may be produced by the stretching of unanesthetized internal organs, whereas cutting of the same tissue may not be an effective precipitant of pain.

Pain as a by-product of intense thermal stimulation is a familiar phenomenon. Experiments with the "burning glass" extend back into the last century. A radiant-heat method of measuring pain thresholds which has come into clinical prominence recently is that devised by Hardy and his associates (145). The schematic arrangement of their apparatus is shown in Fig. 73. Light (and heat) from the 1000-watt

lamp, *L*, is focused by a lens, *C*, through an aperture onto the forehead of the subject, *H*. *S* is a secondary shutter, operated manually
and opened just before the stimulus is to be given. The primary shutter, *P*, is regulated by a pendulum and provides a stimulus duration
of exactly 3 sec. Heat intensity is regulated by the rheostat, *RH*. *R*

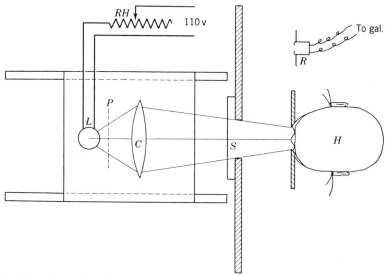

Fɪɢ. 73. The radiant-heat technique for measuring pain thresholds. Radiation
from lamp, *L*, is directed by the condensing lens, *C*, through a shutter, S, to the
forehead of the subject. An automatic shutter, *P*, allows an exposure of exactly
3 sec. In successive trials the level of operation of the lamp is increased, by
variation of the rheostat, *RH*, until the subject feels a sharp stab of pain just before
the closing of the shutter. Substitution of the radiometer, *R*, for the forehead
permits calibration in energy units. From Wolff and Wolf (*317*) after Hardy,
Wolff, and Goodell, *145*. By permission of Charles C Thomas, publisher, and the
authors.

is a radiometer, substituted for the subject's forehead at the time of
stimulus calibration. If the radiometer itself has been calibrated
against a standard, threshold may then be stated in gram-calories per
second per square centimeter. The method of measuring the pain
threshold is to step up the intensity, in successive trials, until the
subject feels a sharp stab of pain, the culmination of an intense sensation of warmth, just before the termination of the 3-sec exposure.
The subject's forehead is usually blackened with India ink to provide
a highly absorptive and uniform skin surface. Care must also be taken
to permit dissipation of heat between trials; a 30- to 60-sec inter-trial
rest period is therefore allowed.

Measurement of the pain thresholds of a large number of normal, healthy people by this technique revealed remarkably little variation from person to person, or from day to day in the same person (*255*). A group of 150 subjects gave a mean threshold of 0.206 gm-cal/ sec/cm². The method appears to be a sensitive one in that the effects of analgesic agents such as morphine, codeine, and alcohol have been shown through its use to raise the pain threshold enormously—as much as 70% in the case of morphine sulfate (*317*, p. 20)—while leaving other

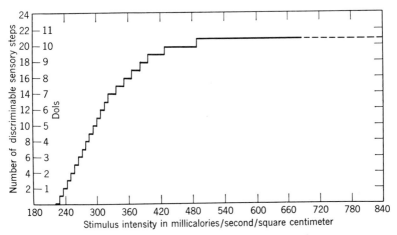

FIG. 74. The "dol" scale of pain intensity. The dol is equal to two successive "just noticeable differences" in pain intensity. From Hardy, Wolff, and Goodell, *146*. By permission of the editors, *Journal of Clinical Investigation,* and the authors.

sensory thresholds (touch, hearing, smell, vibration, and two-point tactual discrimination) relatively unaffected.

The same method has permitted measurement of the differential pain threshold, a practical impossibility with mechanical techniques. Hardy, Wolff, and Goodell (*146*) determined first the approximate limits of painful stimulation with their radiant-heat apparatus. For the standard 3-sec exposure the absolute threshold for pricking pain lay at 0.220 gm-cal/sec/cm² (220 millicalories, for short). The practical upper limit was found to be at about 480 mcal; above this value inconvenient burns were induced. Between the limits of 220 and 480 mcal there were found 21 j.n.d.'s of intensity. Between the threshold and about 320 mcal, ΔI increases in such a way as to render the Weber fraction, $\Delta I/I$, roughly constant at 0.03. Above this point the ratio grows larger. Hardy, Wolff, and Goodell have suggested that the intensive series in pain is capable of scaling, and they have accordingly proposed the "dol" as a unit of pain intensity. The dol is equal to 2 j.n.d.'s. This roughly provides a decimal scale between pain threshold and "ceiling" pain. Figure 74 is a graphic representation of their pain scale (considerably idealized, because the ΔI measurements are really very crude ones statistically). The energy range between lower and upper thresholds is, of course, a narrow one. The 21 discriminable steps are embraced within an energy ratio of little more than 2:1. It is interesting to compare the lower pain threshold and the point farther down the scale at which warmth is first detected. There are some 90 steps in this range, and the two energy values involved stand in the ratio of 2000:1.

Distribution of Pain Sensitivity. Pain has an interesting distribution throughout the body. For most areas of skin and with appropriate stimuli pain "points" or "spots" appear in great profusion. (We can be sophisticated about "spots" now, after having seen in connection with pressure sensitivity that the "spots" are artifacts of experimental procedure!) Table 3, derived from the work of von Frey's laboratory,

TABLE 3. DISTRIBUTION OF PAIN SENSITIVITY

After H. Strughold (275)

Skin Region	Pain "Points"/cm²
Back of knee (popliteal fossa)	232
Neck region (jugular fossa)	228
Bend of elbow (cubital fossa)	224
Shoulder blade (interscapular region)	212
Volar side of forearm	203
Back of hand	188
Forehead	184
Buttocks	180
Eyelid	172
Scalp	144
Radial surface, middle finger	95
Ball of thumb	60
Sole of foot	48
Tip of nose	44

gives some representative results of systematically exploring various regions of the body with a spine-tipped hair. Whereas the absolute number of "points" found in a unit area may not be too significant, since alteration of the sharpness of the stimulus point or of the force exerted by the hair attached to it would certainly change the number of pain "spots" reported, identical procedures were used for all skin samples, and the results for the several regions are therefore presum ably comparable with each other.

It is interesting to note that the "hollows" of the body conformation, the fossae, are among the most readily responsive areas. In passing from the base to the extremity of a limb provisions for pain reception tend to decrease; the reverse is the case for pressure sensitivity.

Two highly sensitive tissues, not included in Table 3, are the cornea of the eye and the tympanic membrane of the ear. The most exquisite pains in the body can originate from these sources. The cornea is of special interest, since it is widely held that this tissue is devoid of all sensitivities except pain. In fact, the cornea may be said to be a veritable battleground on which has been waged for at least half a century a crucial theoretical struggle concerning the neural basis of pain. We shall have to take a good look at the evidence for unique properties of the cornea when we come to the question of the receptor system for pain.

Certain areas of the body are relatively analgesic, and a few are apparently totally so. Among the former may be counted the mucous lining of the cheeks and back parts of the mouth, including the rear portion of the tongue. The lower half of the uvula is completely insensitive to pain, as is also a small region of the inner cheek opposite the second lower molar, sometimes called Kiesow's area. Evidence coming chiefly from surgical experience points to the generality that the "solid" organs of the abdominal cavity are insensitive to direct stimulation, assuming no inflamed or diseased condition to be present. The same may be said for the alimentary canal from the stomach to the rectum and for the gall bladder. The "hollow" viscera, especially those lying in the upper part of the abdominal cavity, may produce pain, sometimes quite severe, when under traction. Probes inserted into skeletal muscle, tendons, fascia, and periosteum reveal these tissues to be supplied with pain endings, though not too liberally in the case of large muscle bundles. Hypodermic injection of irritant solutions into these organs demonstrates the same thing. The bone coverings are especially sensitive, pain from them partaking more of the quality of superficial cutaneous pain and being capable of somewhat accurate localization.

Pain Adaptation. Pain has been widely held to be incapable of adaptation. Its apparent failure to fade out on continued stimulation has led to this belief, and certain biological views concerning the survival value of pain have tended to perpetuate it. Dallenbach (73) has summed up the classic argument (preparatory, it should be added hastily, to showing its falsity): "Pain is deleterious; adaptation would be of anti-survival value, as organisms that become adapted to pain would, in the long run, not survive; hence pain is non-adaptable."

The failure to recognize the adaptability of pain arose from the same sources that prevented for so long a time any sort of quantification of results where pain is concerned—difficulties inherent in control of the conditions of stimulation. Headaches, toothaches, and pains from injuries inevitably involve constantly changing conditions at the site of stimulation, chiefly rhythmic ones based on circulatory events. It is the case in all the other sense fields that the course of adaptation is revealed only when steady stimulation is maintained. Pain should be no exception.

The simple fact is that pain is not an exception in the sensory realm, and it is revealed when care is taken to provide an unvarying stimulus. Many experiments, some of them performed more than 30 years ago, have demonstrated the reality of pain adaptation. A particularly helpful series of studies has been made by Dallenbach and his students (73, pp. 345–346). They aroused pain by mechanical means (sharp needles, the applied pressure being carefully regulated), by intense warmth (radiant heat, without pressure accompaniment), and by cold (a dry-ice stimulator, likewise pressureless). With the needles the typical course of adaptation was a gradual reduction of pain intensity to the point of disappearance, residual pressure sensations replacing the pain. When heat was used the first sensation reported was naturally warmth; this developed into weak pain which became progressively intensified. From the peak intensity it gradually subsided, returning eventually to warmth. Likewise, cold stimulation produced feelings of "cool," then "cold," and eventually pain. After remaining at a high degree of intensity for a time it declined gradually to "cold" and, finally, to "cool." These events are precisely what would be expected if pain adapts independently of the other cutaneous modalities. All three experiments reveal, as residual effects, the types of sensation inherent in their appropriate stimuli. Strong pressure elicits pain but leaves as a residue, when pain has adapted out, a pressure sensation. Heat leaves warmth, and cold, cold.

These adaptation experiments, incidentally, have an important bearing on an old controversy. Earlier in this chapter it was pointed out that the view still persists that pain is not a separate and distinct form of sensibility but that it invariably results from overstimulation of some other sense mechanism. This theory is an old one and was chiefly espoused by Goldscheider. His controversy with von Frey on the subject is classic. It still resounds in the literature.

That pain is a separate and distinct sense is a belief of great antiquity. The crude beginnings of a theory incorporating this supposition have been traced to Avicenna in the eleventh century (73). On
the basis of a considerable body of accumulated evidence—and not a
little speculation—von Frey made the theory quite specific. For him
not only was pain a system of sensitivity apart from pressure, warmth,
and cold but it was mediated by receptor organs of its own, free nerve
endings. The "factual" evidence, in 1894–1897 when von Frey was
stating his theory, was concerned largely with: (1) the distribution of
pain points; (2) the differential action of anesthetics on pain and
other tactual sensitivities; (3) threshold determinations; (4) the apparent pathological separation of pain from other tactual systems in
diseases of the cord and brain; (5) the relatively long latency of pain
sensations following stimulation; and (6) the uniqueness of certain
areas, such as the cornea of the eye(?), in yielding only pain sensations.

Goldscheider, on the other hand, believed that the body possessed
no separate system of nerves for the mediation of pain. He did not
fall into the error, made by so many earlier theorists, of supposing that
pain was a very general consequence of overstimulating just any sensory
nerve. Dazzling lights, loud noises and shrill tones, intense heat and
cold, and pungent odors can all be "painful," but this is to be explained
satisfactorily on the basis that pain has an entirely ubiquitous distribution in the body. There is no mystery about this. Pain endings are
found associated with all organs of sense as with many other organs,
and, given the appropriate muscular tensions and other reactions of
associated tissue, pain is likely to result. Goldscheider's view was that
pain is relatively specific in the sense that only one cutaneous system
was responsible for it; the system was that responsible also for pressure. Pressure and pain differ from each other intensively. What is
pressure on weak stimulation is pain on more intense application of
the stimulus. Summation of pressure impulses in the gray matter of
the cord produces painful sensations.

One of the consequences of this view is that pain, upon being sufficiently weakened, should change into pressure. The adaptation experiment becomes critical for deciding between von Frey and Goldscheider, and, as we have seen, it fails to support the latter's contention. Pain, in the course of adapting, becomes progressively less intense and finally disappears without passing over into pressure. That
is, it fails to leave a residue of pressure unless the adaptation stimulus
is a pressure stimulus as well. Mechanical stimuli cannot answer the
question, but thermal stimuli do so quite decisively.

Identification of the Pain Receptor. As we have seen, the widespread distribution of free nerve endings throughout the body very early formed the basis for the belief that these organs are the receptors for pain. The view has not often been challenged. That the free nerve ending is the pain end organ is a common textbook statement. We need not accept it entirely on faith, however; there is imposing evidence to be considered.

The best support for the correlation of pain sensitivity with activity of free endings is perhaps the incontrovertible fact, which impressed von Frey and others long ago, that unencapsulated terminals of sensory nerves exist generally throughout the body. Plexiform arrangements of fibers ending in minute skeins, loops and whorls, brushes, knobs, and fine twigs abound within and beneath the epidermis and are present in mucous membrane and in a great variety of somatic and visceral organs. These elaborate neural designs seem anatomically to be but variations on a main theme. Their distribution is sufficiently widespread to coincide with that of pain sensibility, so far as can be judged from the available evidence. At least, there is no encapsulated ending having a similarly broad and rich distribution.

If an area could be found which possessed only pain sensitivity and which, at the same time, revealed only a single neural mechanism to be present, this would be strong evidence indeed for a firm correlation between mode of sensation and neural structure. Logically, of course, the possibility would remain that, in other areas, different mechanisms might also mediate pain, but at least one certain correlation would exist. The cornea of the eye has been held to provide exactly the instance sought. It has been repeatedly claimed that the cornea contains only free nerve endings and that pain is the only sensation of which the cornea is capable. It does indeed seem to be the case that the central portion of the cornea has but one type of sensory innervation. Its neural arrangements, a somewhat elaborate network of inter-digitating free terminals, have been described in careful detail by Tower (283). So much for one side of the correlation. However, in completing the other side, pain as a unique product of corneal stimulation proves to be a factual disappointment. The cornea, to be sure, has tremendous capacity for generating pain. Ask anyone who has suffered from a corneal ulcer! Indeed, very special conditions have to be imposed to arouse anything other than pain in the cornea. However, it can be and has been done. Nafe and Wagoner (219) carefully lowered onto the cornea brass cylinders of the type used in thermal exploration of the skin. Stimulation was controlled mechanically by a pulley and counterweight arrangement in such a way that a pressure not exceeding 1.5 gm was exerted on the tissue. A large series of stimulations of six subjects resulted in almost uniform reports of simple contact or pressure. One report was of "sharp contact." No stimulations were painful. Apparently, direct observation under carefully controlled conditions reveals the central cornea to be capable of pressure sensations as well as painful ones.

Another line of evidence points to the multiple sensitivity of the cornea. In 1938 there was introduced to neurosurgery Sjöquist's operation for the relief of intractable facial pain. This operation involves cutting the bulbospinal tract of the fifth (trigeminal) cranial nerve and leaves the face completely analgesic. In cases so operated the cornea is found to have a remnant of sensitivity; appreciation of touch is retained, although pain is missing. The cornea, then, fails to provide the unique relationship sought. Perhaps there are other tissues with which we could do better. The inner reaches of the external ear, the tympanic membrane in particular, have been similarly considered capable only of pain. Careful study of this region has not been attempted, mainly because of its relative inaccessibility, and an answer is not yet forthcoming.

Meanwhile, there are other lines of attack on the problem. One revolves around the much-discussed question of "double pain" and some interesting histological findings connected with it. If pain is elicited by pinprick or intense heat applied to a finger or toe there may be noted two phases in the temporal course of the sensation. There is first a sharp, sudden pain, followed by a longer-lasting second pain. These two phases have been called "fast pain" and "slow pain" or "first" and "second" pain. There is not uniform agreement about the qualities possessed by the two. Some observers have called fast pain "pricking pain" and slow pain "burning pain." Other, equally well-qualified investigators have come to the conclusion that the two are qualitatively identical (37, pp. 82–83). Of the temporal separation there seems to be little doubt. Figure 75 gives a schematic representation of the courses of the two pains and shows, in addition, the prolongation of "second" pain in cases of peripheral neuritis. The significance of the double pain response is that, since both slow and fast pain must be set off at the receptor practically simultaneously, differences in nervous conduction rates must be responsible for their temporal separation in experience. In some admirably conducted histological experiments Weddell (300) has demonstrated that the presumed pain endings occur in connection with two types of fibers—those with myelin sheath (rapidly conducting) and those without (slowly conducting). Terminals of the myelinated fibers end just beneath the epithelium, while endings of non-myelinated fibers are situated more deeply, in the corium and in relationship to tiny cutaneous blood vessels. The same investigator and his colleagues (*321*) had earlier shown that it is possible, by careful manipulation of a sharp needle, to arouse separately "first" and "second" pain. Whereas fast (and only fast) pain could be gotten by penetrating the skin to a depth of 0.25 to 0.50 mm, slow pain was obtained at a depth of 0.50 to 1.0 mm.

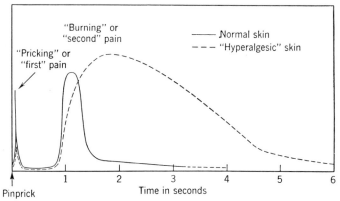

Fɪɢ. 75.   The course of "double pain."   The solid line suggests the normal temporal course of "first" (pricking) pain and "second" (burning) pain resulting from a pinprick.   The dotted line shows the heightening and prolongation of "second" pain in cases of hyperalgesia.   From Bigelow, Harrison, Goodell, and Wolff, *35*.   By permission of the editors, *Journal of Clinical Investigation*, and the authors.

The current conjecture is that the former may be responsible for discharge of fibers in the A group (the delta elevation), while the latter initiate impulses in C fibers (*37*). If this is correct fast pain would be conducted over fibers ranging from 3 μ to 6 μ in diameter, while slow pain would be confined to those having a diameter of less than 1 μ. We should not be misled by such guesses, however. Thus far there has been no simple sorting out of sensitivities by fiber size, and the available evidence seems not to promise that there will be in the immediate future, if ever.

"Protopathic" Pain.   Often, when cuts and other injuries to the skin produce a local anesthesia, there will be found an "intermediate zone" bordering the insensitive region and separating it from surrounding normal areas. This "zone" has special sensory characteristics. In other instances, where the extent of injury is relatively slight, only a superficial branch of a sensory nerve being involved, there will be no absolute anesthesia but there will result a somewhat circumscribed area having the same special properties as the intermediate zone in more extensive injuries. The outstanding characteristic is the greatly altered quality of pain sensation evoked from the abnormal region. Though its threshold may be higher, the pain is exceptionally strong and unpleasant. Moreover, once aroused, it tends to persist and to radiate. Localization is diffuse and grossly inexact. Such a pain pattern is difficult to describe, and it has received a variety of names in the literature: protopathic pain, hyperpathia, paradoxic pain, hyperalgesia, "over-reaction," dysesthesia.

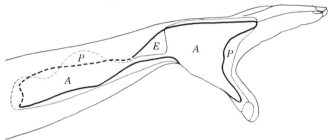

Fig. 76. Epicritic and protopathic sensitivity. Map of Henry Head's hand and arm 1 month after the radial and external cutaneous nerves had been cut. The area marked A is still entirely anesthetic, while "protopathic" sensitivity is found in area P and "epicritic" sensitivity, rarely occurring by itself, is in area E. From Boring, 45. By permission of the copyright owners, Appleton-Century-Crofts, New York.

The British neurologist, Henry Head, performed an experiment a half-century ago that was destined not only to draw attention to this phenomenon but from which he was to derive a whole theory of cutaneous sensitivity (149). Several repetitions of Head's experiment, with modifications, have been performed over the intervening years. They have been as much directed at testing Head's ingenious and provocative theory as at the final establishment of the facts of cutaneous innervation (296).

Head, in cooperation with the psychologist, Rivers, and the surgeon, Sherren, cut two nerves in his forearm and studied the sensory losses resulting. Carefully following the course of the return of sensation as the nerves regenerated (see Fig. 76) he believed he had discovered a basic separation between two types of cutaneous sensitivity. The immediate consequence of knocking out the sensory supply to the forearm was that there appeared a region of total anesthesia. Surrounding this during recovery was an "intermediate zone" having some remnants of sensitivity but behaving in most respects unlike the normal skin lying beyond. In the intermediate zone pain could be aroused, and it was a peculiarly disagreeable pain. High and low temperatures could be appreciated (above 45° C. and below 20° C.), but not moderate ones. Moreover, there was no discernible adaptation to these extremes of temperature. Pressures could be felt if heavy, but only coarse gradations of pressure strength could be appreciated. Head believed these symptoms to be those of a primitive nervous structure, now artificially dissociated from another, more highly developed one which was also present in normal skin. The primitive system he dubbed the "protopathic." The later-regenerating system, the "epicritic," he considered to be a finely discriminative one and one which was probably phylogenetically a later development. The epicritic system was superposed on the protopathic system of nerves and was responsible for partially inhibiting the latter's action. Epicritic functions included the mediation of light touch, fine intensitive gradations, temperatures between 25° C. and 40° C. (and their adaptation), and the spatial features of touch such as localization and two-point discrimination. Pain was never mediated by epicritic nerves.

The protopathic-epicritic distinction was appealing to many, and the concept has been used not only to interpret cutaneous sensory phenomena but, coupled with the further hypothesis that the protopathic system makes its appeal to the thalamus while the epicritic system has its central terminations in the cortex of the brain, the theory has been used quite generally as a basis for a broad neurological interpretation of behavior. Thus Rivers (251) has utilized the notions of protopathic and epicritic forms of *behavior* (essentially, instinctive and emotional responses as opposed to intelligent and manipulatory ones) as devices for explaining various forms of psychoneurosis, "substitution hysteria" in particular. But it is as a theory of cutaneous sensation that we are presently interested in the protopathic-epicritic distinction. As such, it stands in opposition to the classical theory of four cutaneous modalities: pressure, pain, warmth, and cold. To be sure, Carr (55) analyzed in detail the results reported in the Head nerve division experiment and came to the conclusion that, on the basis of his own results, Head should have logically found for no less than seven systems of sensitivity, not two. However, scientific theories never get established or abolished by merely arguing about them. What are the current facts and what shall we conclude about the usefulness of Head's theory?

The most recent and the best-controlled of the nerve division experiments is that of Lanier (193). In three subjects the two main nerves (the lateral and median cutaneous antebrachials) supplying the volar surface of the left forearm were destroyed by injecting their tracts with 95% alcohol. A considerable region corresponding to the peripheral projection areas of the nerves was thus left anesthetic. These areas, carefully located in advance, were explored systematically for several months before denervation. The same care in mapping was used throughout the 2-year period following the operation. Instrumentation and procedure were such as to guarantee comparability between successive tests, a matter too frequently overlooked in some of the earlier work. Moreover, quantitative measures of threshold were secured by means of a calibrated mechanical algesiometer (pain), a "limen gauge" (pressure), and a thermoesthesiometer (warmth and cold). All four modalities were found to recover continuously and gradually throughout the process of nerve regeneration, though the area of initial loss for the temperature senses was markedly greater than for pain and pressure. Pain, pressure, and cold recovered, by circumferential shrinkage of the area unresponsive to a stimulus of constant magnitude, at about the same rate. Warmth was considerably delayed; Lanier found Head's peculiarly unpleasant "protopathic" pain both in the intermediate zone shortly after denervation and in the central anesthetic zone once the regenerating nerve fibers began to grow back into it. But sensations best described as "protopathic pressure" also appeared, and pressure is, of course, not supposed to be a protopathic quality. While there was a return to near normality after 2 years or so, Lanier reported to the author that, more than 15 years after the operation, he still had occasional "protopathic" reactions from the region originally made anesthetic by denervation.

Even though there was some general agreement between the qualitative results of the Head and Lanier experiments, the "protopathic-epicritic" theory was not regarded by Lanier as necessary to account for his findings. After weighing the evidence carefully Lanier concludes (193, p. 454): "The results of the study do not substantiate Head's theory of protopathic and epicritic systems of fibers in cutaneous nerves. Neither the patterns of sensory dissociations nor the sensitivity alterations in affected areas can be accounted for by his theory. The sensory dissociations observed point conclusively to the existence of four types of anatomical mechanisms underlying cutaneous sensibility."

A convincing histological study (301) adds a final note to our understanding of the protopathic pain mechanism. Skin samples were taken from 59 patients who had scars or partially denervated skin. These were stained and subjected to microscopical analysis. In all instances in which pain of protopathic quality had resulted from pinprick in the affected area, the findings were consistently that the underlying nerve nets and terminals were isolated from their neighbors. There was no overlap or interdigitation of terminals in the region; only a single nerve fiber had supplied all the endings. Conversely, in no single case in which such isolation of terminals could not be found microscopically could "unpleasant" pain be produced. It would appear that protopathic pain owes its existence to simplification of the sensory nerve supply. Where normally intricate networks exist pain takes on a more subdued character.

Itching. We saw that pain comes patterned in a great variety of ways. One pattern of special interest is itch. Itching seems to bear about the same relation to pain as tickle does to pressure. It is a durative pattern, usually highly attention-demanding and, like tickle, leads ordinarily to reaction. One usually "does something about it," rubs or scratches the affected region. What are the conditions for the arousal of itch?

It is not possible to provide a complete answer as yet. A number of pathological skin conditions commonly accompanied by itching are known clinically. These presumably involve fairly low-level irritations of free nerve endings in the affected tissue. But itching can occur also in entirely normal skin. In mapping experiments with hairs and needles delays are often occasioned by the unwanted appearance of itching. One well-defined experimental situation for the production of itching has been discovered by Bishop (36) with the use of his electrical "sparking" method. Repetitive shocks, each so weak that by itself it will produce no sensation whatever, may induce a persistent itch not unlike that generated by an insect bite. Here is direct evidence of temporal summation in the pain receptors; in fact, summation occurs when the shocks succeed each other at a rate as slow as 5 per second. Itching may also be brought about as an after-effect of the sharp pricking sensation produced by single shocks of greater strength. Weak but supraliminal single shocks induce pricking pain without itch, and, if the intensity is generally increased in slowly repetitive stimulations, the pattern passes over into sharp stabbing pain, eventually becoming intolerable.

That the pain system and not those for pressure or temperature is concerned is attested by the fact that the absolute threshold to electrical stimuli is much lower for pain than for any other cutaneous modality in most skin regions.

Direct Nerve Stimulation. It is a commonplace that direct stimulation of nervous tissue, without the intermediation of receptor organs, has no sensory effect. Thus brain operations involving cutting and cauterization can be conducted without benefit of anesthetic once the brain has been laid bare. The one exceptional mode of stimulation is electrical. Indeed, a great range of sensory effects can be produced by electrical stimulation of the cortex. One of the values of this principle is seen in its use to reproduce the sensory "aura" in localized (Jacksonian) epilepsy to find the site of a responsible tumor or other brain impairment. Not until quite recently, however, have experiments been performed in which direct electrical stimulation of a peripheral nerve was attempted. The results are important for our understanding of pain.

Pattle and Weddell (227), two British investigators, exposed the digital nerve of Weddell's index finger. Sheet rubber was slipped between the nerve and the surrounding tissue, and a pair of silver-silver chloride electrodes was hooked about the nerve. The skin was then sutured in such a way as to insulate the nerve and its attached electrodes from all tissue. The preparation being readied, electrical stimulation was cautiously applied. Steady d-c potentials were delivered to the nerve, as were inductorium and condenser shocks. With a 6000-ohm resistor in series with the nerve it was found that 7.5 volts were required to produce a just detectable sensation. The threshold sensation was always the same, a pain "greatly resembling a wasp sting." It was always felt as in the finger pad (where the nerve endings were located), despite the fact that throughout the experiment the finger pad proved to be anesthetic to direct mechanical stimulation. A timing arrangement was improvised which permitted the exact registration of the onset of the electrical stimulus and the subject's response, on a key, to the first twinge of pain.

Individual condenser shocks were given in gradually increasing strength, the electrical capacity of the condenser (in microfarads) being a measure of intensity. No sensory result was produced until a value of 0.1 μf (through a series resistor of 6000 ohms) was reached. Then came the "wasp sting." The same quality of sensation with, moreover, the same latency of 1.27 $\pm$ 0.03 sec resulted from all condenser values up to 6.0 μf. A 7.0-μf condenser discharge produced a sharp break in the series, for now "a long-lasting, severe, aching pain, which was completely different in quality from the 'wasp sting' reaction" resulted. The latency remained substantially unaltered, however, at 1.27 $\pm$ 0.06 sec. There was little repetition of the high-intensity

(7.0 μf) experiment.   The aching pain was reported as "not well toler-
ated by the subject," and it could not be systematically investigated.

Of special theoretical interest, in view of what we already know
about the summation of subliminal shocks to produce itching, were
the results obtained with repetitive stimuli.   "When a just sub-thresh-
old shock was repeated six times within 0.5 sec. *no sensation whatever
was aroused.*"   Apparently the summation effect is one occurring at
the receptor level, not in the nerve, as has been long surmised.   Repeated shocks of supraliminal strength, if succeeding each other within
0.1 sec, brought forth a single sharp pain of the wasp-sting variety,
which was felt as about twice as strong as a single shock of the same
intensity.   If the two shocks were separated in time by more than 0.1
sec, two distinct pains were felt, each of its proper strength.

One wonders what happens quite abruptly at the high-intensity
level (between 6.0 and 7.0 μf).   The sudden change of quality from a
"wasp sting" to a prolonged aching pain is a matter of some interest,
since a single nerve bundle was mediating both.   A more intimate
picture of what is happening here might go a long way towards settling
some old disputed points in cutaneous theory.

11

Temperature Sensitivity

The Thermal "Senses." One of the most persistently recurring questions in the whole realm of sensory psychophysiology is that concerning the basic nature of sensitivity to temperature changes. Are we dealing with a single "temperature sense," or are there two systems of sensitivity, a "warm sense" and a "cold sense"? If solely physical considerations were consulted, if stimuli alone could provide the answer, the problem should not detain us long. The absorption of heat by the skin is a simple, straightforward event, describable in the terms of calorimetry. Objects of higher temperature than the skin, upon coming into contact with it, transmit heat to it. The loss of heat by the skin to surrounding air or to objects contacted is the obverse process. There are not two sets of stimuli, warm and cold; there are only positive and negative transfers of a single form of physical energy, heat.

But, as we have seen, appeal to stimuli has never provided the best solution to the problem of classification of the senses. If it could be conclusively demonstrated that there existed in the skin a single anatomical mechanism capable of responding one way to heat gains and another way to heat losses we should doubtless decide in favor of a single "temperature sense." As the facts now stand the weight of evidence is against such a conclusion. Instead there are compelling reasons for believing that we are dealing with two systems of sensitivity, one for warmth and one for cold.

The chief argument for the separation of the two rests on the demonstration that cold and warm sensitivities are not distributed alike. If a sample area on the arm is explored, point by point, with a metal contactor cooled well below skin temperature a pattern of responsive "spots" will be found. Some points will "flash out" strongly with cold sensations, while others will yield moderate, cool feelings. In a 1-cm² area perhaps a half-dozen such spots will be found. If the experiment is now repeated with a warmed contactor the same area will yield

211

perhaps one or two reports of warmth, perhaps none. The probability is that careful mapping of the region will show widely disparate patterns for the two qualities, cold spots nearly always being far more numerous than warm. Table 4, a composite of results from Rein (*244*) and from Strughold and Porz (*277*) gives comparisons for several body regions.

TABLE 4. COMPARISON OF WARM- AND COLD-SPOT CONCENTRATIONS

After Rein (*244*) and Strughold and Porz (*277*)

	"*Spots*" per cm^2	
	Cold	Warm
Forehead	8.0	0.6
Nose	8.0 (side)–13.0 (tip)	1.0
Upper lip	19.0	. . .
Chin	9.0	. . .
Chest	9.0	0.3
Upper arm, volar side	5.7	0.3
Upper arm, dorsal side	5.0	0.2
Bend of elbow	6.5	0.7
Forearm, volar side	6.0	0.4
Forearm, dorsal side	7.5	0.3
Back of hand	7.0	0.5
Palm	4.0	0.5
Fingers	2.0–9.0	1.6–2.0
Thigh	5.0	0.4
Lower leg	4.0–6.0	. . .
Sole of foot	3.0	. . .

There is, of course, the same necessity here, as in our earlier considerations of pressure and pain "spots," to avoid the naive conclusion that the mapping of temperature spots implies the location of individual temperature receptors. "Spots" are products of certain experimental operations. The number found in a given area reflects, to be sure, the sensitivity in that area, but it also reflects the operation of a number of other variables. The number of warm or cold spots found in a given exploration is a function of at least the following factors, in addition to depending on receptor availability in the particular skin area being tested: (1) stimulus temperature, (2) size of stimulator, (3) concomitant mechanical pressure, (4) state of thermal adaptation, (5) duration of stimulus at each exposure, (6) interval between stimulations, and (7) the attentive "set" taken by the observer. Some of these are not as important as one might expect. Thus Heiser (*161*) systematically varied stimulus duration between 0.5 and 4.0 sec, in an experiment on warm sensitivity of the forehead, without finding any significant change in the number of reports of warmth. It is reasonably certain, though, that time could be shortened to the point where it would make a difference. Similarly, increase in stimulus pressure from 1.0 to 6.0 gm brought about an increase in number of warm spots which, however, was so small as to require treatment by probability statistics to make certain that the increase was a real one (*162*). The small increase accompanying a change from 1.0 to 2.0 gm was not statistically reliable.

The effects of stimulus size and stimulus temperature are difficult to separate. Both affect the warm and cold spot counts; increased size improves the probability that warm or cold will be reported in a given application, and increased deviation of stimulus temperature from that of the skin brings the same result. The two variables can, of course, be separately investigated in a systematic manner, but one hardly knows whether increase in frequency of temperature reports, in the case of an enlarged stimulus point, is the result of more end organs being stimulated or a more adequate delivery of heat to a fixed number of them. Increasing the contacting area of the stimulus may be tantamount to intensifying the stimulus. Conversely, increasing the effective temperature may be physiologically equivalent to spreading the stimulus over a larger amount of receptive tissue. Simple mathematical relations between either stimulus area or stimulus temperature and numbers of responsive "spots" have never been established with certainty. Everyone who attempts mapping of cold or warm spots is impressed with the apparent fickleness of their behavior. Test-retest reliabilities are disappointingly low despite careful control of the obvious experimental variables. This is not to say that mapping and remapping of temperature spots inevitably leads to utter lack of consistency. The results are far from chaotic. One is likely to be able to see, in the charts of several successive mappings, strong pattern resemblances. However, if exact correspondences are looked for square by square, agreement between any two maps is likely to run no higher than 70% to 80%. Indeed, far lower degrees of consistency are commonly found.

Where especially responsive individual spots are concerned experience has been quite otherwise. In any extensive exploration of the skin with a cooled temperature cylinder there are likely to be found a few points at which cold comes out promptly and vividly. One can return to such spots time after time and get the same result. In fact, tests separated by relatively long periods of time, even years, will show unfailing responsiveness at the loci of such peaks of sensitivity. There are, then, points of peculiarly ready reaction, and this may mean either that certain receptor aggregates possess abnormally high sensitivity or that they are extraordinarily favorably situated with respect to channels of heat transfer. There is some suggestion that the latter may be true in Gilmer's finding that about twice as many cold-sensitive spots are found on sweat duct openings as are found on loci of stimulation not involving mouths of sweat ducts (119).

Thermal Changes in the Skin. One way we shall get a better picture of the probable stimulation process is to pay some attention to investigations of heat transfers by the cutaneous tissues. If the epidermis, with its relatively simple composition, may be regarded as a somewhat homogeneous conductor of heat, the same cannot be said of the more elaborate tissues beneath it. The dermal layers are, of course, considerably complicated thermally by reason of the fact that they house blood vessels—capillaries, venules, arterioles, and (at deeper levels) veins and arteries. The vascular system has much to do with supplying heat to the skin and with regulating that supply. It obviously cannot be ignored in the thermal stimulation process.

Direct evidence concerning heat interchanges in the cutaneous tissues comes chiefly from the ingenious experiments of Bazett and his co-workers (18, 19, 20, 21). Using tiny thermocouples inserted into the skin of the forearm under previously located warm and cold spots, they were able to measure accurately the extent of heat conduction through the tissue from a thermal stimulator applied to the surface. At a depth of about 1.0 mm below the surface (subsequently measured on X-ray photographs) there proved to be remarkably little heat gained or lost in arousing warmth or cold. With an applicator of 1.5 mm diameter a stimulus 10° C. above the initial skin surface temperature, held on the spot for 6 sec, produced a maximum temperature rise of only 1.05° C. 1.0 mm below the surface. A cold stimulus more than 15° C. below initial surface temperature brought about a drop, 1.0 mm down, of only 0.4° C. during a 5.6-sec period. Results with a much larger applicator (11.0 mm) produced more extensive shifts of subsurface temperature, though none was as large as might be expected. Moreover, the skin surface directly under the stimulator never attained the temperature of the physical stimulus, discrepancies between them of 8° to 10° C. being common even at the moderate temperatures used.

The rate of heat penetration through the cutaneous tissues was found to vary from 0.5 to 1.0 mm/sec, depending somewhat on the vascular conditions at the time. If the blood vessels were in a dilated condition the velocity of heat transfer was reduced. Apparently the circulatory flow serves as a kind of cooling system, picking up heat and carrying it off, thus retarding direct heat penetration into the tissues lying beyond. Local inflammation is a particularly powerful inhibitor of cold sensations, reducing their intensity and exaggerating their latency of arousal. Conversely, hyperemic skin renders warmth easier to evoke.

The presence of blood vessels in the skin, more or less constantly varying in diameter as they do with consequent transient changes in warming and cooling effects, brings about an unstable thermal situation. It is little wonder that it has been impossible to establish experimentally the invariant relationships between stimulus temperature and sensitivity. Blood flowing past a given receptor must effectively contribute to the state of adaptation of that cell and must be regarded as constituting part of the thermal stimulation system. This means that a relatively large area of tissue may affect a given end organ. The situation is not unlike that obtaining in the radiation thermopile of the physicist. The thermocouple junction has soldered to it a metal disc or "radiation receiver" which collects over its relatively large surface enough heat to activate the thermocouple junction and thus greatly improve the sensitivity of the instrument. In like manner the blood supply of the skin imparts its heating and cooling effects to the relatively tiny nerve endings responsible for temperature sensations. In view of this condition it is remarkable that warm and cold sensitivities have anything like punctate distributions.

Out of the studies of heat transfers in the skin have come some interesting ideas concerning the probable mechanism of thermal stimulation. Bazett, McGlone, Williams, and Lufkin (21) performed the somewhat Spartan experiment of suspending with dulled fishhooks the skin of the prepuce, applied a thermal stimulus to one side of the fold, and picked up the transmitted heat with a thermocouple cemented to the other side. Since the stretched tissue of the foreskin is only about 2.0 mm thick, it was possible to stimulate or record from either side, thus permitting calculations of the probable depth of the receptor. Time relations for both sensation (reaction time) and heat conduction were carefully measured. The latency of the cold sensation is short (0.3–0.5 sec), and estimates from these experiments place the receptor at a depth below the skin surface of about 0.1 mm. Warm sensations are aroused more slowly (0.5–0.9 sec latency). Similar calculations place the receptor depth near 0.3 mm. These estimates mean that the end organ for cold lies just above the most superficial venules; those for warmth are at depths where complex patterns of arterial and venous networks exist.

Putting together all that has been learned about thermal inter-changes and calculated receptor depths, Bazett has evolved a theory

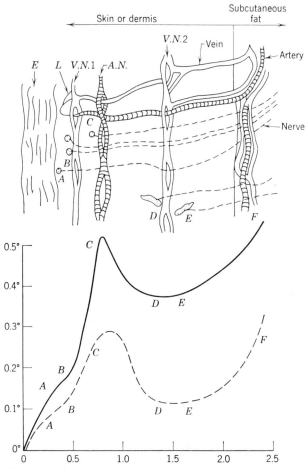

Fig. 77. Thermal gradient theory of temperature sensitivity. The various structures of the dermis and subcutaneous region are represented at the top. Below are pictured two different thermal gradients, one for rapid blood flow (solid line), one for more sluggish circulation (dotted line). The abscissae give distances below the skin surface, in millimeters. The ordinates show temperature above that of the skin surface, in degrees Centigrade. Possible positions of cold receptors under this theory are A, B, and C; warm receptors could be at D, E, or F. From Bazett, 18. By permission of Reinhold Publishing Corporation, New York.

of "thermal gradients" which is illustrated in Fig. 77. The curves represent the normal resting gradients in the skin of the forearm, ordinates being temperature rises above that of the skin surface, abscissae being depths below the surface. The solid line depicts a situation in which the blood flow is increased above that of the normal; the more usual case is represented by the dotted line. Temperature changes in the first 0.5 mm are quite hypothetical, but the remainders of the two curves have considerable experimental evidence to support them. A, B, and C denote possible locations of cold receptors; D, E, and F are loci of possible end organs for warmth. In the normal resting skin, in thermal equilibrium with the external environment, the gradients for warmth and cold are of opposite sign. To be effective a warm stimulus would have to exaggerate the normal gradient. A cold stimulus, to excite cold sensations, would similarly have to steepen the normal gradient. It is to be noted that the hypothetical cold receptor lies in a region in which the gradient is already somewhat steep. Normally cold stimulation comes from without. There is little, if any, vascular tissue intervening between the surface and the receptor. The withdrawal of heat from the system produces promptly a simple augmentation of the temperature difference between the skin surface and the receptor organ, i.e., steepens the thermal gradient. A rapid reaction to cold results. Under certain conditions a warm stimulus might reverse the gradient to a cold receptor and stimulate it ("paradoxical cold," to be described later). The situation for warmth is somewhat different, though similar in principle. The application of heat to the skin surface will also exaggerate the somewhat gentle gradient existing in the region of the receptor and, though complicated by several intervening circulatory events, should produce stimulation of the warm receptor. The process should require more time than that for cold, as indeed it does. The flow of blood from subcutaneous tissue into the arterial network should combine with the heat interchange of external origin either to summate with it (vasodilatation) or partially to counteract it (vasoconstriction). The former should accentuate the gradient; the latter should flatten it.

Whereas many details of the thermal gradient hypothesis work out as the experimental facts demand, there are reasons for thinking that the idea provides no final and complete explanation of the stimulation process. Bazett has himself realized this and has been prompt to point out that certain crucial experiments prevent the acceptance of the thermal gradient principle as the sole one at work. If the hand is immersed in fairly warm water (42° C.) and allowed to remain there for an hour or more sensations of warmth still persist. Thermal gradients should have long since disappeared; a steady equilibrium state should have been reached. If it is argued that the blood flow tends to maintain an ever-renewed gradient, that point can also be met. In experiments on circulatory stasis, in which a tourniquet applied above the elbow has prevented blood from entering the forearm and hand, extreme temperature sensations occur on removing the block and allowing warm blood to flow back into the tissues. This would not be surprising if, as would usually occur, the hand and forearm had cooled during the period of circulatory arrest. Steep gradients should then be formed. But extreme warmth is still experienced on return of circulation when care has been taken to prevent the escape of heat from the hand and arm. Warm blood flowing into warm tissues should not produce extreme thermal gradients. The conjecture therefore is that other events intervene—chemical or osmotic gradients, perhaps—between the establishment of a thermal gradient and the arousal of the receptor. Experiment will doubtless eventually decide.

Adaptation, Thresholds, and Physiological Zero. The phenomenon of adaptation, a very general one occurring in all the sense modalities, has always to be reckoned with in determining thresholds. Prior stimulation, if it is not too far removed in time, is likely to have reduced sensitivity and raised threshold values. This is the case in pressure and pain. When we come to consider adaptation in the thermal senses the situation is a bit more complicated. Adaptation is readily demonstrated for both warmth and cold. Prolonged stimulation with heat reduces warmth sensitivity (raises thresholds to heat), and prolonged cold stimulation reduces cold sensitivity (raises thresholds to cold). What complicates the situation, however, is that stimulation with heat also sensitizes the skin to cold. Adaptation to a hot stimulus brings with it an actual lowering of the cold threshold, in that temperatures which would normally result in thermal indifference or even produce mild warmth now feel cool. In like manner cold stimulation reduces the threshold for warmth; lower temperatures than are normally required arouse warmth.

The simultaneous moving of cold and warm sensitivities in response to a single condition of thermal stimulation is a fact of considerable importance. As might be anticipated, much is made of it by those who support the view that warmth and cold are simply different qualities belonging to a single "temperature sense." The analogy is drawn with color sensitivity in vision. Blue and yellow (or any other complementary pair) likewise move together; adaptation to blue builds up yellow sensitivity and vice versa. If there is this complementary relation between warmth and cold, as manifested in adaptation, there should also be an analogue of neutral gray in vision. There is. For a given area of the skin there is always some temperature representing thermal indifference. The temperature to which a response of neither warmth nor cold can be aroused is known as physiological zero. Assuming a normal heat equilibrium with the surrounding air and no immediate history of unusual thermal stimulation, physiological zero corresponds to the skin temperature. Thus, under these conditions, the skin over much of the exposed body surface has a temperature in the neighborhood of 32° C. This is physiological zero until warm stimulation raises it, or cold stimulation lowers it. Then it migrates temporarily to a new level. Some protected areas have normal temperatures much higher than this (36°–37° C.); some, such as the ear lobe, where circulation is sluggish, normally stand at about 28° C.

Physiological zero is not to be thought of so much as a point on a scale as a scalar distance, a small zone of thermal indifference. Stimulus temperature must deviate appreciably in one direction or the other to transcend the zone and elicit warmth or cold. In the neighborhood of 32° C. for the fingers, the zone is not a large one. It is of the order of 0.3° C. (plus and minus 0.15° C.) when the measurements are made by dipping the fingers in slightly warmed and cooled water. At much higher or lower starting points the neutral zone is wider. Thus, after the fingers are adapted to warm water of 40° C. an increase of 0.5° C. is required to feel warmth and a corresponding decrease of 0.5° C. to feel cold, the two summing to make a neutral zone of a whole degree.

Determinations of the amount of heat energy needed to produce a threshold feeling of warmth on the forehead have been made (144) with the Hardy radiant heat technique, the one discussed earlier in connection with pain thresholds. Sensation is evoked in 3 sec by exposure of a skin area of 200 cm² at a rate of 0.00015 gm-cal/cm²/sec. This compares with a value of 0.218 gm-cal/cm²/sec needed to reach the pain threshold in the same period of time. Thus warmth is experienced at an energy level representing but a small fraction of that required to elicit pain. A further calculation reveals threshold energy for warmth to be but 0.09 gm-cal. This is a tiny figure, as heat energy values go in the bodily economy, amounting to no more than one nine-millionth of the normal hourly radiation loss from the body surface.

It is clear that, however sensitive the temperature receptors to thermal stimuli impinging upon them, the sheer fact of adaptation prevents the system from serving as a good thermometer. Where accurate temperature judgments are required one does well to rely on the expansion and contraction of alcohol, mercury, or other substances rather than trust the evidence of his cutaneous senses. At the same time the temperature system of the skin is designed to preserve comfort and permit quite rapid accommodations to a constantly and sometimes quite rapidly changing thermal environment. The phenomena associated with thermal adaptation will bear looking into more intimately.

Numerous studies have been directed at adaptation rates and adaptation limits for large skin areas. A few have been concerned with punctiform stimulation. As early as 1846 Ernst Weber did the "three-

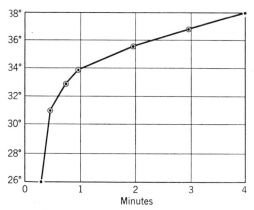

Fig. 78. The course of temperature adaptation. The ordinate shows the temperatures (in degrees .Centigrade) which yield the same thermal impression, to one hand kept in water at 38° C. until the time of testing, as that received by the other hand, kept in 26° C. water for the times shown on the abscissa. At the beginning of the experiment both hands were adapted to 38° C. From Woodworth (319) after Hahn, 137.

bowl" experiment. Three containers of water at 20°, 30°, and 40° C. were used. One hand was placed in the 40° water and allowed to adapt. At the same time the other hand was adapted to the 20° water. Then both hands were removed simultaneously to the 30° water where, of course, it was demonstrated that the same physical temperature can feel cold to one hand and warm to the other. Similar crude experiments can tell us a good deal about adaptation rates. The results of Hahn (137), shown in Fig. 78, demonstrate that the course of thermal adaptation, like all similar processes, proceeds in accordance with a negatively accelerated curve. These experiments were performed by simple immersion of the two hands in baths of varying temperatures and for various adapting periods, judgments of equality of cold sensations being required of the subject. At the end of 4 min (following an initial adaptation period of 5 min at 38° C. for both hands) adaptation appears to be complete in that 38° feels the same to the right hand as 26° does to the left. Both are thermally indifferent.

Will all temperatures, however high or low, similarly induce complete adaptation, i.e., will they all appear to fade out totally if stimulation is continued long enough? The uniform finding is that, for areal stimulation, extremes of temperature never proceed to complete adaptation. There is considerable blunting or dulling of the sensation but never total cessation. Hold the hand in chilled water at 10° C. and, so long as the temperature of the medium remains constant, cold sensations will persist indefinitely. The same lack of complete adaptation is found for temperatures of the order of 45° C. Warmth never quite completely disappears. The zone within which total obliteration of thermal sensation can be produced through adaptation is usually put at 16°–42° C. Within this range moderate temperatures reach physiological zero relatively rapidly, while higher and lower temperatures require longer to disappear.

If there is some failure of adaptation to go to completion in the case of extreme temperatures and areal stimulation, there appears to be none where punctiform stimuli are concerned. Warm and cold spots have been subjected to continuous exposure to a wide range of temperatures (15, 196, 171) and, in all instances, complete adaptation has resulted. At extreme temperatures that would fail to extinguish sensation, were they applied to a large areal surface, local stimulation (1.00–1.25 mm diameter) produces total disappearance in a matter of seconds. The course of the fading-out process is generally observed to be an undulating or discontinuous one, especially in the case of warm spots. Adaptation times seem to be less related to the temperature of the stimulus than to the absolute sensitivity of the spot, the initially more responsive spots requiring longer to adapt. Moreover, the after-effects are relatively prolonged and apparently cumulative. A recovery period at least equal to the adaptation time is required to bring the spots back to normal threshold. This factor is, of course, a complicating one in experiments involving serial exploration of spots with temperature stimulators.

Of the several possible interpretations of the facts of thermal adaptation, one is interesting for the parallel it provides with a concept of pressure adaptation already considered. It will be recalled that one way of viewing the fading and ultimate cessation of pressure sensations is to look upon the phenomenon as an instance of stimulus failure. In the presence of a constant objective stimulus the cutaneous tissues readjust themselves; the movement creates sensation, until all tensions have been resolved and no tissue movement can occur. Adaptation is then complete. Very much the same idea has been applied to thermal sensations, ultimate adaptation to a constant temperature being regarded as an instance of stimulus failure. The hypothesis is due to Bazett (18). He has introduced it as part of his theory of thermal gradients (Fig. 77). The mechanism of adaptation would work somewhat as follows: If the arm were to be immersed in water at, say, 38° C. the gradients for warmth sensation should at first be much exaggerated, yielding a positive sensory response. Later, as the tissue is generally warmed the gradients will lose their steepness and eventually flatten out to the point that they no longer have as much as a liminal slope. The stimulus for the receptor has failed; adaptation is complete. At a higher temperature, say 43° C., the gradients are never reduced to a negligible slope, the conditions of positive stimulation remain, and adaptation never proceeds to entire completion. A comparable picture may be built up for cold. This view of thermal adaptation must withstand the same criticisms, of course, that may be urged against the whole theory of thermal gradients (see p. 216), and it may well be that the ultimate gradients in question will turn out to be chemical ones.

Paradoxical Cold and "Heat." In 1895 von Frey made a singular discovery with respect to the behavior of cold spots. He noted that spots previously identified as sensitive to cold would, on occasion, respond with cold sensations if touched with a very warm (45°–50° C.) stimulus. Since it seemed paradoxical that a hot stimulus would yield impressions of cold, the phenomenon was named "paradoxical cold." The range of temperatures adequate for the arousal of paradoxical cold is, of course, well above that necessary to arouse warm spots and only a little below that needed to produce thermal pain. The latter normally has a threshold in the neighborhood of 52° C.

Paradoxical sensations of cold are encountered commonly enough in the mapping of warm spots. Cold sensations in response to other types of stimuli are occasionally found also. Thus the movement of a hair may elicit "flashes of cold." Alternating currents of low frequency applied to the skin by relatively confined electrodes may produce "cold vibration" (119). The fact that cold feelings result from the stimulation of a cold spot, whatever the nature of the effective stimulus, was regarded by von Frey and, indeed, by the vast majority of current theorists as the best possible evidence in support of Johannes Müller's doctrine of "specific nerve energies" and of the clear separation of warmth and cold as qualities belonging to two distinct cutaneous senses.

An analogous phenomenon to paradoxical cold, "paradoxical warmth," is alleged to occur, though even its co-discoverers (Rubin and Goldscheider, in 1912) specified radically different conditions for its arousal. Rubin believed faint warmth could be called forth by stimuli just below (0.1°–1.5° C.) skin temperature. Goldscheider gave 6°–10° C. below physiological zero as the temperature range necessary to paradoxical warmth. The fact seems to be that, if it is a genuine effect at all, the necessary and sufficient conditions have yet to be established. Many have sought it; few have ever reported finding it. In his long series of experiments Bazett reports with conviction on paradoxical warmth only once (*19*). Gilmer states (*119*, p. 324), "Out of a total of approximately 13,000 cold stimulations in this experiment only one report of paradoxical warmth was made. Repeated stimulation of this one spot on several different days failed to bring about another report of the experience." Since warmth, like cold, may occasionally be evoked by mechanical means the suspicion is strong that it is the mechanical rather than the thermal component of the stimulus that is responsible.

An effect presumably dependent on paradoxical cold for its occurrence is that known as psychological "heat." Though the designation is perhaps an unfortunate one, the word "heat" having a common physical meaning, there is no doubt that the phenomenon it refers to is a very real one in experience. The simplest condition for the perception of "heat" is provided by an areal stimulus between 45° and 50° C. applied to a region, such as the forehead or arm, having good warm and cold sensitivity. Under these circumstances there should be aroused warmth (the normal response of warm spots) and in addition cold (paradoxical cold from cold spots). The two sensations fuse to produce an overall impression of intense "heat." To most observers the salient feature of the experience is a stinging quality added to the thermal background.

If psychological heat is indeed a fusion or mixture of warmth and cold sensations it should be possible to produce the effect synthetically, for all that is needed is simultaneous stimulation of warmth and cold (without depending on the latter's paradoxical arousal) in the same general cutaneous area. The experiment is made with the "heat grill" (see Fig. 79), which provides the specified conditions. One alternate set of tubes gives a cold stimulus (12°–15° C.), while the other is warm (42°–44° C.). Though there is nothing really physically "hot" about the grill, the first impression on placing the arm on it is that it actually is dangerously so, and the uninitiated will quickly withdraw to avoid being burned.

This synthesis of psychological heat seems to bear out the analysis. "Heat" is compounded of warmth and cold. Whether it is a stable compound, so to speak, has been debated in what is by now a somewhat involved literature. To some, heat has seemed to be a complete fusion, a new quality which resembles neither warmth nor cold, just as gray is a fusion resembling neither the blue nor yellow of which it may be compounded. Others have viewed it as an imperfect fusion, in which warmth and cold are intermingled with heat. The visual

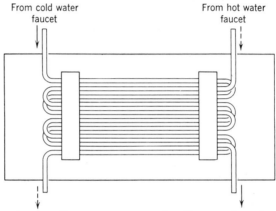

From cold water faucet   From hot water faucet

Fig. 79. The "heat" grill. Warm water and cold water flow through alternate tubes. If a broad skin area, such as the underside of the forearm, is placed firmly on the grill "psychological heat" may be synthesized from mild warmth and cold. From Munn's *Laboratory manual in general experimental psychology.* Boston: Houghton Mifflin, 1948. With the publisher's permission.

analogy for this would be orange which, while neither red nor yellow, resembles both. Perhaps the most interesting result of experiments on synthetic heat has been the demonstration by Alston (*10*) that the stinging heat quality can be produced by simultaneous stimulation of a single cold spot (with cold) and a single warm spot (with warmth). The synthetic perception of heat occurs even though the two spots are separated by as much as 15 cm. This fact, as we shall see, is not easy to accommodate in theory.

The Classical Theory of Temperature Sensitivity. As with pressure and pain, there exists no absolute certainty as to the identity of the end organs responsible for warm and cold sensations. There is no dearth of hypotheses, however, and we are led at once to the realm of theory to build up a picture of how the temperature senses operate. The classic theory is von Frey's. It is that warmth and cold are separately mediated, each having its own set of nerve fibers specific to the quality in question and each system having its own specialized receptor organs. The Krause end bulb is the receptor for cold; the deeper-lying Ruffini cylinder is the end organ for warmth.

The correlations hypothesized by von Frey have never been established as incontrovertible fact. As Dallenbach has pointed out (71), "Von Frey was duly cautious and conservative in stating his theory. He said, 'the end-bulbs are probably for that reason the organs of cold sensation'; 'there appears to me a probable correlation between Ruffini's end-organs and the sense of warmth.' He was, moreover, straightforward in pointing out the defects and weaknesses of his theory. . . . The further we get away from von Frey the more dogmatic in general become the statements regarding his correlation. The writers of textbooks during the first decade following the formulation of the theory were reserved in their statements concerning it, in the next decade they were less so, and during the past decade [1920–1930] the writers have very frequently given the correlation as established fact." In general, Dallenbach's remarks could be extrapolated into the following two decades. Meanwhile, there have been both strengthening and weakening experimental evidences and the appearance on the scene of a rival theory.

This virtue must be attributed to von Frey's theory (or the more dogmatic restatements of his theory): it is specific enough to have served as a powerful stimulus to experimental investigation. In the light of it several important studies were directed at testing the assumed correlations. Perhaps the most spectacular were those of Strughold and Karbe (276). They first amassed considerable presumptive evidence that the Krause end bulb was indeed the receptor organ for cold, finding that: (a) areas of the surface of the eye most sensitive to cold also showed, in anatomical studies, the greatest concentration of Krause end bulbs; (b) cold thresholds were low where end bulbs characteristically lay near the surface, and vice versa; and (c) the count of cold spots was in good agreement with the end-bulb counts made histologically. Their next step was to embark on an experiment in which they undertook, in three subjects, to produce vital staining of the eye. They used an aqueous solution of methylene blue, which has a strong affinity for nervous tissue, and continued to apply it to the surface of the eye at intervals until 1.5 to 2.0 mg had been used. Observation of the sclera with a corneal microscope and slit lamp revealed the successful staining, after several hours, of two end bulbs in one experiment and a group of four in another, while only nerve fibrils responded to the stain in the third. No cold responses could be aroused at the time of staining and, whereas the coloring faded out fairly rapidly, a generally anesthetic condition remained for some time. With a view to future exploration detailed maps were made to serve as guides. Three days after the application of the dye, cold stimuli (tiny wire cylinders, with a round bead at one end) produced weak responses. However, "after 8–10 days there were aroused in the previously marked places clear sensations of cold, while their nearest neighbors proved to be anesthetic or numb." Naturally, Strughold and Karbe concluded that the Krause end bulb was the cold receptor.

Another set of experiments upholding the von Frey correlations is that of Bazett, McGlone, Williams, and Lufkin (21), previously described as the "prepuce experiments." Here the conclusions have to be less direct, since they depend solely on determinations of the population density of cold and warm spots, the calculated depths of the receptors, and histological studies of comparable tissue samples. For cold, the number of spots was found to be 6 to 12 per square centimeter and the depth to be 0.1 mm. About 15 end bulbs of the Krause type per square centimeter were found to be distributed at a depth of about 0.1 mm, just below the arteriovenous region immediately under the papillae. For warmth, the concentration of spots was found to be about 1 per square centimeter, with the receptor lying at a calculated depth of 0.3 mm or a little more. The histological results placed Ruffini cylinders at a depth of about 0.28 mm. Their distribution in the prepuce agreed fairly well with the warm spot count. Bazett's conclusion is constrained, despite the close agreements found. He states (18): "The special receptors for cold and warmth have received provisional, though not absolute, identification."

Other attempts to correlate structure and function have been, in the main, entirely disappointing. Excision experiments extend back to 1885, when Donaldson charted warm and cold spots, extirpated the tissue, and made a histological examination of it. "There were numerous nerves beneath these spots, but these were almost as numerous in neighboring parts. The result . . . is completely negative" (84). Häggqvist, in 1913 (136), similarly found no special end bodies. He did report bundles of smooth muscle tissue under cold spots, a finding which has never been confirmed by anyone since. Pendleton, in 1926 (229), excised tissue at carefully located cold spots; he found nothing of note in the tissue examinations. Dallenbach, in 1927 (70), plotted and replotted warm and cold spots, meticulously controlling for a number of the usually disturbing variables and getting in consequence good test-retest reliabilities. The mapped tissue was then extirpated, incisions being made to a depth of 3 mm, and prepared for histological study. Methylene blue was used as the staining agent. Not a single specialized end organ of any kind was found, though there were numerous nerve fibers and undifferentiated nerve terminations.

Somewhat more encouraging results, from the viewpoint of adherents of the classical theory, came out of the experiments of Belonoschkin in 1933 (*31*). He charted the cold sensitivity of female breast tissue about to be removed for carcinoma and post-operatively searched for nerve endings. Bielschowsky's silver stain was used. In the region of the nipple, where cold sensitivity is such as to present a practically continuous surface of high responsiveness, individual "spots" not being discriminable, nerve terminations were discovered in great profusion. In an area of 160 mm² more than 100 end bodies were present. The commonest had a form resembling the Krause end bulb. However, a diversity of other structures existed also. Simple terminal networks were of frequent occurrence. Other types of specialized endings were identifiable. So many variations appeared, in fact, that Belonoschkin found it useful "not to distinguish between them according to their customary designations but simply to speak of them as encapsulated and non-encapsulated nerve end-bodies." We saw earlier, in our general consideration of the nervous apparatus of the skin, that this view is gaining currency with histologists.

Now, with the major evidences before us, what shall we say of the adequacy of the classical theory of temperature sensitivity? It is clear that it leaves much to be desired. Resting as it does chiefly upon an assumed correlation between distribution of sensitivity and distribution of end organs, it cannot be said to be in a firm position so long as equally well-performed experiments point to diametrically opposed conclusions with respect to that correlation. As matters now stand we shall have to suspend judgment. Krause end bulbs and Ruffini cylinders may eventually prove to be specialized receptors for cold and warmth. That they are *the* receptors is far from having been established. On the basis of certain of the findings one might as readily conclude for free nerve endings as temperature organs, and yet, as has been seen, both pressure and pain can make some legitimate claims to these also. There is obviously much more to be learned before any of the systems of cutaneous sensitivity can be unequivocally assigned to a particular type of receptor organ.

The Neurovascular Theory. The chief rival to von Frey's formulation is Nafe's neurovascular theory, first elaborated in the early 1930's and the subject of much discussion and no little controversy since then. Taking as a primary consideration the essential intimacy of relation between warmth and cold, forming as they do a single continuum passing through physiological zero, Nafe looked for one mechanism that might be responsible for both kinds of sensitivity. The only adequately distributed tissue which, moreover, might contain sensory nerve endings capable of generating impulses for temperature sensations he believes to be the smooth muscle walls of the blood vessels of the skin. As we know, the smallest of these extend to the upper reaches of the corium, vascular loops being common inhabitants of the papillae. Capillaries would seem not to be candidates; they are non-muscular and are not supplied with sensory nerves. Venules are possibilities but appear not to have a sufficiently rich innervation to serve the purpose. The arterioles, then, are likely prospects. These and the smaller arteries house in their smooth muscle walls (at least in the outermost layers, the *adventitia* and *tunica media*) both afferent and efferent nerve terminations. Sensory termini in the forms of free nerve endings, button-like endings, and terminal loops are found. They can be traced chiefly to relatively large myelinated fibers, though some have small myelinated and unmyelinated parent fibers. Contraction and relaxation of arteriolar walls could set up trains of impulses in afferent nerves which, at the brain, could say "warm" or "cold." Temperature sensations are then, under this theory, kinesthetic sensations; they are proprioceptions of arteriolar movements.

The direct responses of smooth muscle tissue to thermal changes are such as to suggest that the correlations of movement and sensation necessary to a neurovascular theory of temperature sensitivity are possible. Nafe cites Sir Thomas Lewis as having shown (198) that denervated smooth muscle tissue responds directly to warmth by relaxation, to cold by contraction. These are then the assumed correlations. In response to a warm stimulus the arterioles dilate because their smooth muscle walls relax. Cold produces contraction of the arteriolar walls and constriction of the vessels. The pattern of nerve impulses created by relaxation (providing it is rapid enough) is interpreted as warmth; that produced by contraction is interpreted as cold (again, assuming the contraction to be vigorous enough).

Nafe also sees in the reactions of smooth muscle to relatively extreme temperatures the possible bases for "heat" and for thermally aroused pain. Table 5 reproduces his assumptions with respect to the action of smooth muscle at different temperatures and the accompanying sensory events.

It is to be noted that "heat," with its pricking quality, is assumed to result from the complete constriction of scattered muscle elements in

TABLE 5. THE CORRELATIONS ASSUMED BY NAFE'S NEUROVASCULAR THEORY

After J. P. Nafe (218), p. 1055

Experience	Temperature (°C.)	Action of Smooth Muscle
Pain		Spastic contraction
	52	
Heat	45	Constricting elements in dilating muscle
Warm		Relaxation
Zero	33	Physiological zero
Cold		Contraction
	12	
"Cold heat"		Muscle elements showing severe constriction in general contraction
	3	
Pain		Spastic contraction

a general background of relaxation. Presumably those elements having the highest contractibility introduce the painful note. This happens normally just above 45° C. At about 52° C. all or nearly all elements have constricted maximally, and pain alone is felt. "Cold heat" and the pain associated with extremely low temperatures are analogous occurrences at the other end of the scale. Here, however, the constricting elements superpose their effects on a general background of contraction. The essential continuity of the warm-cold series and the further continuity with heat-pain and cold-pain must be counted as strong supporting considerations for the neurovascular theory.

Several other temperature phenomena find ready interpretation within the framework of the theory. The shift of physiological zero with temperature adaptation and the resulting changes in warm and cold thresholds speak most strongly for a theory based on a single underlying mechanism. The occurrence of warm and cold sensations, reflexly aroused through vasomotor action as in the case of chills during fever, finds ready interpretation and may well constitute one of the best lines of evidence favoring the neurovascular theory. This would be true, of course, of any temperature theory (such as Bazett's restatement of the von Frey doctrine) that recognized the importance of blood vessels in the general temperature economy of the skin. The failure of high test-retest reliabilities to appear in the mapping of temperature spots—what we have spoken of as the "fickleness" of warm and cold spots—finds some accountability in the neurovascular theory.

The shifting of responsive points may be due to changes in state of tonus of the blood vessels. They are known to have their contractile state altered by blood pressure changes, variations in blood content, and other autonomous and reflex effects, including emotional reactions. The observational properties of warmth and cold also "make sense" in terms of the theory. Cold ordinarily puts in its appearance in an abrupt, clear, and well-defined manner, whereas warmth is more gentle in its mode of occurrence, "welling up" rather than "flashing out." Arteriolar contractions are more prompt and definite responses than dilatations. Even paradoxical cold produces no embarrassment for the theory. Smooth muscle is known to respond to intense stimuli with contraction, especially if the stimulus has a mechanical component, and it has been chiefly in connection with very warm thermal-mechanical stimulation that paradoxical cold is most commonly reported.

Not all is clear sailing for the neurovascular theory, however. Some serious objections may be urged against it. One wonders first about the obvious facts of relative distribution of warmth and cold. If the same underlying mechanism is responsible for both, why should the two have such radically different distributions? Why are there so many more cold spots than warm spots? Why do maps of the former yield so many discrete points as compared with the latter, and why do not warm spot maps fit exactly over those for cold? Moreover, if they are generated by impulses passing over the same fibers and constitute products of one and the same mechanism, why do not cold and warmth have similarities in observation? Why do not cold and warmth feel alike? If they are both basically kinesthetic in origin there should be some resemblances in their felt patterns, and yet they seem to be characterized more by a sharp qualitative difference than by similarity.

A number of other established facts find no ready explanation in the neurovascular theory. Why should an increase in concomitant pressure bring with it an increase in number of warmth responses, as found by Heiser and McNair (162)? One would suppose that either heat or paradoxical cold would result, since the direct action of mechanical stimuli on relaxed smooth muscle tissue is to produce contraction. Why is the two-point limen, the separation of two punctiform stimuli that can just be discriminated as two, larger for warmth than for cold, and why is the normal error of localization for warmth greater than for cold? A mechanism common to warmth and cold should not produce differences of this sort. Why are the facts of intermittent stimulation with radiant heat as they are? It has been shown that a "critical fusion point" for radiant heat can be established; discrete and temporally equally spaced warm stimuli yield a continuous feeling of warmth when repeated every half-second or thereabouts. Picturing the direct responses of arterioles to such a mode of stimulation, one would suppose that a typical summation of smooth muscle responses might ensue and that the effect of such repeated stimuli might be tetanus (heat, then heat-pain?) or, at least, alternation of relaxation and contraction (alternate warmth and cold). How account for the findings of Alston (10) with respect to the generation of the heat experience from single warm and cold spots separated by as much as 10 or 15 cm? There is hardly provided a "general body of relaxation" within which constricting elements can operate, as demanded by the theory.

Many of the foregoing objections to the neurovascular theory deal with minutiae, of course, and it should be hastily added that the classical theory of temperature does no better with them. However, a completely satisfactory theory must deal with them. The basic difficulty with the neurovascular theory seems to be that, invoking as it does a complex and as yet only poorly understood mechanism, it both predicts too little and too much. One can find in the physiological literature of smooth muscle responses instances of nearly every kind of reaction. Thus, for example, although a strong mechanical stimulus produces sudden contraction of relaxed smooth muscle, such a stimulus, applied to partially contracted muscle, may produce a sudden relaxation. Why should not paradoxical warmth occur commonly and predictably, then? These are the necessary conditions for it. Other instances of unrealized predictions could be cited.

It is yet too early to attempt a final evaluation of the neurovascular theory. That it possesses both virtues and defects is apparent from the foregoing. In general, it meets the requirements of a good theory in that it comes into harmony with a fair share of the established facts in the temperature realm and it is, moreover, eminently testable. What is needed is serious investigation conducted in the light of it. Until much more is known about the reactions of arterioles in situ and of the correlations between their responses and sensitivity changes we shall not be in a position to decide whether blood vessels play a primary role or only a supporting one in temperature reception.

Nerve as Temperature Receptor. So accustomed have we become to thinking in terms of specialized receptor organs to perform particular jobs of energy absorption and conversion—rods and cones for light, hair cells of the organ of Corti for sound, and the plethora of encapsulated and free nerve endings for the various forms of energy impinging on the skin—that the possibility that no such specialization may be needed for temperature has pretty much escaped us. The observation has been made, however, that nerve fibers themselves have an interesting response to the direct application of thermal stimuli and, in fact, meet certain of the specifications for a thermal receptor. Not many of the details have been worked out as yet, but some of the fundamental phenomena, which at least indicate the possibilities, have been described by Bernhard and Granit (33). Rapid warming or cooling of a mammalian nerve preparation is found to set up a local electric current at the point of application of the thermal stimulus. This disturbance, the so-called electrotonic current, is capable of initiating a discharge in the nerve and, so long as the potential created by the temperature change is maintained, will continue to produce a train of nerve discharges. The cooled or warmed portion of the nerve is electronegative relative to the region at normal temperature. Apparently local thermal imbalance is an adequate stimulus for direct nervous discharge. The heat flow may be in either direction. It is important only that it be of a sufficiently high order of magnitude. This effect is not to be confused with a more general one, known for a long time, in accordance with which nerves discharge at one or another frequency, depending on the temperature to which they are subjected. Generally, cold suppresses and heat enhances nerve response, though an optimal temperature has also been shown to exist in some experiments. These more general effects can be demonstrated by slow warming and cooling. The active potentials here in question are strictly local ones and may be created in sufficient strength to produce a nerve discharge when a drop of only 1° C. is involved. In the intact organism, surrounded by what must be considered to be far more favorable circumstances for stimulation, a much greater sensitivity must be realized.

It would be ironic if, after years of debate as to whether the specialized receptors for warmth and cold are Krause end bulbs and Ruffini cylinders or sensory endings in arterioles, it should turn out that there are no specialized endings at all but that nerve is its own receptor for temperature. Time—and a great deal of experimentation—will be needed to provide an answer.

12

Kinesthetic and Organic Sensibilities

"Deep" Sensibility and Kinesthesis. All receptor systems thus far considered—those for vision, hearing, and the cutaneous senses—may be classed, according to the scheme introduced by Sherrington (258) long ago, as *exteroceptors*. All sense organs belonging to this class are stimulated from without the body and provide knowledge of events external to it. The chemical senses, smell and taste, likewise belong in the exteroceptive category. Many internal bodily changes also have their effects on receptor organs and result in sensation. These organs are the *interoceptors* and have as their receptive field the gastro-intestinal tract. We shall encounter them later as the mediators of the so-called "organic" sensations.

Between the outer and inner bodily surfaces there exist other sense organs—in subcutaneous tissues, in the walls of deep-lying blood vessels, in muscles and tendons, in the coverings of bones (periosteum), and at the articulations of bones. Because these receptors are stimulated mainly by actions of the body itself they are called *proprioceptors*. This class of sense organs also includes, according to the original classification of Sherrington, the very special receptor system which is located in the non-auditory labyrinth of the inner ear and which, through the generation of an elaborate set of postural reflexes, is responsible for the maintenance of general bodily equilibrium.

Separate study of the receptors lying between the outer and inner walls of the body is not easy to arrange, and there is consequently something of a dearth of reliable information concerning them. If they are stimulated in their normal surroundings other tissues containing responsive nerve terminations are necessarily involved, thus producing confusion in experience. If they are investigated in physiological preparations the data are then restricted to electrophysiological indications, and the picture of the sensory process is only indirectly obtained and quite incomplete. Of course, it is possible to approach certain of the deep-lying receptor systems by way of the body surface, eliminating either by anesthetization or surgery the contributions of the purely cutaneous nervous components. This was what was done by Goldscheider in a series of experiments in which he investigated deep pressures and pains after dulling the overlying skin with cocaine. This was also what was done by Henry Head and a succession of researchers who repeated his experiment of dividing the median cutaneous nerve and rendering anesthetic a substantial area of the forearm and hand (see pp. 204–207).

It was, in fact, in connection with Head's original work that the designation "deep sensibility" first came into being. Upon severing the nerve and testing in the center of the affected skin area he found that, whereas light pressure, needle prick, and temperature stimuli aroused no response, heavy pressure evoked a deeply localized feeling of dull pressure which, if increased in intensity, passed over into dull pain. Presumably subcutaneous nerve endings were being stimulated. Just how deeply situated they were it would be important to know. Head believed them to be terminations of sensory nerves running their courses with motor nerves and thus unaffected by destruction of superficially disposed sensory nerves like the median cutaneous. The endings involved could, of course, be free terminations extending no further toward the surface than into the connective and adipose tissues of the subcutaneous regions. There are known to be many such. The endings could have been Pacinian corpuscles; in some parts of the body deep-lying tissues are somewhat freely supplied with these large, encapsulated end organs. Were sensory nerve terminations in muscles, tendons, and joints brought into play? They could conceivably have been. We know little of the distorting forces necessary to arouse these receptors. Possibly heavy pressures exerted on the skin are conducted to underlying muscles and bones with sufficiently small loss to be effective there.

Such "passive" appreciation of pressure properly comes within the meaning of "deep sensibility," as conceived by Head. A far more important set of sensations—important for its consequences in behavior— is that comprising the mass of feeling generated by movements of the body itself. This kind of sensitivity has been known, since the origination of the term by Bastian in 1880 (45, p. 525), as kinesthesis (literally, "feeling of motion"). Here belong the more or less continuous—and little-attended—sensations originating in muscles, tendons, and joints. Bastian included the labyrinthine receptors as part of the "kinesthetic" system. Current usage tends, in most contexts, to restrict the term "kinesthesis" to feelings aroused by movements of muscles, tendons, and joints or, in Goldscheider's terminology, the muscular, tendinous, and articular senses. Had they any peculiar qualities to contribute to experience these sensations would perhaps be better known and would receive distinctive names. As it is, they seem only to yield pressures and, very occasionally, pains. Their patterns are generally massive ones, deeply and diffusely localized and, moreover, combined in a multitude of ways with sensations arising from the superficial cutaneous senses. All of this makes observation of kinesthetic patterns difficult and uncertain. However, some facts are established.

Relative Roles of the Kinesthetic Receptors. It was originally discovered by Goldscheider, in a notable series of experiments (*122, 123*), that the appreciation of passive movement imparted to the limbs comes chiefly from the joints rather than from the muscles. By cocainizing the overlying skin and muscles he was able to show that the "articular sense," joint sensibility, was mainly responsible for providing the sense data upon which discrimination of limb movement depends. Contrariwise, passing strong faradic currents through the joints rendered them much less sensitive, greatly elevating thresholds for the detection of movement. Historically, Goldscheider's discovery represented an interesting turn of events, for, since the days of Charles Bell (c. 1826), the "muscle sense" had been pretty generally looked on as a sixth sense (to be added to Aristotle's original five), and it was believed that receptors embedded in muscle were chiefly responsible for originating the feelings underlying appreciation of posture, weight, resistance, and bodily movement.

Other proofs of the importance of the role of joint sensibility come from abnormalities. Cases are known in which anesthesia has invaded the muscles and overlying skin with, however, full retention of articular sensitivity. In such instances there is little, if any, disturbance of the ability to perceive passive movement in the affected limb. The converse type of pathological separation of function is also known. Bone disease may abolish the joint receptors and yet leave the muscles and skin unaffected. Here the result is also the predicted one; capacity to appreciate posture and movement is destroyed.

Discrimination of motion at joints proves, on measurement, to be remarkably good. Goldscheider (*op. cit.*) devoted a lengthy and thoroughly systematic set of experiments to threshold determinations, over 4000 observations being entailed. Whether measured in terms of the minimum angular displacement that could be detected (rate of movement being held constant) or in terms of the minimum velocity of motion that was discriminable, it was found that, of the nine joints tested, the shoulder was the most sensitive and the ankle was the least. Displacements of 0.22 to 0.42 degree (at a speed of 0.3 degree/sec) could be discerned at the shoulder. The wrist and knuckle of the index finger were nearly as sensitive (0.26–0.42 degree and 0.34–0.43 degree, respectively), while the ankle required relatively larger displacements (1.15–1.30 degrees). More recent measurements by Laidlaw and Hamilton (192) on 60 normal subjects yielded results generally in agreement with Goldscheider's figures, thresholds at different joints varying on the average between roughly 0.2 and 0.7 degree, though in these experiments the speed of movement was much less (10 degrees/min). The hip proved to be somewhat more sensitive than the shoulder, and the main joint of the big toe (the metatarsophalangeal, not measured by Goldscheider) gave the highest values of the 12 joints investigated. In both sets of results it is clear that movement at the larger and more important joints, such as the hip and shoulder, is apprehended somewhat more readily than at the finger and toe articulations.

For the appreciation of movement of a limb, whether the motion is passively imparted to it or actively initiated by the organism, the best evidence seems to indicate, then, that receptors in the neighborhood of joints are primarily responsible for providing the raw data on which the perception of such motion depends. What of the role of receptor organs situated in muscle and tendon?

Their importance seems to lie chiefly in the feelings of strain added to the total kinesthetic picture when resistance to limb movement is encountered. Let something more than the normal demand of moving bones be placed upon their attached muscles, and evidence for feelings originating in muscular and tendinous tissue becomes evident by direct observation. Either require a heavy weight to be lifted or, more vividly still, continuously exercise a muscle group under conditions of diminished blood supply (by applying a tourniquet above it), and the feeling of strain—and, eventually, ache or even sharp pain— will assert itself. Most muscles and tendons are, indeed, well supplied with sensory endings. In the case of muscles the innervation is a somewhat complex one.

Kinesthetic Receptor Organs. Since the extensive and painstaking work of the British physiologist, B. H. C. Matthews (207, 208), the end organs responsible for initiating proprioceptive messages have been quite well understood. Four sets of receptors are involved, two in muscle proper, one in tendon, and one in the fascia associated with muscle. Matthews has designated them, respectively: A_1, A_2, B, and C endings. The anatomical arrangement of all but the last type is illustrated in Fig. 80.

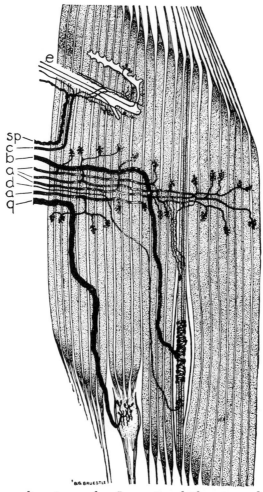

Fig. 80. Nerve endings in muscle. Innervation, both motor and sensory, of a group of muscle fibers. Motor neurones are those marked a. Three kinds of sensory fibers subserving kinesthesis are shown: Matthews' Type A_1 ("flower-spray" endings) at the termination of fiber d; Type A_2 (annulospiral endings) at the end of b; and Type B (Golgi tendon organs) terminating g. The structure labeled e is a small blood vessel innervated by sensory fiber c (pain?) and a sympathetic plexus, sp. From Fulton, *101*. By permission of Oxford University Press.

The form of termination picturesquely called "flower-spray ending" is the A_1 type and is found, in the diagram, at the end of the small-diameter fiber, d. A_1 fibers are found to be stimulated by passive stretch of the muscle. Active contraction brings about an abrupt cessation of A_1 activity. A slight tension exerted on the muscle invariably brings the flower-spray endings back into play, and a strong, sudden stretch may excite a sufficiently high level of activity to produce sensory impulses from A_1 at frequencies up to 500 per second. A_1, then, signals muscle stretch and makes no report during active contraction. About 50% of the fibers in muscle are of the A_1 type.

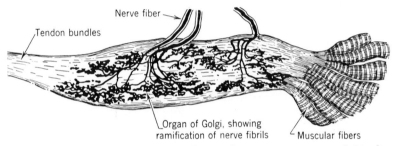

Fig. 81. Kinesthetic receptors in tendon. The B-type receptors of Matthews (207, 208) or Golgi tendon organs. From Lickley, 200. By permission of Longmans, Green and Company, New York.

A_2 fibers (b in the diagram) are of larger diameter, hence more prompt to report. However, situated as their endings are, they provide much the same data as do the A_1 type. They likewise normally respond to stretch by initiating impulses and cease firing upon active contraction of the muscle. However, the terminations of A_2 (called "annulospiral" endings) do show heightened activity during a very strong contraction. This is presumably because they are wound around so-called "intrafusal" fibers, modified red muscle cells which also contract when the main body of the muscle contracts vigorously. Then the annulospiral endings are stimulated mechanically. Both A_1 and A_2 fibers will continue to fire with great regularity when the muscle is slightly stretched. They adapt very slowly, an important characteristic in a mechanism reporting postural adjustments.

Receptors of the B type are presumably the tendon organs of Golgi (see Fig. 80, g, and Fig. 81). These have been known since 1880, though no clear records of the responses of their attached fibers became available until the experiments of Matthews. B receptors have higher thresholds than do either A_1 or A_2. However, they respond with some regularity to tension, however it is imposed. Thus they signal both stretch and active contraction. Measurements of action potentials in their attached fibers show that their response (impulse frequency) is roughly proportional to the common logarithm of the tension. B receptors are, then, general tension recorders, and their function is somewhat less specialized than those of the A_1 and A_2 types.

The receptor designated "C" by Matthews is perhaps the Pacinian corpuscle. Unlike the other forms of proprioceptors, this encapsulated ending is found to adapt very quickly. If the fascial sheaths of muscles are cut away the C type ending disappears. In any case they are few in number and cannot be very important in the total picture of muscular response. They do, however, go into action during muscle movements, as do endings of the B type. The suspicion is strong that their contribution is to report mechanical deformations whether imposed from without ("deep pressure") or from within (muscle movement).

The foregoing analysis of the receptor systems in and around muscle is complete except for the omnipresent free nerve ending. Muscles are, of course, highly vascularized tissues, and blood vessels are sensitive structures. At least, they are well supplied with sensory nerves of the freely terminating variety. Whereas many of these doubtless have the primary duty of initiating reflex reactions concerned in the maintenance of thermal equilibrium, it is perhaps also the case that they can arouse sensation. Small, unmyelinated endings are found distributed widely throughout muscle, tendon, fascia, ligaments, and joints. The exquisite pains associated with muscle cramps and sprains, the severe aches connected with muscles exercised under conditions of diminished blood supply, and the breathtaking sharp pains consequent upon puncturing the fascia with a needle all bespeak a wealth of sensory innervation, and the free nerve ending is, of course, suspect as the originating agent. The details are as yet obscure, but the weight of evidence favors the interpretation that, in all these subdermal organs as in the skin, the free nerve ending is a pain receptor. As in the skin, whether it is *the* pain receptor future research will have to decide.

Organic Sensibility: Visceral Sensation. It has long been a commonplace in surgical experience that organs of the abdominal viscera may be freely manipulated, even squeezed, torn, or cauterized without benefit of anesthetic, provided only that traction on the mesentery and direct mechanical or thermal stimulation of the body wall be avoided. Visceral organs are, in general, peculiarly undemonstrative. Anatomically, it is the case that there are far more motor fibers supplying the viscera than there are sensory fibers reporting on their action. Moreover, the vast majority of afferents from the viscera have nothing to do with sensation. They are exclusively concerned with the mediation of reflexes, themselves controlled at relatively low levels of the central nervous system, which are necessary to the maintenance of the vast and intricate economy involved in circulation, respiration, digestion, excretion, and related vegetative functions.

However, it is not the case, as has frequently been stated, that "the viscera are insensitive." They are only relatively so. On occasions, when large distending forces are present (e.g., "gas pains"), or when their smooth muscle tissues go into a state of strong contraction (spasm, "cramps"), or when subjected to the action of unusual chemical irritants, certain of the viscera are demonstrative enough. It is no solace to the angina sufferer or the victim of a kidney stone to be told that "the viscera are insensitive"; he knows better, at least about some of them. But the large and sudden distentions responsible for such pains are not of usual or normal occurrence, and, fortunately, enough is known about their neural bases to permit a certain amount of management of them. A generality which is useful here is that pains originating in organs of the viscera are reported almost exclusively over fibers belonging to the sympathetic division of the autonomic nervous system. Contrariwise, afferent impulses concerned in visceral regulatory reflexes and in reporting non-painful visceral sensations are conducted over parasympathetic fibers. There are known exceptions to this rule in the case of some of the pelvic organs, e.g., the bladder. This clear separation of function makes possible a variety of neurosurgical attacks on persistent and unbearable pain arising from visceral sources. By stripping the artery supplying the organ (since sympathetic axons usually follow the artery closely), removing the appropriate sympathetic ganglia, cutting several posterior roots at the proper cord level, or sectioning the anterolateral tract of the cord it becomes possible to interrupt the pain pathway without seriously disturbing the normal functioning of the organ so denervated.

By any practical criterion the problem of pain is, of course, the most urgent one to raise in connection with the visceral organs. But, as has been intimated, some of the viscera are capable of yielding other sensory patterns, several of them such as hunger, thirst, and nausea quite elaborate in their modes of appearance. Organs of the alimentary tract can, up to a point, be explored for their sensitivity to mechanical pressure, electric currents, and thermal changes. With somewhat less accuracy their reactions to chemical stimuli can be ascertained also. In the majority of the few studies directed at revealing normal sensitivity of the gastrointestinal tract the technique has been that of the stomach balloon. Varying pressures, with slow or rapid onset, can be produced by inflation of the balloon, and the pneumatic system can itself be used as a recording device for muscular contractions of the stomach wall. Thermal sensitivity can be investigated by means of a simple stomach tube through which is conducted hot or cold water, a smaller rubber tube running through the larger one carrying the wires of a thermocouple to record temperature of the stomachic contents. Similar techniques may be used for studying responses to pressure and thermal stimulation of the colon. Electrical sensitivity of the esophagus has been demonstrated with the use of a stomach tube bearing on its external surface a series of metal rings, each capable of serving as an "active" electrode in the stimulation process.

The classic study here is that of Boring (41, 42), who, repeating many of the earlier experiments that had yielded conflicting results and at the same time avoiding many of the previous errors of control, was able to show that parts of the gastrointestinal tract are sensitive to pressure, warmth, cold, and chemical stimuli. The pressures effective for the alimentary canal are not those of contact or simple deformation but relatively large distending ones. Slow inflation of a rubber balloon against the walls of the esophagus (or the colon) results in the eventual arousal of a broad pattern of muscular pressure. Rapid inflation may produce deeply localized pain or ache. Release of air pressure from the balloon promptly brings the painful or pressural feelings to an end. Similar pressure variations introduced in the stomach proper are without effect. However, the stomach does prove to be thermally sensitive, as is also the esophagus. An increase in stomach temperature of 5° F., brought about within 6 sec by pouring 25 cc water at 60° C. through a stomach tube, is felt as warm. A similar amount of icewater will reduce stomach temperature by 5° C. in the same period of time and will be felt as cold. That these changes are appreciated by way of deep-lying receptors in the stomach tissue is attested by the fact that skin temperatures, recorded simultaneously from the adjacent body wall, remain virtually constant throughout such experiments. Thermal conduction to cutaneous receptors thus cannot be responsible. Chemical stimuli such as alcohol, oil of peppermint, and mustard in suspension introduced directly to the stomach by way of a rubber tube can be appreciated.

Localization of visceral sensations is not infrequently faulty. So constant and reproducible is the error of localization in the case of certain pains that the phenomenon constitutes a commonplace of clinical practice, so-called *referred pain.* The classical example of referred visceral pain is that associated with angina pectoris. An acute pain arising in the heart is localized in the chest wall and is felt to radiate outward to the underside of the arm. Another clearly recognizable instance of referred visceral pain is that occurring in renal colic. A stone passing down the ureter produces a sharp pain which, however, appears not to move but to be referred constantly to the groin. This happens despite the anatomical fact that the upper end of the ureter is situated under the last rib! Not all referred pains involve such large errors of localization, nor are all referred pains of visceral origin. Certain somatic pains, e.g., those originating in the margins of the diaphragm, may be referred considerable distances away from the site of stimulation. In general it seems that those sensations which have a fairly superficial and easily identifiable mode of initiation tend to be localized with some accuracy; those having a deeper origin are subject to larger localization errors. The full explanation of this is not obvious. It may be that the relative infrequency with which deeply disposed tissues are ever restimulated in identical fashion militates against the building up of a localization schema for these organs. Localization, so far as present evidence attests, is a product of learning, and, hidden from sight as the viscera are, the chances are remote of learning directly much about one's own viscera and particularly of verifying the sources of their stimulation.

Much of the apparent mystery surrounding the faulty localizations of "referred" sensations disappears when attention is paid to the underlying neurological facts. Spread of excitation within a dermatome (see p. 172) is a natural consequence of the intimacy of neurological relationship existing within a given spinal segment. Especially in the case of the strong stimuli necessary to the production of visceral pain, "flooding over" at the spinal level is to be expected. It is not surprising, therefore, that a common reference for pain is to the opposite side of the body to that affected, localization being in the area of the corresponding dermatomal segment. Nor is it surprising, once the dermatomal projections of the spinal segments have been studied, that certain unilateral anomalies of localization should occur. In the instance of the seemingly odd radiation of anginal pain into the left arm, for instance, it is actually the case that the same thoracic segment that sends fibers into the chest area over the heart also innervates the inner side of the upper arm. "Synthetic" angina has been produced by Lewis and Kellgren (*199*) by injecting the appropriate interspinous ligament with 5% saline solution, which produces a strong irritation of the spinal center and pain projected to its dermatome. The pain in this case was indistinguishable in localization from that of true angina pectoris.

One interesting anomaly of localization is that occurring in the esophagus. It may be noted that very cold or hot food seems to disappear, on being swallowed, only to reappear in the stomach region. The supposition would be that the esophagus is thermally anesthetic. Actually, if the esophagus is explored carefully it is found to be sensitive throughout its length to both warmth and cold. Why, then, the apparent contradiction between everyday experience and experimental result? This question was answered by Boring, who performed the instructive experiment (41) of electrically stimulating five levels of the esophagus, separated evenly by 5-cm spaces. The subjects were required to localize each internal stimulation by pointing to the appropriate place on the chest or neck. Whereas all five loci were effective, it turned out that there is not a one-to-one correspondence between position within the esophagus and that of the overlying thoracic wall. Stimulations near the upper and lower ends of the esophagus were fairly accurately localized; there was a tendency for higher stimulations to be referred upward to a point above the clavicle, while the lowest tended to be shifted still further down, below the end of the sternum. Stimulations in the middle reaches of the esophagus were rarely accurately localized, being commonly referred either up or down. Sometimes they had a double reference, both up and down.

Organic Sensory Patterns: Hunger. It was suspected more than a hundred years ago that hunger pangs have their origin in contractions of the stomach walls. Ernst Weber, writing in 1846, said that "strong contraction of the muscle fibers of the wholly empty stomach, whereby its cavity disappears, makes a part of the sensation which we call hunger." Weber's conclusion was based on surmise; it remained for Cannon and Washburn (54), in 1912, to furnish experimental proof. Their technique was that of the stomach balloon. (See Fig. 82.)

Over a period of several weeks Washburn, the observer, introduced daily to his stomach a tube terminating in a small balloon. For several hours each day the tube was carried about, balloon in the stomach, until Washburn was thoroughly habituated to it. Then, when records were to be taken, the balloon was gently inflated to conform with the stomach walls. The stomach tube was joined to a manometer, and a float on its mercury column recorded on a kymograph variations in gastric size. A pneumograph was also attached about the waist to record any movements of the abdominal muscles. Washburn, out of sight of the kymograph, pressed a key whenever he felt hunger pangs.

As the record in Fig. 82 reveals, hunger indications were found to coincide exactly with the occurrence of powerful stomach contractions. The contractions were fairly rhythmic ones, each developing to a peak and subsiding again within a span of about 30 sec. They recurred at a frequency of 30–40 per minute, though this was somewhat variable from one hunger episode to another. In any given "attack" of hunger the contractions are likely to begin somewhat feebly, long periods of

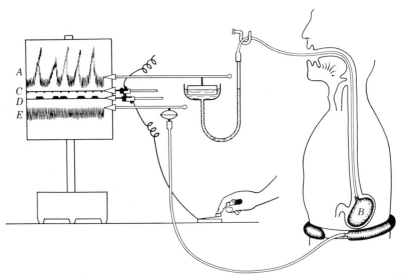

FIG. 82.   Recording of hunger contractions.   The Cannon-Washburn technique (*54*), devised in 1911 and widely used since, for revealing motions of the stom-ach wall in hunger.   Note the correspondences between record *D*, which registers hunger pangs, and record *A*, which is of stomach contractions.   *C* is a time line, *E* a record of abdominal breathing.   From Cannon, *53*.

relative quiescence separating them.   As time goes on the contractions become more powerful and recur with greater frequency.   Assuming that nothing is done to assuage the hunger, the series of contractions may be prolonged for an hour or more or, somewhat more typically, may run its course in one-half to three-quarters of an hour.   The peaks of contraction may be as few as 20 or as many as 70.

The coincidence of stomach contractions and hunger pangs is cer-tainly not accidental.   Since the original Cannon and Washburn ex-periment gastric contractions in relation to hunger have been studied by many, notably by the Chicago physiologist, Carlson, and his students.   Always the one-to-one correspondence between the sensory and the gastric events has been demonstrated.   The simple conclusion would seem to be indicated that feelings of hunger are caused by stomach contractions and thus are kinesthetic sensations of a certain pattern. However, the mere fact that gastric contractions can be shown to be taking place when hunger is reported does not prove that vigorous motion of the stomach wall is either sufficient or necessary to arouse hunger feelings. Both events may be traceable to another, more deeply seated mechanism. That strong contractions are not of themselves *sufficient* to produce hunger pangs is demonstrated time and again in gastric records. Violent contractions may occur in the absence of any experienced hunger. There is, of course, nothing surprising about this; stimulation, however strong, does not necessarily result in either sensation or response. Inattention, fatigue, or some other inhibitory influence may prevent it. That stomach movements may not be necessary to hunger is a conclusion forced by clinical experience. In a case in which the stomach was totally removed and the esophagus joined directly to the intestines (297) desire for food continued to be felt, and the patient ate normally. Similar implications are involved in the finding that rats surgically deprived of their stomachs will perform normally in maze learning even though the "hunger drive" is used as a motivating force. The same animals show as much activity in hunting food as normal rats do, and they yield normal scores on an obstruction apparatus designed to measure the strength of the "hunger drive."

It is at this point in the search for an explanation of hunger that ambiguity of meaning begins to perform a disservice. "Hunger" is at once the name for an organic sensory pattern, the "pangs" or "aching pain" experienced when the stomach is empty, and also for the desire for food or urge to eat—in short, appetite. If eating were entirely a matter of satisfying hunger pangs, meals would become very brief affairs, for the first few mouthfuls of food are sufficient to reduce the strong gastric contractions to a level subliminal for sensation. Food is not the only agent having this effect. Even non-nutritive and indigestible substances—bits of leather, moss, or clay—will temporarily allay hunger pangs. Swallowing hard, tightening the belt, or smoking will do the same. It is well known that strong emotions will promptly produce a thoroughgoing cessation of all digestive activities. The prolongation of eating, then, is not in the interest of satisfying hunger pangs but must be accounted for somewhat more elaborately in terms of deep-seated desire or motivation—what it would be better always to call appetite. It is appetite, not hunger, that gets us as far along in a meal as dessert.

The origin of hunger contractions themselves is still veiled in mystery, though some facts concerning the relation between them and the organism's need for food have been unearthed. Blood transfused from a starved dog into a satiated one will set up vigorous gastric contractions in the latter. Conversely, blood from a recently fed dog will inhibit stomach contractions in a starving one. Clearly there is a chemical principle at work here. What is it? At one time the answer seemed entirely obvious and simple. Blood sugar level was thought to control the hunger mechanism. A deficiency of blood sugar, brought about either by abstention from food or by the use of insulin, has been shown to augment gastric contractions. Also, glucose injected into the blood stream will, under some circumstances, abolish hunger contractions. However, the close correlation between the onset of hunger and fluctuation of blood sugar concentration that would be predicted on the basis of these relationships did not materialize as further experiments were performed. Apparently the answer is somewhat more complicated than was at first suspected. Perhaps a "hunger hormone," as yet unidentified, is at work. Possibly the genesis of hunger contractions is to be found in the workings of central neural mechanisms rather than the peripheral ones that seem to have been favored up to now by the experimental evidence. The facts yield themselves up slowly, and a final conclusion is not yet in sight.

Organic Sensory Patterns: Thirst. Just as hunger seems to be most immediately connected with strong contractions of the stomach walls, sensations of thirst can be shown to be set off by dryness of the mouth and throat. That local conditions in the throat region are directly related to thirst sensations is not only the conclusion from experience; it can be demonstrated by experiment as well. Any set of conditions which will produce drying of the tissues of the mouth and throat will induce thirst in some degree. Thus the breathing of hot dry air, the chewing of desiccated foods such as crackers, or prolonged speaking or singing are familiar thirst-provoking situations. In all these the normally moist surfaces of the buccal cavity become partially dehydrated, and distressful feelings of dryness and stickiness result. Very intense thirst may be induced experimentally by the subcutaneous injection of atropine. In one such experiment Cannon (52, Chap. 16) measured the output of the salivary glands before the injection of atropine and found it to be 13.5 cc for a 5-min sample. After the drug had fully taken effect the flow was reduced to 1.0 cc, and "all the feelings that were noted in ordinary thirst—the sense of dry surfaces, the stickiness of the moving parts, the difficulties of speaking and swallowing—all were present." Flushing out the mouth with water produced an immediate cessation of the symptoms.

Further light on the mechanism of thirst comes from a consideration of ways in which it may be allayed, once present. Whereas no
permanent solution comes from it, holding in the mouth acid substances which will increase saliva flow or sipping water and swishing
it about in the mouth will, as all athletic coaches know, temporarily
reduce or abolish thirst. A very much more dramatic device is that
of painting the back of the mouth with novocaine. Once the tissue is
dulled in this manner thirst is effectively subdued. In cases of polyuria,
with its incessant and tormenting thirst, relative comfort has been
brought about by anesthetizing the throat.

The output of the salivary glands in relation to dehydrating influences in their immediate neighborhood would appear, thus far, to be
the key to the understanding of thirst. It is the chief factor, but it
can also be shown that others are involved. Influences of a general
kind can produce thirst. Thus profuse sweating or excessive loss of
fluids by way of the bladder and intestines will upset the water balance of the organism and, sooner or later, cause thirst. The yielding
up of milk by the nursing mother is followed by a strong desire for
water. Loss of blood through hemorrhage is likely to result in excessive thirst; the universal cry of the battlefield is, "Water, water!"
States of emotion, all of which affect the organism in a widespread and
indiscriminate manner, inevitably have thirst as one of their common
components. The distressing thirst accompanying stage fright is a
notable part of the torment suffered by the novice in public speaking.
What have all these very general conditions of the organism to do
with local moistness of the pharynx?

The considerations here are the analogues of those we encountered
in connection with the interpretation of hunger. Thirst must be
thought of, on the one hand, as a pattern of sensation (comparable to
the "pangs" of hunger) and, on the other, as a complex motivating
force (like appetite). "Appetitive thirst" doubtless dictates how long
we shall continue to drink at any one time. Dryness of the mouth and
throat should, after all, be brought to an abrupt end by the first gulp
of water. Sensations from the throat presumably cannot serve either
to motivate in the direction of prolonged drinking nor inform one as
to how much to drink. Yet, through careful regulation of intake all
normal humans—and a great variety of differently constituted sub-
human species—maintain a nice water balance. The precision of balance is most obviously manifest in the blood, which is preserved in a
nearly constant state at the expense of water reserves in all other
bodily tissues. The essential connection between thirst as locally initiated by the tissues of the throat and thirst as originated by a bodily

need is to be found, according to Cannon, in the mechanism of the blood's water balance. Among the structures which are called upon by the blood to yield up water are the salivary glands. Whereas the three sets of salivary glands comprise only one group of tissues upon which the demand is placed, the salivary glands are especially unfavorably affected by the water deficiency. They differ from almost all other tissues in that they need an entirely adequate supply of water if they are to perform properly their service to the organism. Their own secretion is almost pure water (97–99%), and the consequences of bodily water depletion are for them very great. Strategically situated as the salivary glands are and responsive as they are to the slightest changes in water balance, they constitute delicate indicators, sensitive reporters of body hydration. By permitting the epithelial tissue of the pharynx to dry out, the salivary glands are responsible for initiating the sensory pattern we know as thirst. When water is imbibed it becomes available to the salivary glands, which once more moisten the buccal cavity and keep it lubricated. According to this view, then, the salivary glands provide the necessary link between thirst-as-appetite and thirst-as-sensation. It becomes clear why excessive sweating should cause, among other symptoms, a parched mouth and also why it is possible to slake thirst somewhat by introducing water to the body by way of a stomach tube or injecting it into the veins.

13

Labyrinthine Sensitivity

Equilibrium Mechanisms of the Inner Ear. It was earlier pointed out, in a description of the auditory response system (p. 108), that the bony labyrinth of which the cochlea constitutes one portion also contains two other parts, non-auditory in function. These are the *vestibular sacs* and the *semicircular canals.* In our consideration of audition we set them aside as not germane to the discussion. Now, as we pay attention to the receptor systems involved in internal sensibility, they come to be important to us. Within the vestibule and semicircular canals are initiated many of the sensory processes responsible for muscular tone and postural adjustment. Thoroughgoing injury to the labyrinth has many consequences other than total deafness; flabbiness of the neck, limb, and trunk muscles and disturbed action of the eye muscles are likely to ensue. All these changes, taken together, inevitably mean disordered movements and equilibrium failures.

Though there must be a very intimate coordination between the activities of receptors situated in the semicircular canals and those in the vestibular sacs, the two sets of end organs are clearly different in detailed construction, and they function in accordance with somewhat different principles. One important characteristic they have in common, however. Both participate in neural systems which make no direct report to the cortex of the brain. The "labyrinthine sense," as it is sometimes called, yields no sensations! That is, it yields none directly in the same way that vision, audition, and the other senses do. It appears to have no "qualities" of its own. After a vigorous swirling about in a rotating chair, for example, observe carefully what the resulting "dizziness" actually feels like. It will be found to have a quite complex pattern of which prominent components are: kinesthetic sensations from the eye muscles, which are making powerful and rapid compensatory adjustments; pressure sensations from the chest, head, and visceral regions; and perhaps a series of pulsating sensations which depend on vascular changes. If the eyes are open there will be elaborate and rapidly changing visual sensations also. Note that all these experiences are accessory and indirectly aroused. There is nothing coming out of the analysis of feelings of dizziness to tell one that the primary source of stimulation is the inner ear.

While the distinction rests on somewhat shaky foundations, the current belief is that the semicircular canals and the organs of the vestibule subserve two somewhat different functions. The canals are thought to be solely responsible for initiating reflex responses to rotary motion imposed on the organism, whereas the vestibular organs, the utricle and the saccule, are believed to respond to changes of head position involving linear motion. There is no denying that the receptor cells, the anatomy and disposition of which are fairly well known in each case, are admirably adapted to this particular division of function. There are, however, some experimental evidences which indicate that the semicircular canals may play at least a secondary role in static positional adjustments and that the utricle may participate in reactions to strong rotary motions.

The manner in which they are constructed tells one a good deal about how the various organs of the non-auditory labyrinth must operate. Let us consider the semicircular canals and the vestibular sacs separately.

The Semicircular Canals and Their Stimuli. Lying approximately at right angles to each other, one for each major plane of the body, are the three semicircular canals. Their relations to other parts of the labyrinth and to each other are shown in Fig. 83. Considering the two labyrinths together (right and left sides of the head), the two lateral canals fall approximately in the same bodily plane, the right anterior and left posterior do the same, and so do the left anterior and right posterior. The six canals thus form a three-coordinate system to which gross bodily motions may be referred; the three "spirit levels" of the body, William James called them. The bony semicircular canals vary from 15 to 22 mm in length, the posterior being the longest and the lateral the shortest. The internal width of the bony canals averages about 0.8 mm. Within the bony labyrinth lies the membranous labyrinth, all parts of which are continuous with each other and with the sacs of the vestibule. Surrounding the entire membranous labyrinth and apparently serving as a lubricant to prevent it from rubbing against its bony surroundings is a watery fluid, *perilymph*. The membranous canal itself contains a liquid, *endolymph*, which plays an important part in stimulation. In response to pressures it either shifts its position or circulates within the canal. If it circulates it flows through tubes which have a "bore" of only about 0.2 mm over most of their length, and a great deal of frictional resistance must have to be overcome.

At one end of each semicircular canal, just as it enters the vestibule, there appears an enlargement. This region is known as the ampulla. It is important because, as is suggested by Fig. 83, it contains the end-

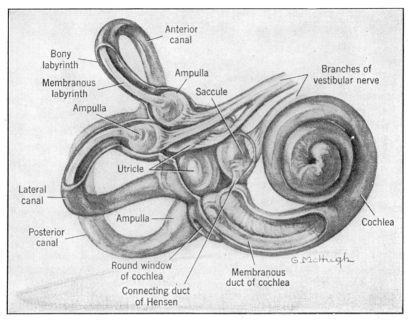

FIG. 83. The semicircular canals and their relation to the cochlea. The right labyrinth is shown, large portions of the protecting bone being cut away to reveal the membraneous canals and sacs inside. The three semicircular canals are approximately at right angles to each other.

ings of the vestibular or non-auditory branch of the eighth cranial nerve. The internal structure of the ampulla is remarkable and provides the key to the understanding of how the canals operate. Within each ampulla is a structure, the crista, which houses the terminations of the vestibular nerve. The nerve endings have a not uncommon form, one with which we are familiar from our study of hearing: hair cells (see Fig. 84). The hair fibers project into a gelatinous mass, the cupula, which extends from one wall of the ampulla to the opposite one. The cupula is fixed at its base (where the hair cells enter) but is free to swing at the distal end. This it does in response to hydraulic pressures created within the endolymph. The immediate stimulus for the discharge of nerve impulses in the hair cells is, therefore, bending of the cupula with consequent distortion of the crista. Though no one has ever actually witnessed it happening, the supposition is that motion of the cupula stretches the hair cells on the side away from the bending and slackens those on the side toward it. Impulses set up in some such fashion in the dendritic endings of the vestibular fibers pass over these fibers to the medulla, where synaptic endings occur

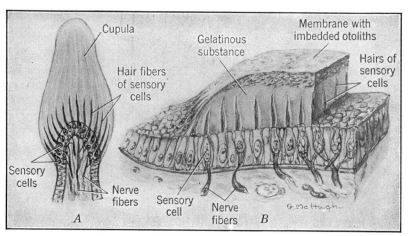

FIG. 84. Receptors of the non-auditory labyrinth. *A*, diagram of the crista, showing the hair-cell terminations of the non-auditory branch of the eighth cranial nerve projecting into the cupula, a gelatinous structure. *B*, diagram of the macula, a structure found both in the utricle and the saccule. This similarly houses hair-cell nerve endings.

in the vestibular nuclei of that organ. The vestibular portion of the eighth nerve (about 19,000 fibers, comprising half the total nerve bundle) contains chiefly large fibers (10 μ to 15 μ in diameter), though small ones down to 2 μ are also present. This means that impulses from the non-auditory labyrinth are, in general, rapidly conducted ones, as might be expected in a system responsible for emergency reflexes.

The normal or "adequate" stimulus for the receptors of the canals would seem, at first glance, to be bodily motion. But motion, whether straight-line or rotary, can be shown to be insufficient, in itself, to stimulate the cristae. Gently rotate a blindfolded subject in a noiselessly turning chair of the barbershop variety, and it will be found that he perceives motion only when the chair is gaining or losing speed appreciably. If the rate of rotation is held approximately constant he will not feel himself to be turning. It is not motion but change of rate of motion, acceleration or deceleration, that constitutes the adequate stimulus for the semicircular canals.

In the vast majority of normal situations changes in rate of bodily motion are the only stimuli encountered.   However, there are other kinds of stimuli, for the most part experimentally applied only, that initiate ampullar activity.   Heat or cold (caloric stimulation) is effective.   Syringe the external ear with hot or cold water, and there follows immediately a series of reflex responses of the eye muscles, so-called nystagmic movements, that cause the eyes to sweep slowly in one direction (slow phase) and then snap back to the original position (quick phase).   Subjectively such repeated motions are accompanied by dizziness; in the extreme they lead to nausea.   Hot water produces nystagmus with the quick phase toward the side of the head stimulated.   Cold water does the reverse; it sets up nystagmus with the quick phase towards the opposite side of the head.   The mechanism of coloric stimulation is presumably that of convection currents in the endolymph.   Whereas nystagmic responses to thermal stimuli are the common stock-in-trade of otologists, who are able to put them to excellent clinical use, there has been little study of them experimentally.

Another way to excite the semicircular canals is by direct mechanical pressure.   There are relatively few situations involving human subjects in which this can reasonably occur.   In some cases of deafness due to hardening of middle ear tissues it becomes possible to restore hearing by making an opening or "window" between the middle and inner ear cavities.   Such "fenestration" operations are often attended by the most violent disturbances of equilibrium because of the involvement of the non-auditory parts of the labyrinth.   Hydraulically it is all one system, it will be remembered, and temporary difficulties of balance are therefore not surprising when the auditory mechanism is disarranged.   For the fenestration operation to remain permanently successful it is necessary for the artificial window, which is covered over by a tissue flap, to stay open.   The bone tends to grow back over the window and undo all that the operation has accomplished.   Accordingly, frequent tests are made, mechanical pressure of the index finger being applied at the proper point in the external auditory canal.   If there is no occlusion pressure will be transmitted through the hole to the labyrinth, evoking reflex nystagmic responses.

In animal preparations, where the semicircular canals can be laid bare for experimental purposes, direct mechanical (or thermal) stimulation becomes possible.   Ewald, in the last century, attained good control with his "pneumatic hammer," a tiny device for mechanically stimulating the canals directly. The hammer consisted of a cylinder, 9.0 mm long and only 1.4 mm in diameter, which contained a movable piston. A small hole being drilled in the wall of a semicircular canal and the foot of the cylinder being securely sealed against the bone, movement of the piston would now apply a mechanical force against the membranous canal and affect the endolymph. In the case of the horizontal canal compression most readily produced movement of the endolymph, while with the two vertical canals decompression was the more effective. The index of effectiveness was the turning of the head and eyes by the animal.

Still another agent capable of stimulating the canals, or at least the nerve fibers leading away from them, is electricity. Both direct and alternating currents have been used experimentally, and a few facts have come to light. With direct current somewhat specific responses can be aroused. Thus, if the cathode (negative pole) of the circuit is applied to the left labyrinth of the pigeon a reflex movement of the head to the right will result. Reverse the electrodes, and a left turning of the head is evoked. Whether the site of stimulation is the crista or the vestibular nerve fibers themselves is still uncertain, though suspicion rests strongly on the latter probability. Nystagmic eye movements can also be produced by direct currents applied to the head. A negative electrode placed on the human mastoid, the positive one being grounded at any convenient bodily locus such as the neck or shoulder, will elicit nystagmus in which the slow phase is away from the side stimulated. Interchange of the electrodes reverses the slow and fast phases. Alternating currents have been used little in labyrinthine experiments, and there appears to be some confusion in the literature concerning the main effects obtained with them. They seem not to produce nystagmus, but compensatory head movements do occur, faradic stimulation of the mastoid leading to rotation or tilting of the head away from the stimulated side. This needs further investigation, especially at low frequencies of current alternation.

Reactions to Rotation of the Body. Responses of the semicircular canals have been studied chiefly by means of the rotating chair. The prototype is the Bárány chair, which became well known in World War I as a test for vertigo in prospective aviators. Any heavy rotating base which has relatively noiseless bearings and which can be accelerated and decelerated smoothly may be used. A comfortable chair mounted rigidly on such a base and equipped with a head rest or biting board provides a suitable platform for rotating the body about its vertical axis. It is common practice to arrange it so that the head is inclined forward at an angle of about 25 degrees to bring the horizontal canals to a plane parallel with the floor, viz., to render them really horizontal. This will be accomplished if the head is tipped so that an imaginary line from the corner of the eye to the ear canal opening is horizontal. As a matter of fact, it turns out that somewhat greater sensitivity to rotary acceleration is realized if the head is held erect, rather than tilted forward in the customary manner (284). There is no requirement, of course, that the center of rotation be the body axis. An increasing number of experiments is being carried out on the human centrifuge, a kind of merry-go-round in which the subject may be some distance from the axis of rotation, ordinarily facing the center and with a shield surrounding his head to protect the face against telltale air currents.

To measure absolute sensitivity any one of three indicators may be employed: (1) kinesthetic and cutaneous feelings of total bodily motion; (2) nystagmic eye movements; (3) the "oculogyral illusion." The magnitude of the absolute threshold will be a function of the response selected as an indicator, for the three are not equally sensitive. In general, the first and second—perception of bodily motion and observation of nystagmic movements, especially of the slow phase of nystagmus—yield results which are in substantial agreement. Accelerations of the order of 1 degree/sec^2 prove to be liminal. The third method is somewhat more sensitive, however; it gives considerably lower threshold values.

The "oculogyral illusion," as it has been called by Graybiel and his associates, who have investigated it extensively (130), is a visual effect occurring under angular acceleration of the body in a human centrifuge. It refers to the apparent motion of an isolated visual object (six radial lines of dim light forming a star pattern and viewed against darkness) which is rigidly fixed in space relative to the head of the subject. The observed motion following angular acceleration is in the direction of turn. Shortly after the body has attained a uniform angular velocity there is experienced no further visual motion. Deceleration reverses the apparent direction of visual movement. After stopping, once the seen motion has subsided, it may revive itself but this time it appears to be in the opposite direction (the same as that in response to initial acceleration). The visual effects are presumably correlated exactly with nystagmic responses and, as such, are delicate indicators of labyrinthine stimulation. As compared with threshold accelerations approximating 1 degree/sec^2, obtained by the two cruder methods, the oculogyral illusion begins to appear with accelerations or decelerations of as little as 0.12 degree/sec^2.

Direct study of the eyes' responses to rotatory acceleration and deceleration reveals the nystagmic sequences to be quite elaborate. They are particularly complex if vision is allowed to intervene. Then there occur interactions, especially those of inhibition, between voluntary eye movements and ocular reflexes aroused by action of the canals. If, however, vision is excluded by dark surroundings or by the use of a blindfold, pure labyrinthine nystagmus can be studied. Since the effects of acceleration and deceleration are identical in character (though opposite in direction), observation can be facilitated by bringing the chair to a steady velocity (conventionally, 180 degrees/sec), continuing at that speed until all effects of acceleration have subsided, and then decelerating to a fairly rapid stop. Nystagmic movements, with the slow sweep in the direction of rotation, will be observed throughout the period of slowing down and coming to a stop. The slow phase of nystagmus increases in velocity for slightly longer than the duration of deceleration, then very gradually declines in speed, the repetitive sweeps continuing on for about a half minute. Up to this point what has occurred is "primary rotation nystagmus." The total response is not over, however, for with the subsidence of the primary phase there begins, without noticeable interruption, a series of eye movements in the opposite direction. This is *secondary* or *inverse nystagmus.* Its speed develops gradually for well over a minute, attaining a velocity at the peak of perhaps 5 degrees/sec, then shows a very gradual decline for the next several minutes. Altogether, the entire eye movement sequence, with its primary and secondary nystagmic phases, may occupy as much as a 10-min period. The protracted secondary phase is largely missing, of course, if vision is permitted. Fixational efforts easily overcome the relatively weak movements of inverse nystagmus. While for a given individual, under constant experimental conditions, the duration of the primary phase, that of the inverse phase, and the speed attained at the height of inverse nystagmus are likely to be reproducible quantities, there are large and perhaps important individual differences in all these response characteristics.

In addition to eye movements a number of reflex responses of the neck, limbs, and trunk are evoked by rotation. A blindfolded subject, spun in a smoothly rotating chair, may show certain of these reactions. During the initial acceleration the head may make slow sweeping motions in the direction opposite to that of rotation, with frequent quick returns in the opposite direction (just as the eyes do in nystagmus). If the spinning is somewhat vigorous a sudden cessation of whirling brings forth compensatory movements of the head, arms, and legs, all responses that tend to prevent the subject from falling over. If, after rapid rotation to the left for a dozen or so turns, the subject is abruptly stopped and is instructed to get out of the chair and stand erect with his arms straight out in front of him he will stand with his head and arms to the left, the right arm up, and the left down, a stance which has been called "the position of the discus thrower." If, under this post-rotatory influence, he changes the position of his head radically he will be in serious danger of falling. In fact, quite apart from the accessory reactions produced, any gross change in head position following strong stimulation of the canals elicits the "falling reaction."

But responses involving adjustments of this magnitude are the result of somewhat intense stimulation. A more common sequence of events would run more nearly as follows. After having instructed the blind-folded subject to raise his right hand whenever he feels himself moving to the right and his left hand to signal left movement, begin with very slow rotation and gradually step up the speed. Once an acceleration of 1–2 degrees/sec^2 has been reached, the appropriate hand will go up, reporting correctly the direction of rotation. If now a constant speed is maintained the hand will go down and, assuming no accessory cues to the detection of motion to be given (sounds, air currents on the face, etc.), the subject will be unaware of his continued turning. Quite high rotational speeds may go undetected provided the acceleration used in reaching them is subliminal. If brakes are then silently applied, rapidly slowing the chair down, the opposite hand will go up. The sensation is that of turning in the reverse direction and is a direct consequence of supraliminal deceleration. This feeling may last for some time after the subject comes to a halt. In the most extreme instance, however, it will not continue strongly for more than 20–30 sec. This is a figure which reappears time and again in measurements of rotational after-sensations and after-nystagmus. We shall have to confront it later with a view to explaining its ubiquity.

Mechanism of Ampullar Action. Direct observation of labyrinthine events is not at all easy to arrange. In vertebrates the structures concerned are quite inaccessible, and in most of the lower forms they are extremely small. In view of the difficulties it is not surprising that until quite recently the mechanism of stimulation was less a subject of experiment than of speculation. Interestingly enough, however, as subsequent events proved, much of the early theorizing was basically sound. In the 1870's the fundamental theory was laid down, it being the joint product of the thinking of the Germans, Mach and Breuer, and the Englishman, Crum Brown. Today we speak of the Mach-Breuer-Brown theory of labyrinthine functioning.

The theory holds that stimulation of the crista comes about through inertia of the endolymph. The semicircular canals, being set approximately in the three dimensions of space, must be affected by all motions of the head. As a canal accelerates or decelerates in rotary motion the endolymph lags behind its containing tube. The back thrust thus created exerts a pressure against the cupula, bending it and stimulating the nerve endings of the crista. As turning continues, the endolymph, subject to the frictional influence of its enclosing walls, takes up the motion of its canal, and stimulation subsides. The cupula is no longer moving relative to the hair cells and imposing a strain on them. If an abrupt braking of the canal's motion occurs, the endolymph, through its own inertia, flows on for a time, and the cupula is bent in the opposite direction.

There are difficulties with this theory, some of which were seen from the beginning. Thus Ernst Mach, the physicist, considered it somewhat improbable that viscosity would permit the flow of endolymph through a tube having a diameter no greater than a fraction of a millimeter. Breuer believed it had to be that way, however. Brown thought it unlikely that a single canal could signal movement in one direction, then reverse its message. What about the principle of nerve specificity? Accordingly, he modified the theory to let a given canal on one side of the head always report movement in a specific direction. Its mate on the other side, silent during the first movement, was to come into play when the direction of rotation was reversed. This amendment to the theory, though ingenious, was most certainly wrong. Experiments involving destruction of semicircular canals in pigeons and rabbits demonstrated that the receptors of a single ampulla must function for motion in both directions (85, pp. 212–213).

Crucial evidence verifying the Mach-Breuer-Brown theory was a long time in coming, and the ideas involved remained the subject of controversy for nearly 60 years. Then, in 1931, came the dramatic experiments of Steinhausen (268). These, by demonstrating unambiguously the appropriate movements of the cupula in response to positive and negative rotary accelerations and to mechanical and caloric stimulation, proved the essential correctness of the early guesses. The success of Steinhausen's work depended on the judicious selection of an experimental animal and the invention of a novel technique. He made his observations on the pike, which has relatively large and accessible semicircular canals. By cutting away the covering cartilage he was able to render visible a portion of a canal with its ampulla.

Injection into the canal of small quantities of dye made visible the gelatinous cupula, which could then be photographed. A small drop of oil inserted into the canal facilitated observation of the movements of the endolymph. Figure 85 shows a typical response to angular acceleration. Displacement of endolymph with resulting hydrodynamic pressure on the cupula has resulted in extreme tipping of that body with, no doubt, mechanical distortion and excitation of the hair endings of the vestibular nerve. Steinhausen's experiments on the pike

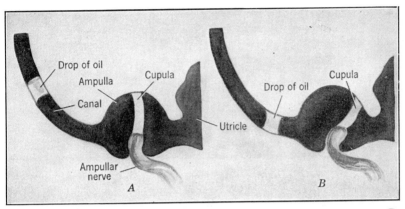

FIG. 85. The effect of angular acceleration on the position of the cupula. The displacement of the endolymph was revealed by an injected drop of oil. The cupula was rendered visible by dyeing it with china white. A, the cupula in its normal position before rotation of the preparation. B, shift of endolymph and consequent change in position of the cupula as a result of rotary acceleration. After Dohlman, 82. Reproduced from Proc. roy. Soc. Med., 1935, 28, 1374, by permission of the Honorary Editors and Professor Gösta Dohlman.

and Dohlman's subsequent ones on the cod (83) make it clear that, in these forms at least, the cupula completely fills up the lumen of the ampulla. "Streaming" of endolymph can hardly occur if this is the case. Until we learn whether the same situation obtains in higher forms perhaps we do well to think of endolymph as only temporarily displacing the free end of the cupula by hydrodynamic pressure rather than "flowing past" it. However, some circulation of endolymph is demanded by the facts of caloric stimulation; convection currents require a fluid medium.

What happens in the sensory nerve fibers leading away from the ampullae? Records of action potentials in single fibers of the vestibular nerve, while being stimulated by angular accelerations, have been obtained by Löwenstein and Sand (203) in 1940 and, more recently, by Gernandt (117). The former investigators picked up discharges from nerve fibers leading away from the horizontal ampulla of the skate. While still unstimulated, the typical fiber had a "spontaneous" discharge rate of about 5 per second. At angular accelerations of the order of 3 degrees/sec² threshold was reached, this being signalled by *either* an increase in impulse frequency (when rotation was toward the side of the head from which the recording was taken) or a de-

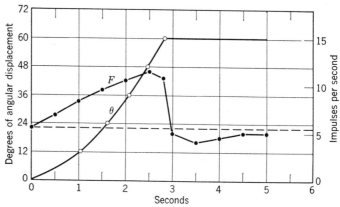

FIG. 86. Vestibular action-potential frequency as a function of acceleration. The line labeled θ shows the amount of angular displacement from the initial position of rest and is to be referred to the left axis. Impulse frequency at each half-second interval is shown on curve F, which uses the axis on the right. Acceleration was about 15 degrees/sec², and rotation increased in velocity up to a total turn of 60 degrees. At this point motion abruptly ceased. Note the increase in discharge frequency with increasing stimulation and the subsequent precipitous decline. Rotation in the opposite direction produced a corresponding reduction in impulse frequency below that of the "spontaneous" discharge of 5 per second. From Löwenstein and Sand, *203.* By permission of Cambridge University Press and the authors.

crease (when rotation was toward the contralateral side). For a given amount of angular acceleration the increase (or decrease) was always the same, impulse frequency being related in a linear fashion to degree of acceleration. (See Fig. 86.) The maximum impulse frequency is attained promptly, coincidentally with completion of the initial acceleration. If, now, *speed* is maintained at a constant level, impulse frequency falls off until it has reached the normal "spontaneous" rate of 5 per second after about 20–30 sec. The cupula does not remain in its extreme position during continuous whirling but, acting like a very slow and heavily damped pendulum, gradually resumes its normal position of rest. It will be remembered that earlier the question was raised, "Why always 20–30 sec as the typical period of rotary after-effects?" Apparently the answer is that we are dealing with an elastic pendulum, the cupula, which has a natural period of that magnitude. If displaced only slightly it would, of course, not require as much time to regain equilibrium. Only the most extreme positive or negative acceleration could produce an after-effect lasting a full half-minute. This explanation serves quite adequately to account for *primary* post-rotation effects. The phenomenon of inverse nystagmus and its corollary, inversion of movement in the oculogyral illusion, are not accommodated by it, of course. These effects would seem to demand that the "pendulum" overshoot and describe at least one more movement in the direction of the original (acceleratory) displacement before finally coming to rest.

The experiments of Gernandt are revealing in that they show in the vestibular fibers of a vertebrate, the cat, similar events to those found by Löwenstein and Sand in a much simpler organism. Using a technique very much like that employed by Galambos and Davis (see Chap. 8) in their study of elements of the auditory branch of the eighth cranial nerve, Gernandt plunged a needle electrode, insulated except at the tip, into the vestibular branch leading from the horizontal ampulla. Single elements could be isolated by appropriate manipulation of the electrode. One hundred such responding elements were examined in relation to rotational acceleration of the animal, their frequencies of spike discharge being recorded. Not all fibers responded in the same way; in fact, three different "types" of fibers were found. By far the commonest performance, recorded in 83% of the fibers, was like that in the Löwenstein and Sand study, viz., when the needle was in the left vestibular nerve and rotation of the cat was to the left, an increase in frequency above the level of the resting "spontaneous" frequency occurred. Rotation in the opposite direction either reduced or entirely obliterated the nerve's response. Elements of Type II, accounting for 12% of the sample, gave a reaction to rotation in either direction by increased frequency of discharge. Type III response, met in only 5 of the 100 fibers, involved a more or less complete inhibition of discharge upon accelerating or decelerating the animal. Normally active, fibers of this type go into a "silent period" on being stimulated. That these three varieties of nerve response do not result from artifacts introduced by movement of the experimental animal or other accident is attested by the fact that substitution of caloric stimulation for acceleratory motion does not change the result. All three types of nerve response can be aroused in the proper fibers by irrigation of the external auditory canal with cold (20° C.) and hot (43° C.) water.

This discovery of three characteristically different patterns of response in fibers of the vestibular branch is difficult to interpret as yet. It is reminiscent, of course, of a similar state of affairs in vision, where several different types of discharge sequence are encountered in optic fibers. In both instances the phenomenon is much in need of thoroughly systematic study. In the Gernandt experiments, as in those of Galambos and Davis in audition, there is some uncertainty as to whether first- or second-order neurons were actually the source of records (103). The presumption is that cell bodies of second-order neurons were chiefly involved. As yet no one has succeeded in overcoming the great technical difficulties that are bound to be present in recording directly from ampullar (first-order) fibers.

The Vestibular Sacs: Utricle and Saccule. The portion of the membranous canal housed within the vestibule proper is divisible anatomically into two separate structures, the utricle and the saccule. The importance of the utricle is clearly established; it contains nerve endings necessary to the preservation of normal posture. However, the indispensability of the saccule is less certain, though it also contains nerve endings of the type found in the utricle. In animal preparations destruction of the saccule results in no obvious defect of equilibrium or locomotion. Some have claimed that the saccule participates in responses of the auditory system, a contention far from having been proved, at least in humans.

Endings of the vestibular nerve impinge upon an area, one in the utricle and one in the saccule, known as the *macula*, an oval, flat thickening of the wall of the vestibule (see Fig. 84). The saccular macula is disposed in a plane approximately at right angles to that of the utricular macula. As in the case of the ampullar endings, the nerve terminations are hair cells embedded in a gelatinous substance. The mode of stimulation of the hair endings seems to be somewhat different in the vestibular sacs, however. The hair cells are more nearly columnar in shape and have suspended above them tiny crystals of calcium carbonate. This granular mass, called the otolith organ, is believed to be so constituted as to "load" the hair cells and cause them to be stimulated by gravitational pull. When the body is speeding up or slowing down in straight-line motion, the inertia of the otoliths would presumably bring about a bending of the hair cells with consequent discharge of their attached nerve fibers. Tilting of the head in any direction would be expected to produce the same result.

Just as the rotating chair has provided the means of studying responses to positive and negative acceleratory forces, the tilt table is the common laboratory device for investigating the effects of gravitational pull on the vestibule. It has been assumed that all that is needed is a way of tilting the entire body away from the vertical and horizontal to various measured extents. A stout board to which the body may be securely strapped, equipped with a substantial bearing and set up in the manner of a see-saw, with a protractor and plumb line attached, is a familiar accoutrement of the psychological laboratory. As a device for measuring thresholds of otolithic action the tilt table is an entirely ineffectual instrument. Cues from the skin and muscles, generated by restraining straps and head holder, tend to mask those initiated by the otoliths and thus yield misleading measures. The fact is that currently there are available no reliable threshold figures for either bodily tilt or linear acceleration. Several interesting phenomena of static sensibility can, of course, be studied qualitatively by means of the tilt table.

A diffuse pattern of strains and pressures having cutaneous, kinesthetic, and visceral origins constitutes the sensory indicator of vestibular action, the "feel" of bodily position. As with the semicircular canals, the neural pathways involved are indirect. With the assumption of each new head position stimulation arising in the hair cells of the maculae starts impulses over the vestibular nerve to the medulla and cerebellum. At these lower centers connections are made with motor fibers going to neck, eye, trunk, and limb muscles. In each of these groups there may occur "tonic" reflexes, patterns of muscular tension appropriate to the body position involved. In lower organisms many of these positional reflexes may be identified and catalogued. Thus there occur entirely predictable deviations of the eyes of fishes when they are slowly turned on the long axis of the body. In some of the reptiles, lizards and turtles notably, and birds—the pigeon has been intensively studied in this regard—the head will be held absolutely still (within mechanical limitations) irrespective of the position in which the body is placed. In higher forms the picture becomes complicated, and in the human it is vastly so. As we ascend the animal scale the vestibular apparatus is connected with postural responses more and more complexly. Both the sacs and canals become diminished in importance as control devices for equilibrium. It follows that damage to the labyrinth is a relatively less serious matter in humans than it would be in simpler organisms where there are not the substitute mechanisms available. In congenital deaf-mutes, for example, whose labyrinths may be completely degenerate, postural adjustments are still made effectively in most everyday situations. Only when vision is excluded or when visual cues become ambiguous is equilibrium threatened. Thus some deaf people report that they dare not go under water when swimming since "up" and "down" then get confused and they are in danger of drowning. Deaf-blinds have been studied with respect to their vestibular sensitivity (325) with the not unexpected finding that they are unable to maintain balance more than a second or two when required to stand on one foot. Nine of 10 deaf-blind subjects showed no post-rotational responses whatever. After whirling in a chair there was no dizziness or nausea, no illusions of movement appeared, and there was not even a hint of nystagmus.

The Non-Auditory Labyrinth and Aviation. If the array of facts and principles concerning the non-auditory labyrinth is less formidable than in some other sense fields—and the judgment of the historian of sensory psychophysiology would be that it is—it can also be said that developments in aviation bid fair to change all this. With commercial, private, and military aircraft flying at ever higher speeds new and somewhat extreme demands are being placed on their occupants. The sheer requirements of survival demand that all available sensory and motor capacities be brought to bear on the problem of adapting to a complex and kaleidoscopic environment. In response to the needs of modern aviation, research on labyrinthine phenomena is presently receiving more nearly adequate attention and support than in an earlier time, when rotational and gravitational forces were of practical concern only to the acrobat, the ballet dancer, and, if he thought about them, the whirling dervish!

In the maintenance of equilibrium and bodily orientation visual, labyrinthine, cutaneous, and organic cues all commonly come into play. Occasionally auditory sensations have a supporting role. In the flying situation it is, of course, vision that usually provides the most precise data of orientation. The pilot sees the cockpit and external objects, especially the nose of his plane and the horizon, in relation to each other. In night flight and in "weather" he has his instruments which visually give accurate, if somewhat indirect, indications of the plane's attitude in space. Ordinarily, then, the pilot's sensory world is mainly visual and yields sufficiently exact and complete information to permit of the nice adjustments required in complicated maneuvers as well as in straight and level flight, takeoffs, and landings.

However, information obtained visually is not always correct, subject as it is to illusory influences, and returns from other sensory systems cannot always be suppressed. The sense data most frequently coming in conflict with the visual are those arising from the operation of the non-auditory labyrinth. In flight the occupant of an airplane may be subject to three sets of acceleratory forces: angular, radial, and linear. Angular accelerations and decelerations are fortunately only briefly and transiently encountered in flying; stimuli appropriate to the semicircular canals are not commonly long sustained. However, as we shall see, they are potential sources of disorientation in the air. Radial acceleration and deceleration (centrifugal and centripetal force) occur more commonly, being involved in any rotation about an axis at some distance from the plane. Thus radial forces exert themselves on the pilot whenever he goes into a turn, climb, or dive. But the most common acceleratory and deceleratory stimuli, in all kinds of flying, are linearly disposed ones. Any change in speed unaccompanied by change in direction involves either a positive or negative linear acceleration and becomes a potential stimulus to the vestibular sacs. If the change in velocity is sufficiently marked it can serve to initiate some very serious errors of perception.

The effects of linear acceleration and deceleration in a plane have been investigated at the Pensacola Naval Air Station (58). An observer sat blindfolded in the rear of a two-place training plane, his head held rigidly in place. His job was to give a running account of all perceptions of bodily position, the reports being taken down on a wire recorder and synchronized with an objective record of the plane's performance as revealed by a three-dimensional accelerometer. The pilot put the plane through its paces of speed changes by suitable manipulation of throttle and flaps, but maintained as closely as possible straight and level flight. The observer was, of course, ignorant of the plane's true performance. Uniformly, all observers reported strong perceptions of tilting forward when the plane was rapidly slowed down and of tilting backward when speed was suddenly increased. The frequency with which such reports were made, the estimated angle of tilt, and the duration of the feelings of tilt all proved to be proportional to the strength of the stimulus, i.e., to the amount of acceleration or deceleration. The threshold for the perception of tilt was surprisingly small, $0.02g$, or only 2% of the acceleration that would be imparted by a force equal to that of gravity. This is the value for positive acceleration. For deceleration the threshold is higher, about $0.08g$. In either case the feeling of tilting is elaborated into the judgment that the plane is actually changing altitude, climbing in the case of positive acceleration and diving in the case of negative. An acceleration of about $0.1g$ was interpreted as a climb at a 20–25-degree angle. The feeling lasted somewhat beyond the real accelerative force. A deceleration of the same magnitude was felt as a dive at a 15-degree angle below the horizontal. No such estimates would be given, of course, if visual cues to position and motion had remained in the picture. However, this experiment demonstrates what might happen to spatial orientation if visual information were to be obliterated. The pilot flying in fog, having just reduced his throttle setting, may see from his instruments that he is still flying level but his otoliths may tell him he is in a dive. Among a great many things an aviator must learn is the difficult lesson of coming to disregard the direct evidence of his senses, in such situations as this, and to place his trust in the less direct but sounder evidence offered by his flight instruments.

A study which combines the effects of angular and radial accelerations and which, therefore, involves the functioning of the entire non-auditory labyrinth, has also been conducted at Pensacola (205). With very much the same arrangements as those of the linear acceleration experiment, the reactions of observers to varying degrees of lateral tilting and turning were studied. Six different angles of bank, at a constant altitude, were tried: 10, 18, 30, 40, 50, and 60 degrees. Angular accelerations varied from 0.10 degree/sec^2 (onset of the 10-degree bank) to 0.80 degree/sec^2 (recovery from the 60-degree bank). The observer reported on his perceptions of turning and tilting, judging direction and amount, and also estimated the magnitude of the forces in operation. The first fact that becomes apparent, on analysis of the records, is that feelings of tilting and turning are dangerously unreliable indicators of the true state of affairs. At small angles of bank the plane's change of direction and position went unnoticed much of the time. The absolute threshold for the perception of turning falls between the 10- and 18-degree banks, where the acceleratory force is about 0.15 degree/sec^2. Positive and negative accelerations give about the same value. Within the limits of the study there is no angle of bank which provides absolutely certain information; even the 60-degree tilt was not detected 100% of the time. Even though the existence of the banking movement is appreciated, there may still be an erroneous judgment of the direction of turn. Moreover, perceptions of tilting and turning have their onset only after a considerable lag; the maneuver has already been in effect for 5 or more sec. A great deal can happen in the air in this time.

Estimates of the amount of lateral tilt are markedly in error. Going into the turn, while the degree of tilt was being varied between 10 and 60 degrees, the observers made average estimates ranging between 4.2 and 11.9 degrees. Recovery from the bank, which was performed somewhat more rapidly and thus involved relatively greater accelerations, was accompanied by an even smaller range of estimated angles: 4.1 to 6.8 degrees. The duration of the feelings of turning and tilting was quite out of line with reality. All angles of bank were held for about a minute; on the average the feelings had subsided in about one-third that time. In view of what we have already seen about linear accelerations it is not surprising to find a fore-and-aft tilting component present in this experiment as well. The onset of turn and the turn itself are both accompanied by clear feelings of backward tilt, estimated to be as high as 45 degrees in the case of the 60-degree bank. After recovery from the turn, and after a noticeable lag, the observer may feel himself to be tilted forward somewhat.

The one datum that was accurately estimated throughout the entire experiment was the magnitude of the g force. While the true g was changing from 1.02 (at 10-degree bank) to 2.00 (at 60 degrees) the observers' estimates were, respectively, 1.00 and 1.95. Estimated and real forces coincided closely all along the line. Yet, from the standpoint of manipulating the controls of an airplane, this is one bit of information that is practically useless! At least, if g needs to be known for any purpose it would be better to measure it with an instrument. All the potentially useful data, which might serve to supplement visual information when it is meager, turn out to be grossly illusory.

Another way in which the non-auditory labyrinth may alter the perceptual field in flying is through the operation of the oculogyral illusion. We have already seen what the general conditions for the occurrence of this phenomenon are—a relatively dim but structured visual target viewed against darkness. If such a target is observed in the air during a banking maneuver the target appears to move, the induced motions being both those of total displacement in space and of rotation about the center. The rotary movements are always in the direction of the banking motion of the plane and have a maximum extent of 15 degrees. There is a lag of 4 to 6 sec between the beginning of the banking maneuver and the reported target rotation. The effect lasts varying amounts of time depending on stimulus intensity, from less than 10 sec (10-degree bank) to nearly 30 sec (60-degree bank). Total displacement of the target is a little less predictable but occurs, along with rotary motion, at all angles of bank. This form of distortion of the visual field apparently requires special conditions for its occurrence and thus does not constitute a very serious threat to the flyer. In ordinary daylight flying the visual field is too well illuminated and too replete with geometrical detail to be subject to the oculogyral illusion. In most night flying situations runway illumination, signal lights, cockpit illumination, and general ground lighting all aid in its avoidance. A more serious threat to safety in night flight seems to be occasioned by the so-called autokinetic phenomenon. This effect occurs when a single, relatively confined light source is stared at continuously over a period of time. The light appears to move, gliding, wavering, or wandering in an unpredictable manner through space. This phenomenon is not confined to aviation, of course; one can demonstrate it to himself quite readily in a dark room provided with a "point" source of light. But the autokinetic effect has special implications for aviation in that the conditions of its arousal occur not uncommonly in night flying. It has been responsible for many near accidents and probably, in military aviation, for some fatal ones. In formation flying at night the pilot "flying wing" on a squadron leader will attempt to maintain a constant distance between planes by steadily fixating the light on his leader's wing tip. After a prolonged period of this the autokinetic phenomenon may supervene. The light ahead may appear to describe an arc as in a "wingover" or other radical change in flight path; the hapless pilot makes rapid stick and rudder adjustments in an attempt to "follow," then finds himself either in a collision path with another aircraft or in a spin, recovery from which may be impossible. The use of flashing signal lights and higher illumination levels, together with repeated injunctions to pilots to keep their eyes moving about during night flights, have helped to reduce this particular hazard.

The non-auditory labyrinth enters into aviation, especially commercial flying, in yet another way; it is concerned with the production of air sickness. This malady, as much the plague of the airways as its relative, seasickness, is of the sea lanes, constitutes for many people a major deterrent to air travel. Air sickness and seasickness are members of a large family of which train sickness, car sickness, and the somewhat rarer illness experienced on roller coasters, during parachute descents, and while riding on camels are others. The feature all these forms of transportation have in common is regularly repeated motion of fairly low frequency. Motion sickness seems never to come from walking, running, or otherwise repeatedly jarring the head in a rapidly recurrent fashion. Marathon runners become exhausted but not nauseated. Nor is motion sickness ever an immediate effect of rhythmic motion; some little time is required for a "build-up" of the reaction.

The only comprehensive study of motion sickness ever to be undertaken is that of Wendt and his colleagues at the University of Rochester (307). They installed a vertical accelerator or "wave machine," a kind of elevator in which it is possible to vary waveform, degree of acceleration, velocity, and amplitude of movement, and frequency of wave repetition. These components of motion are combined in various ways to test their relative efficacy as generators of motion sickness. It turns out that sickness rate depends on the frequency with which wave motion is repeated, on waveform, and on total wave energy. As wave frequency is increased sickness rate increases, at first slowly then more rapidly, until a peak rate is reached at about 20 cycles/min. Above this frequency, where each phase of the motion recurs every 3 sec, the stimulus becomes less effective. Rapidly repeated waves result in very little illness. In one experiment more than one-third of the subjects became ill within 20 min when stimulated with a 9-ft wave repeated 13 times a minute, while only 7% became sick in response to a 1-ft wave having a frequency of 32 cycles/min. In another study a motion having an amplitude of 7 ft, occurring at the more moderate frequency of 22 per minute, induced illness in somewhat over half the members of a sizable group of naval officers.

Individual differences in susceptibility to motion sickness are notoriously large, as is also the number of alleged preventatives and cures. With the coming of the air age there has been a revival of nostrums and superstitious rules for conduct associated with seasickness and its "remedy." More happily, there have also been a few forward strides in the quest for the drug that will prevent motion sickness without at the same time depressing important bodily functions. During World War II it was important to prevent both air sickness and seasickness among troops during invasion operations. Considerable success attended the use of the hyoscine derivatives for this purpose. More recently significant promise, as motion sickness preventatives, has been shown by certain of the antihistamine drugs, notably dramamine.

Whatever the eventual solution of the problem of motion sickness, one knows in advance that it is not likely to be arrived at simply. Many different conditioning factors, both physiological and psychological, are known to be related to susceptibility. Moreover, there is an important adaptive effect with repeated exposure to motion which at present is both unpredictable and unexplained.

14

The Sense of Smell

Smell and Taste Confusions. Foods and beverages, once taken into the mouth, make at least a dual, usually a triple, appeal. The tissues of the mouth, throat, and nasal cavity are so innervated, and so disposed in relation to one another, that any or all of three sensory systems can go into operation simultaneously in response to the same stimulus. The cutaneous sensibilities of the mouth region are inevitably brought into play. They not only report on texture of foods but contribute the "biting," "burning," or astringent elements of certain of them and the "coolness" or tingle of others. The sense of taste is also obviously involved, end organs in·the tongue and palate accounting for a limited but basic repertory of sense qualities. It is, however, olfaction that furnishes the most elaborate of experiences connected with food, for it is the receptor system situated high in the nostrils that supplies the overtones for the fundamental tastes, that adds "aroma," that transforms sheer acceptance of food into appreciation of flavor. Were there no sense of smell there would be no gourmets, only consumers of nutriments.

We are constantly ascribing to taste those sensations that really belong to smell. The confusion is a natural one. Unless one takes the trouble to block off the nostrils and make the test to determine what the tongue by itself can do to identify food flavors, one may never discover how poor the sense of taste is and what a great richness and variety of experience are contributed by smell. The sense of taste, unassisted, is able to detect the sourness of acid, the sweetness of sugar, the bitterness of quinine, and the salt taste of sodium chloride. It fails utterly to encompass the full flavor of meats, fruits, butter, and coffee. These, together with nearly all other foods, depend for their appreciation mainly on their appeal to the sense of smell. Hold the nose and, except for the cues that may be offered to the sense of touch by textural features, a cube of raw potato may be indistinguishable from one of apple. Only the slight sweetness of each comes to register under these conditions. In a similar situation oil of peppermint has only a weakly bitter taste, while making its most forceful impression on cutaneous nerve endings to give a strong feeling of "coolness." With the nose out of action powdered cinnamon yields only a mild sweetness.

The relative sensitivities of the three systems encountered in the mouth and nose region—smell, taste, and feeling—can be assessed by using one of the relatively few substances which serves as a stimulus both to smell and to taste and which, in sufficiently high concentration, also chemically irritates the cutaneous fibers. Such a stimulus is ethyl alcohol. Thresholds of the three kinds of sensation show that smell is evoked with about 1/60,000 the concentration needed to produce a cutaneous ("burning") sensation, while taste results from about ⅓ the strength necessary for minimal arousal of the skin. Other stimuli would yield somewhat different indices of relative delicacy, but, by and large, they would show olfaction to be considerably ahead of the other two systems in absolute sensitivity. As Parker has said of taste and smell, ". . . the two senses may be said to differ from each other more or less as ordinary scales do from a chemical balance; taste is used in determining the presence of relatively large amounts of substance, smell for only the most minute quantities" (226, p. 238).

Physical Properties of Odors. A wide range of differently constituted materials possesses odor. One property they all have in common, however; they are all *volatile* substances. To stimulate the sense of smell materials must be air-borne and in a finely divided state. Solids, unless they pass over readily into the gaseous state at ordinary temperatures, cannot be smelled. Liquids do not become odorous until they vaporize.

Since volatility is a *sine qua non* for odors, the ease with which substances evaporate should provide an index of their relative stimulating power. If volatility were the only prerequisite the efficacy of a material as an odor stimulus would be given directly by its vapor pressure, since this is a measure of the facility with which molecules escape the parent substance and pervade the surrounding atmosphere. In a general way the relation holds. Highly odorous liquids are likely to have high vapor pressures; liquids of faint scent are likely to be of low vapor pressure. But there are prominent exceptions. Musk, for example, is one of the most powerful odorants known and is, for this reason, used effectively in the manufacture of perfumes. It is of low volatility, however. The answer in this case seems to be that musk owes its power as a smell stimulus to its favorable chemical composition; only relatively few molecules need be released for this material to be effective. Pure water has a relatively high vapor pressure but is, of course, odorless. Volatility seems to be a necessary but not a sufficient condition for the generation of odor.

Another physical characteristic of possible importance is solubility. The presumption is that odorous materials must be captured by the mucous lining of the nostrils before they can stimulate. This implies that the particles go into solution. If so, they presumably have to be water soluble. Perhaps the odorant must enter the cells containing the actual nerve endings. If so, the odorous material would have to be lipoid soluble as well.

A great many odorous substances are both water soluble and lipoid soluble, and a simple relation between ease of odor production and solubility has not been easy to establish. There are some provocative facts, however. The family of alcohols, which forms a so-called homologous series having the general chemical formula, $C_nH_{(2n+1)}OH$, contains some weakly odorous members, others which have strong odors, and still others that are odorless. The "lower" alcohols (those having few carbon atoms: methyl alcohol, CH_3OH, and ethyl alcohol, C_2H_5OH) have relatively feeble odors. These are readily soluble in water but are practically insoluble in fatty materials. The "higher" alcohols either have no odor at all or, like the lower ones, give only faint odors. Thus, cetyl alcohol, $C_{16}H_{33}OH$, is entirely without odor. In general, the higher alcohols are lipoid soluble but not water soluble. Between the two extremes of the series are a number of compounds which are both water and fat soluble. Butanol, C_4H_9OH, is such an alcohol; it has the powerful odor characteristic of rancid butter. Compounds in the middle of the series are uniformly quite odorous. This would suggest that an odorant, to be effective, has to possess both water and fat solubility. However, as in the case of the attempt to link odor production with volatility, there are exceptions to any such simple rule. One finds, for example, that acetone has low fat solubility but a strong odor. There are other cases which violate the rule and which prevent a straightforward linkage of solubility with odorousness. There remains the possibility, of course, that it is neither water nor fat solubility that is important. The mucous lining of the upper nostrils may have become specially modified, chemically and physically, to do its unique work and may, therefore, be of quite elaborate composition. Some attention has been given to the protein solubility of odorants (214, pp. 285–286), with the finding that certain odorants are more readily soluble in protein solutions than in water. This is a promising relation which needs to be investigated with systematic thoroughness, a treatment it has not received as yet.

In addition to volatility and solubility in one or another solvent, odorous materials necessarily possess a large number of other physical properties, some of which may conceivably have something to do with odor production. Many of these properties have been subject to study, and there are some suggestive results, though no sweeping generalities have as yet emerged. Several of the physical characteristics investigated have to do with the manner in which odorous substances absorb, scatter, refract, or otherwise react to light. It was noted long ago that many odorous solutions strongly absorb waves from the infrared portion of the electromagnetic spectrum. Recently there has been a revival of interest in this phenomenon, and one of the theories of olfaction we shall consider later takes this property of odorants as its starting point. Similar absorption in the ultraviolet region of the spectrum has been shown to occur, and this fact has also prompted a theory of odor. The interesting transformation of odorous solutions into colloidal suspensoids consequent upon ultraviolet irradiation, the curious fact that the vast majority of odors have refractive indices occupying a very narrow range of values in the neighborhood of 1.5, and the special behavior of odorants with respect to the so-called Raman shift have all been viewed as possible clues to the discovery of the central stimulus property for smell. The last mentioned, the Raman shift, may yet turn out to be important. Many liquids, odorants among them, have the property of so changing monochromatic light shining through them that some of the emergent waves are found to have frequencies both higher and lower than the one received. The difference between the wavelengths of incident and transmitted lights is the Raman shift. The claim is that only substances having shifts between 140 mμ and 350 mμ are odorous. Much remains to be learned about this relationship. Thus far we only know that the effect occurs with great regularity in odorous solutions, that it presumably is a direct indicator of quite specific intramolecular vibrations, and that many odors which have similar smells also show similar behavior with respect to their Raman spectra.

Odor and Chemical Composition. If there is uncertainty about the physical characteristics necessary in odors there is still more concerning their chemical qualifications. This is not for lack of chemical knowledge about odorous materials. We were perhaps better off in this respect in an earlier time when we knew less chemistry. As matters now stand it is quite impossible to devise any sweeping generalities about the chemical composition of odors. It is found that some compounds of quite different composition smell alike, while others of similar chemical structure are readily distinguished by smell. Even some compounds having identical molecular constituents, differing from each other only with respect to the spatial arrangement of certain of their atoms (stereoisomers), may yield different odors.

This is not to say that no predictions whatever as to odor can be made from a knowledge of chemical composition. Within certain families of substances it is possible to state fairly accurately what the substitution of one radical for another will do or how the addition to or subtraction from the molecule of a particular atom will affect odor. But the rules joining chemistry of odorants with olfactory sensitivity are certainly not uncomplicated, nor are we in possession of any master generalizations linking the two.

By and large, odor stimuli belong to the class of organic rather than inorganic substances. None of the chemical elements which occur free in nature is odorous under usual conditions. If heated to the point of vaporization elementary arsenic yields an odor, one strongly resembling garlic. There are 29 other elements which are also found in the free state; not one of them is capable of exciting smell without first combining with other elements to form compounds. Thus, both hydrogen and sulfur fail to stimulate the nostrils; let them combine to make hydrogen sulfide, and they set up a veritable stench. Of the remaining elements, which are normally to be found only in a combined state, only a few are of olfactory interest. These are the halogen family: chlorine, bromine, iodine, and fluorine; phosphorus, in the yellow form, P_4; and oxygen, as ozone, O_3. The halogens do not occur, at normal temperatures and pressures, in their atomic state. It is the diatomic molecules, Cl_2, Br_2, I_2, and F_2, that excite the sense of smell. The odor of chlorine is familiar from bleaching agents and disinfectants. Bromine and iodine somewhat resemble chlorine, though they are less irritating. Fluorine one handles with great respect, since its chief use (in the form of hydrofluoric acid) is to etch glass! In very dilute solutions it may be smelled, however. Like the other halogens it is an irritant and poisonous. Its odor somewhat resembles that of hypochlorous acid, HOCl, to which it is not too distantly related.

The fact that the only seven elements that excite olfaction lie in a somewhat restricted region of the periodic table (the halogens in Group 7, phosphorus and arsenic in Group 5, and oxygen in Group 6) has naturally been of interest to more than one theorist. It would appear that the capacity to function in a high state of valency has something to do with odor production. Yet one is barred from coming to a firm conclusion here by the equally evident fact that other elements in these groups are olfactorily inert.

Another "near generalization" arises from a consideration of the positions of the odorous elements in the so-called *electrochemical series*. The chemical elements may be arranged in sequence, from high to low, depending on the potential difference between the element and an aqueous solution of its salt. The greater the potential difference, the higher the element in the series. Those occupying the top positions, all metals, are able to displace lower elements from their salts. Now it turns out that six of the seven odorous elements occupy six of the last seven places in the series. Arsenic seriously violates the rule by appearing in the middle of the total series, however, and thus prevents the formulation of what might have become an important law of olfactory chemistry.

The key to the mystery of the chemical properties of odors is unlikely to be discovered either within the periodic table of elements or in the electrochemical series. These constructions are too simple. The vast majority of odorants are organic compounds and are relatively complex in constitution. With a few notable exceptions, such as carbon tetrachloride (CCl_4) and hexachlorethane (C_2Cl_6), organic materials always contain both carbon and hydrogen atoms. In addition, they are likely to contain oxygen. Commonly nitrogen, sulfur, or the halogens are represented in their structure. A wide range of other elements appears in organic compounds, though none other as frequently as those listed above.

Many families of organic compounds have been studied systematically with respect to their odor-producing characteristics. To be sure, there are resemblances of odor pretty clearly traceable to chemical similarities. In general, one expects compounds of phosphorus, bismuth, and arsenic to have odors reminiscent of garlic. Sulfur compounds, by and large, are vile smelling, as are also those of selenium and tellurium. Ethers and esters generally have fragrant odors; the fragrances yielded by many flowers and fruits are due to the esters exuded by them. However, exceptions to even such rules as these are frequent enough. Thus a prominent sulfur compound, ethyl sulfite, far from having an offensive odor, smells like peppermint. Some of the higher esters, such as refined beeswax, have no odor whatever, owing to their being insoluble and thus incapable of stimulating.

If there are direct and invariable links between chemical makeup and odor we certainly do not know what they are. The whole picture is further confounded by the fact that some organic compounds, certain of the substituted ammonias (amines) among them, change their odor with dilution. Ambergris and civet, both of which are animal secretions, behave in a similar manner, being repulsive in concentrated form but attractive, in fact used as constituents of expensive perfumes, when in great dilution.

The Olfactory Receptors. The airway of the nostril gives access to the sensitive nerve endings, all but hidden high in a crypt at the top

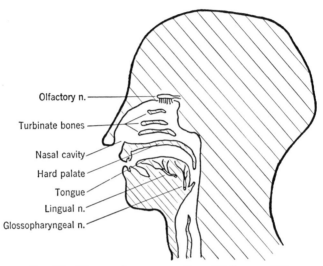

Olfactory n.
Turbinate bones
Nasal cavity
Hard palate
Tongue
Lingual n.
Glossopharyngeal n.

FIG. 87.   The nasal passages.   From Pfaffmann, 232.

of the nasal cavity. The sensitive region, called the *olfactory cleft,* occupies an area of about 2.5 cm² in each nostril. The two olfactory clefts are separated by the nasal septum.

Figure 87 diagrams the nasal passage and suggests some features of the aerodynamics of odor reception. The average volume of the human nasal chamber is 17.1 cc (34.2 cc for the two nostrils combined), and a considerable amount of odor-laden air may thus be in a position to bring about olfactory stimulation. The main movement of air, in ordinary breathing, takes place throughout a high arc in the streamlined nasal cavity, nearly all the inspired current passing through to the pharynx and lungs without affecting the olfactory cleft at all. Such air masses are not rigidly confined to a strictly limited path, however. Both by way of convection and diffusion odorous particles escape the main air stream and find their way to the uppermost reaches of the nasal chamber, where the sensitive olfactory epithelium lies. In mastication of food, motions of the palate and throat create small air movements that send odorous material up to the cleft by way of the rear access provided by the nasopharynx. Particularly during exhalation, but also during the irregular breathing created by sniffing, swirls of air are generated in the region of the superior turbinate (see Fig. 87), and "eddy currents" can then transport odorous particles to the sensitive region with some force.

Once having reached the olfactory cleft odorous materials can affect the sensitive receptors. In just what manner, whether by chemical or physical means, we do not know with certainty. But we do know something of the anatomical and physiological features of the presumed receptor cells. The system of nerve endings responsible for smell is, in many respects, the most primitive to be encountered in the body.

The entire patch of tissue which constitutes the surface of the olfactory cleft is known as the *olfactory mucosa* or *olfactory epithelium*. It consists of several million tiny endings of the first cranial (olfactory) nerve, together with an even larger number of columnar or *sustentacular* cells. As their name implies, the latter mainly serve the function of support, though it is the case that the columnar cells are also pigmented and give a brownish yellow appearance to the area. This tends to set the sensitive region off from the neighboring unpigmented epithelium. The nerve terminations, projecting through the supporting cells to the surface, are called *olfactory rods*. At their distal ends they have slight swellings, cup-shaped on the end, from which a cluster of a dozen or so hairs arises and projects out into the nasal cavity (*61*). The rods are true endings of olfactory nerve fibers. There is no synapse at the level of the epithelial tissues, each rod serving the roles of generator and conductor of nerve impulses. One might regard the olfactory rod as a kind of combined receptor and ganglion cell. Such duality of function is not uncommon in the relatively primitive nervous systems of some of the lower vertebrates. In this case it perhaps reflects the great antiquity of the olfactory system in phylogenetic development.

Figure 88 shows a strip of olfactory epithelium of the rabbit, whose cleft is better known by far than is that of the human. The density of receptors in the rabbit's mucosa is estimated to be 120,000 per square millimeter (*9*). As the nerve fibers leave the epithelium they are seen to converge into larger and larger bundles. There are no lateral connections to join one part of the sensitive area with another, nor is there any overlap in distribution of fibers. The nerve bundles pass through a number of perforations in the *cribriform plate* of the ethmoid bone, to which the olfactory epithelium is attached, and im-

278   The Sense of Smell

mediately enter the olfactory bulb, the farthest forward of the brain's extensions. Near the bulb's surface are encountered formations known as *glomeruli*, where the first synapse in the system occurs. In the human olfactory bulb there are perhaps 2000 glomeruli, each receiving many nerve fibers from the olfactory epithelium. A vast network of fibers arises at this point to complicate greatly the picture of nervous conduction. Two types of nerve cells participate, *mitral* cells and *tufted* cells. Dendrites of mitral cells are found in the glomeruli; their cell bodies lie deeper in the bulb. Some of the axons of mitral cells pass directly backwards to form the olfactory tract. Others connect

FIG. 88. The olfactory epithelium of the rabbit. A main bundle of olfactory nerve fibers is shown in the region of its termination in the mucosa. From Clark and Warwick, *61*. By permission of the editor, *Journal of Neurology, Neurosurgery and Psychiatry.*

with nearby tufted cells, which in turn send axons back to enter the glomeruli. A circular pathway is thus created, a so-called "reverberatory circuit." The guess is that this kind of arrangement makes for "amplification" of the nerve message, behaving much like a regenerating radio receiver network, and may thus serve to improve the general level of olfactory sensitivity.

In view of this elaborate set of pathways it would be important to know to what extent there is preserved point-to-point transport of impulses from the sensitive epithelium to the beginning of the olfactory tract. Is it possible for olfactory impulses to be organized spatially, as those of all other modalities conceivably are? Adrian (3) has adduced some evidence that there is at least a primitive spatial patterning, some parts of the olfactory tract responding somewhat differentially to different groups of odors. Prompted by this discovery, Clark (60) has carefully followed out the degeneration patterns in the olfactory epithelium of rabbits who had been given localized lesions of the olfactory bulb. Some degree of regional projection was found. Both the anatomical and neurophysiological possibilities for spatial organization are apparently present.

We shall not attempt to trace in detail the complicated and as yet little understood pathways from the olfactory bulb back to the cortical smell centers. Considering the relatively minor role that olfaction plays in human life we have a remarkably elaborate olfactory tract. It is, of course, a bequest from our animal ancestors, whose noses were much closer to the ground and for whom olfactory decisions were often life or death affairs. Currently, a many-sided experimental approach is being made in an effort to determine just what parts of the brain are involved in olfaction (215, pp. 113–116). The techniques in use are, in general, those found successful in the other sense departments: (a) removal of animals' central nervous tissue in varying amounts and in different locations, with a view to noting the effects on a pre-established discrimination or conditioned response; (b) stimulation, electrically or chemically, of the motor areas of the brain in an effort to arouse muscular responses associated with olfaction (e.g., chewing and swallowing movements); (c) recording of action potentials at various levels of the central nervous system when the sense organ is being stimulated. The evidences coming from these diverse approaches have then to be put together with those offered by neural anatomy.

Insofar as the various lines of evidence speak with a common voice they point to the cortical areas lying deep in the center of the brain mass as the projection zones for smell. Areas that are suspected occupy a nearly closed ring in the lower part of the mesial surface of the rhinencephalon (the "smell brain"). A prominent candidate is the pyriform area, since it readily reveals electrical activity during olfactory stimulation. The olfactory tract differs from all other sensory systems in that it fails to pass through the thalamus on its way to the cortex. By indirect connection the hypothalamus presumably gets involved, however; at least, the anatomical pathways for such connection are present.

Olfactometry. If we raise the question of the minimal stimulus for olfaction, as we did for vision, hearing, and touch, we shall be able to get some answers, though they will not be as satisfactory as for the other senses. It is possible to make the measurements but, thus far at least, not in terms of energetics. We shall not be able to say what amount of physical energy is transferred from the stimulus to the sense organ in passing the absolute threshold for odor. Methods are available, however, for determining fairly accurately the threshold amounts of odorous materials. It is even possible to calculate the number of molecules present at threshold concentration. In the case of the strongest odorants the amount that has to be released, to be just detected by the nostrils, is so small that there are no means, chemical or physical, of directly measuring it. The threshold quantity is not indeterminate, however. By starting with a known concentration of the odorous substance and evaporating it into a known volume of air, then repeatedly mixing this with equal parts of air to produce progressive dilutions of ½, ¼, ⅛, etc., a point will be reached where odor sensation will just fail to be elicited. A series of connected containers which will produce such a systematic weakening of an odorant is known as a *dilution osmoscope.*

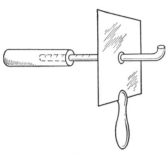

FIG. 89. The Zwaardemaker (single) olfactometer. A hard rubber cylinder, impregnated with odorous material, fits loosely on one end of a glass tube, the other end of which enters the nostril. Variations in odor strength are obtained by changing the cylinder's position. From Pfaffmann, 232.

By this method of measuring the absolute threshold it has been found that the minimum perceptible concentration of vanillin is of the order of 2 ten-millionths of a milligram per cubic meter of air, that of mercaptan (C_2H_5SH) is 0.00004 mg/m^3, while diethyl ether (the anesthetic, $C_2H_5OC_2H_5$) has a threshold concentration of about 1.0 mg/m^3 of air. In the case of mercaptan, it has been calculated that there need be only 1 molecule per 50 trillion molecules of air for this foul odor to be detected. Of course, it should be pointed out that we are talking of molecules, and a "sniff" of 20 cc volume, at the same threshold concentration, could be expected to contain about 10 trillion molecules of mercaptan (*214*, p. 79).

Most studies involving the determination of smell thresholds have made use of the *olfactometer,* an instrument designed by the Dutch physiologist, Zwaardemaker. It is illustrated in Fig. 89. In its simplest form it consists of a glass tube, open at both ends, over which is loosely slipped a hard rubber or plastic tube, the inner surface of the latter being impregnated with an odorous material. A scale etched on the inner tube indicates the position of the outer one and thus the extent of odor-bearing surface exposed to the stream of air created by the subject's inhalation. The olfactometer exists in two forms, single and double, for stimulation of one nostril (*monorhinic*) or for two simultaneously (*dirhinic*, same odor in both nostrils; *dichorhinic*, different odors). As standardized by Zwaardemaker the odor cylinder has an inner diameter of 0.8 cm, a length of 10 cm, and a volume of

50 cc. The instrument's scale may be calibrated in smell units, "olfacties," one olfactie being the number of centimeters exposed when
threshold is reached. Instead of relying upon a "standard sniff" to
deliver the odorous particles, some experimenters have attached a
small continuous-flow pump to the instrument, and air moving at 100
cc/sec has been blown through the sys-
tem for an exposure period of ⅓ sec.

It is this difficulty of insuring that
a constant amount of odorous material
will be conveyed to the olfactory cleft
in successive exposures that has led
to the substitution, more recently, of
another olfactometric technique for
the one devised by Zwaardemaker.
Elsberg and Levy (88) have developed the so-called "blast injection"
method of odor stimulation (Fig. 90).
In this procedure an odorous liquid is
poured into a 500-cc bottle. An outlet tube leads to the nostrils; an inlet
tube is attached to a hypodermic
syringe. A pinchcock on the outlet
is kept closed while a few cubic centimeters of air is forced into the bottle,
using the syringe as a pump. With
the nose piece in place the pinchcock
is suddenly removed, releasing a
"blast" of odorous vapor into the
nostrils. In successive trials the air

Fig. 90. Apparatus used in the
blast injection technique of Elsberg and Levy (88). An odorous
solution is contained in a 500-cc
bottle. A known small pressure is
created with a hypodermic syringe
(seen on the right), and the release of a stopcock sends a "blast"
of saturated vapor through the
nosepieces. From Pfaffmann, 232.

pressure is varied to find the threshold, which then may be specified
in terms of syringe graduations, viz., amounts of excess air pressure
in cubic centimeters. As in the case of the olfactometer a continuous
stream of air may be supplied, of course, by attaching the inlet to a
compressed air tank or rotary pump. When so modified, the technique
is called the "stream injection" method.

The blast injection technique, though fairly widely used for both
experimental and clinical purposes, possesses a serious inherent fault.
Pressure variations, as well as causing differing amounts of odor-laden
air to be "blasted" up to the olfactory cleft, make a differential appeal
to the cutaneous receptors of the nostrils. In threshold determinations,
therefore, air pressure, rather than odor intensity, may provide the
cue. This seems to be the source of the difficulty in Wenzel's (308)

attempted measurement of the differential threshold for one of the alcohols, even though she improved the original Elsberg technique notably by arranging for uniform pressure to be exerted throughout the duration of a given exposure.

The most elaborate of all attempts to measure olfactory sensitivity is found in the "olfactorium" (96), an instrument consisting of a glass double chamber of 250 ft³ capacity. In the inventors' view the taking of olfactory thresholds in an ordinary room is like attempting to perform audiometric measurements on a busy street corner. In the use of the olfactorium the experimental subject first bathes to eliminate residual body odors, then slips into a plastic envelope before entering the inner glass chamber, a "completely controlled odor environment." Pure air or odor-bearing air of predetermined composition, temperature, humidity, and pressure can be introduced at different places and by different methods to the cabinet. This much preparation for odor stimulation may seem like the ultimate in experimental precautions, but it is probably the case that the low reliability attending measurements in olfaction are due, more often than not, to failure to effect the obvious controls of important variables.

Differential Olfactory Sensitivity. The question of ΔI, and the further one of Weber's fraction, $\Delta I/I$, may be raised for smell as for the other sense modalities. Experimental determinations of ΔI, made by several different investigators and covering a span of half a century, are in fair agreement. If absolute smell sensitivity is high, differential sensitivity is not; values of ΔI, for several different odorous substances, prove to be uniformly large. According to the results obtained by Zigler and Holway (328), who used a modification of Zwaardemaker's olfactometer to measure ΔI for India rubber, the Weber fraction varies systematically with absolute intensity. Thus $\Delta I/I$ has a value close to 1.0 when I is at the low level of 10 olfacties. At 400 olfacties, the highest intensity used, the Weber fraction diminishes to about 0.2. Intervening values show a progressive lowering of $\Delta I/I$ as absolute intensity is increased. Apparently Weber's "Law" ($\Delta I/I = K$) holds no more exactly for olfaction than it does for the other senses.

The Olfactory Qualities. It has been seen that chemical composition seems not to serve as an entirely adequate basis for the classification of odors. What happens if we rely on direct observation of smell sensations? Many attempts have been made to classify odors on the basis of their resemblances and differences. Odor systems abound. One of the oldest of them, dating from the middle of the eighteenth century, was devised by the Swedish botanist, Linnaeus. It was his odor system, developed primarily as an aid in the classification of plants, that was amplified slightly by Zwaardemaker to give the frequently-repeated ninefold arrangement of odor qualities: ethereal (fruits, wines); aromatic (spices, camphor); fragrant (flowers, vanilla); ambrosiac (musk, sandalwood); alliaceous (garlic, chlorine); empyreumatic (roasted coffee, creosote); hircine (goaty odors, rancid fat); foul (bedbugs, French marigolds); and nauseous (feces, carrion flowers). There are some obvious difficulties with this grouping of odors. Among the thousands of specific smells that have to be accommodated by the nine categories there are doubtless many hundreds that could not reasonably be pressed into so simple a scheme. Moreover, it is quite possible to find odors in two different categories of Zwaardemaker's listing that have more resemblance to each other than they do to their fellows in the same odor class. Of course, these are the common difficulties of classification systems, particularly where distinctions are difficult and the number of classificatory rubrics is limited.

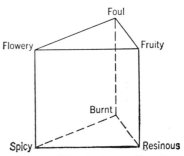

Fig. 91. Henning's smell prism. The figure is a hollow one with the six "primaries" occupying the corners and all surfaces being the loci of odors which bear resemblances to several primaries.

Another attempt at odor classification is that of Henning, who has given us the analytic scheme represented by the smell prism (Fig. 91). The triangular prism is intended to be a hollow one with a multitude of discrete odors occupying each of the surfaces. The "primary" qualities are found at the corners: flowery, fruity, foul, spicy, resinous, and burnt. Like all such models of sensory qualities Henning's smell prism is partly based on experimental findings, partly on purely rational considerations. And, like many such geometrical constructions, the figure has a number of unwanted implications inherent in it. Any odor appearing on a line bounding one of the prism faces should have a dual reference. It should resemble both the qualities terminating the line on which it stands. Thus, the odor of thyme should equally resemble "spicy" and "flowery," since it stands on the edge midway between these two corners. Similarly, sassafras is equally "spicy" and "resinous," acetone is equally "resinous" and "fruity," and oil of roses is equally "fruity" and "flowery." Odors standing on one of the square faces of the prism should have a quadruple reference but should most strongly resemble the qualities at the nearest corners. In the same way, odors lying along diagonal lines that bisect a prism face should have four reference points, since they are at the same time on a face of the prism. An odor lying at the center of a face should equally resemble all the four primaries from which it is equidistant.

There has been, in the main, quite general failure to establish the validity of Henning's smell prism through experimental check. Large individual differences in reaction are encountered, and analytical judgments of odors possess less reliability than could be desired, even where observers have had some training. Difficulties of this sort are found—an observer will report that menthol, say, has an equal resemblance to "resinous" and "flowery" yet deny that it is either "spicy" or "fruity." Moreover, the position his analysis gives it is the center of the flowery-fruity-resinous-spicy face of the prism, and this is already occupied by the odor of arbor vitae. And menthol does not smell like arbor vitae!

The triangular prism, with its limitation to six fundamental odors, seems not to do justice to the complexities of odor sensation. Woodworth, who has made a careful evaluation of Henning's system (*319*, pp. 482–492), believes that much of the difficulty arises from the non-olfactory components in odor reception. Many odorants stimulate the cutaneous endings in the walls of the nostrils, the resulting sensation being reported over the trigeminal nerve as well as the olfactory. Many other scented materials make a separate appeal to taste. The result is a complex perception, smell plus sweet, sour, cold, warm, or pain—and mixtures of these—which prevents the formation of a simple, reliable judgment concerning the odor component.

If it appears impossible to force all smell sensations into Zwaarde-maker's ninefold arrangement or Henning's sixfold one it is perhaps not surprising that another odor system, which attempts to get along with but four categories, should have some difficulty establishing itself (*64*). The Crocker-Henderson system posits four fundamental odors: fragrant, acid, burnt, and caprylic (goaty). Three of these are familiar from other odor classifications, but "acid" is a term more commonly associated with taste than with smell. Each of the four fundamental qualities is supposed to occur in most complex scents but with varying intensity from substance to substance. The presence of each is presumably detectable in the complex, and not only may it be analyzed out with a little practice but a numerical rating may be given to it, based on relative sensory intensity. The scale selected is a nine point one, 0–8 inclusive. Thus phenylethyl alcohol is said to be fragrant in degree 7, acid in degree 4, burnt in degree 2, and caprylic

in degree 3. Phenylethyl alcohol may thus be designated in num
code: 7423. In the same way a 20% solution of acetic acid is n
fragrant and goaty, intensely acid, and not at all burnt. Its symbol is
3803. Methyl salicylate stands at the top of the scale of fragrance
(8453), while toluene is near the bottom of it (2424). Damask rose
has few objectionable qualities (6523). Anisole, with the designation 2577, seems best to be described as having a somewhat sour,
quite burnt and goaty odor.

The scheme is an ingenious one, and there are some obvious advantages in specifying odors by numerical code. The test of the Crocker-
Henderson system, however, would seem to lie in its adequacy to
yield reproducible and unvarying analyses of odorants. Thus far
there seems not to have been an entirely unobjectionable evaluation of
the system in this regard. One should be forthcoming, for the basic
standards of the system have been made commercially available, and
there is only required the properly designed experiment to make the
rendering of a verdict possible.

Other attempts at systematizing odor sensations have been made,
none of them with conspicuous success. It has been supposed that
some central principles of smell organization might come from the
application of the mathematical technique of factor analysis, and
several sets of data involving olfactory judgments have been treated
in this way. Thus Hsü (169) has factor analyzed the ratings made
of 31 odors with respect to the dimension of pleasantness-unpleasant-
ness. Three clusters of odorants appeared in the analysis, one group
characterized by chemical unsaturation (a benzene-ketone group),
another having oxygen uniformly present in the molecule (a "plant"
group of odors), and a third possessing nitrogen (an "animal" group).
Statistical interrelations were sufficiently intimate to prevent a high
degree of discreteness in the groupings. One would certainly do as
well, in devising a classificatory system, to sort out smells on the basis
of the chemical structure of their stimuli, and, to be sure, we have
already seen what comes of that. Moreover, affective ratings of odors
would hardly seem to be the stuff of which to fabricate an odor system.

Adaptation. In common with all other sensory systems in the body
the olfactory sense displays the phenomenon of adaptation. In the
absence of any odor stimulation there is a gain in sensitivity, reminiscent of dark adaptation in vision. Also, like the analogous phenomenon of visual light adaptation, there is a decline in sensitivity with
continuous odor stimulation. The latter effect, also known as smell
fatigue or smell exhaustion, is responsible for some quite abrupt re-

ductions in acuity, changes which on occasion come to be of very real practical concern. Miners long ago recognized the principle, at least implicitly, in their use of canaries and mice for the early detection of the presence of methane which, because of the operation of adaptation, might go unnoticed by human nostrils.

The high levels of sensitivity obtainable through complete removal of olfactory stimuli have not often been studied. Entirely odor-free surroundings were provided, however, by the *camera inodorata* of Komuro (*189*), one of Zwaardemaker's students, and it was possible to measure sensitivity to a number of odorants under the contrasting conditions of (*a*) prior exposure to the purest of air, and (*b*) previous adaptation to the air of the laboratory. Threshold measurements to nine organic reagents were made with the olfactometer. Reductions in threshold values, from the contaminated to the pure air situation, ranged from 9% in the case of pyridine to 39% for artificial musk. The average drop in threshold was of the order of 25%. Apparently we go about partially odor-adapted most of the time.

Sensitivity changes of the opposite variety, reductions attendant upon continued exposure, have not in general received the complete and systematic experimental treatment they deserve. It should theoretically be possible to learn a great deal about the fundamental properties of smell receptivity from curves depicting the course of olfactory adaptation. In fact, it would be safe to say that we should be in a position to solve many of the problems already posed, e.g., the basic one of odor classification, if we had an intimate picture of the adaptation process, including its dependency on stimulus composition and intensity, for a wide range of smell stimuli. The failure to quantify the olfactory adaptation picture is, of course, not entirely due to oversight. We have already seen something of the difficulties of stimulus control in this area.

Adaptation rate, in whatever sense department it is investigated, proves to be a function of stimulus intensity. Some experiments performed by Zwaardemaker show that the sense of smell is not exceptional in this regard. Figure 92 reveals the progressive raising of the absolute threshold to two different concentrations of benzoin and of India rubber as the time of exposure is increased. In the case of benzoin, to which adaptation is the more rapid, a concentration measuring 9 olfacties with the olfactometer produces a nearly fourfold heightening of the absolute threshold in 5 sec, a change requiring about three times as long with the lower concentration of 3.5 olfacties. Similarly, in the case of the more slowly adapting India rubber, a stimulus having a strength of 14 olfacties brings about the same fourfold threshold increase in a half-minute, whereas the 10-olfactie stimulus requires 45 sec to effect a change of this magnitude.

It is apparent from the straight-line relationships shown in Fig. 92 that the adaptation process in these cases has not as yet been brought to completion. Either there should be a leveling off of thresholds at some high point on the olfactie scale, adaptation having brought about a new equilibrium with the olfactory environment, or thresholds should become infinitely high. As a matter of fact, the latter should occur because, unlike visual and auditory sensations, which adapt down to a lowered brightness or loudness level but which never reduce themselves to zero intensity so long as the adapting stimulus remains unchanged, odor sensations normally adapt out completely upon prolonged stimulation. This is at once a blessing, in the case of the tannery worker, and a hazard, in the case of those whose "best friends will not even tell them"!

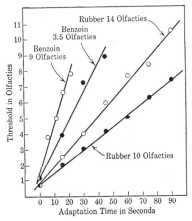

Fig. 92. Olfactory adaptation to two concentrations of benzoin and India rubber. Thresholds are progressively raised as adaptation proceeds. The rate of adaptation is faster for benzoin than for rubber. In each case there is more rapid adaptation to the stronger stimulus. After Zwaardemaker, 329.

Several other phenomena connected with adaptation appear to be important, but much more work will have to be done on them before their full import can be known. Thus, certain odors undergo qualitative changes along with the intensitive one caused by continuous exposure. A case in point is that of ionone, a ketone used extensively in the manufacture of perfumes. In strong concentrations it resembles cedarwood, but with continuous smelling it changes to its more familiar odor, one simulating that of violets. Similarly, nitrobenzol has a "bitter almond" odor when first smelled but takes on a quality more nearly resembling that of tar as adaptation proceeds. If the qualitative changes produced by adaptation were charted for all odorants we should be in possession of a powerful set of facts.

Another effect which is known, but not systematically explored as yet, has to do with the selective nature of adaptation. Many odors behave in a relatively specific fashion when adaptation takes place; i.e., not only is their own threshold raised but those of other odors suffer as well. Adaptation to camphor severely affects thresholds of Eau de Cologne, oil of clove, oil of eucalyptus, and ether. To a lesser extent sensitivity to citral (oil of lemon) and safrol (oil of sassafras) is also reduced, while that to some other odors, e.g., benzaldehyde, are relatively unaffected. The relations seem to be mutual; complete adaptation to benzaldehyde leaves camphor, clove, and eucalyptus likewise unaffected. The occurrence of specific fatigue effects of this kind implies some natural groupings of odors.

Odor Mixture. That we are as yet quite ignorant of even the simplest relations between different odors is abundantly evident from the current uncertainties regarding their classification. Many thousands of different scents can be discriminated; just how many is not known. And with each passing day the organic chemist is adding new ones. It is quite possible, however, that only a few *elementary* odors are needed to account for the whole range of possible smells. The situation may be much as it is in color, where three primaries are sufficient to synthesize the total gamut of visible hues. Were we as certain of the facts of odor mixture as we are the facts of color mixture, we should be able to approach with confidence such problems as those of odor specification and flavor analysis. As matters now stand our information along these lines is at best characterized as sketchy.

In a general way the procedures available for the mixture of odorous stimuli are analogous to those used in color mixture. Just as one may produce composite colors by superposing on a reflecting screen two different spectral samples, then observing the single result of their union at the retina, "composite" odors may be arrived at by physically mixing two odorous liquids or vapors in a container and sniffing the combined product. There is this difference, however. The spectral samples will lose their identities in the new fusion. Orange may "resemble" both red and yellow, but one does not first see red, then yellow, in the blend. Odors, unless they bear a close qualitative resemblance to each other to begin with, are unlikely to mix with this degree of intimacy. The possible results of the simple mixture of two dissimilar odorous stimuli seem to be: (1) a composite which yields a unitary impression, the new odor resembling both the original constituents; (2) a loosely organized blend in which the originals are successively perceived, each being momentarily present to the exclusion of the other; (3) a fusion, somewhat like a musical chord, where the "partials" can be attended to separately but a unified *Gestalt* is never lost; (4) complete masking of one of the two originals so that only the other survives the combining process; and, more doubtfully,

(5) neutralization of each by the other so that the net result is total cancellation of odor.

This last possibility, odor neutralization or "compensation," has been the subject of controversy. Zwaardemaker found it to occur with a number of opposed odors (e.g., cedarwood and India rubber; balsam and beeswax), but Henning regarded the effect to be a sheer myth. It should be said straightway that the bringing together of odorous materials to permit their possible chemical interaction is not at all concerned here. Such "mixture" only produces stimulus alteration, of course. Usually the result of such a change is quite predictable from a knowledge of the component qualities and concentrations. In the case of compensatory mixtures what we are interested in is the result of simultaneous arousal of two antagonistic olfactory processes which may interfere with each other and tend to obliterate sensation. To settle the question it would seem to be necessary to keep the two opposed odorants apart, letting each stimulate a separate receptive area. This can be done, of course, with a double olfactometer and dichorhinic stimulation, since the nasal septum insulates the two clefts from each other. The procedure is analogous to binocular color mixing where blue, presented to one eye, cancels out complementary yellow, presented to the other, to give gray.

Dichorhinic mixing has been performed with many odorants and by many experimenters, but there seems not to be much agreement on the facts. Zwaardemaker regularly combined different odors, always of low intensity, to produce odorlessness. He cautioned that complete neutralization can come about only by the most careful selection of stimuli and graduation of their strengths. Even then the zero point may be only fleetingly observed. Complete neutralization in a three-component mixture he reported to be more difficult of achievement. He obtained it only once in the exploration of 252 mixtures, then by combining terpineol, ethyl bisulfide, and guaiacol (*330*, p. 502). Henning, who also experimented extensively with odor mixtures, denied the possibility of complete neutralization. In dichorhinic smelling, which he regarded to be unnatural and therefore untrustworthy as a technique, there could be unions of two odors which he called "coincidence smells," blends having a unitary character but in which the components could be held apart by straining attention. There could also be "duality smells," where the two odors seemed to have separate but simultaneous existences, each being clearly localized in its own nostril. However, complete abolition of odor through cancellation he thought occurred only through chemical interaction, never through true "physiological mixing."

The resolution of this question lies in the future. Meanwhile, it is possible that Henning was looking for an effect having far greater stability than odor neutralization is supposed to have. It is certainly the case that mixtures tending toward cancellation occur commonly enough. In medical practice Peruvian balsam may be used to neutralize the odor of iodoform. Carbolic acid is often used to counteract objectionable biological odors. Florists know that some flowers, more desirable for their appearance than their fragrance, may be rendered olfactorily inoffensive by adding other odorous flowers or leaves to the bouquet containing them. Within the chemical industry there is a well-developed effort to "engineer" odors. Thus, because many people find sponge rubber, increasingly being used in upholstery and bedding, to have an objectionable scent about it, there is used in its manufacture a "reodorant" which makes the product more generally acceptable. All this may be "masking" rather than "mixing." If so, a separation of the principles should come out of properly designed quantitative experiments; further qualitative ones are unlikely to decide the issue.

The Electrophysiology of Smell. The changes occurring in the olfactory nerve when odors stimulate the receptor cells have been studied, but they are not known as intimately as are analogous events in other sense departments, vision and audition in particular. Part of the difficulty in getting a better picture of the nerve's response should be suggested by the obvious anatomical barriers to such study. Fibers leading from the olfactory epithelium to the bulb are completely inaccessible and, in any case, are fine, unmyelinated threads with little structural strength. No one has ever succeeded in recording the electrical activity in them. However, secondary neurones can be gotten at in favorable preparations. In some fishes—the catfish, carp, and tench have been studied—the olfactory bulb is attached to the forebrain by a relatively long "olfactory stalk" in which the fibers are medullated ones. By careful dissection the bundle can be gotten down to relatively few surviving fibers and their action potentials can be picked up, amplified, and recorded. Several mammalian forms have also proved to be susceptible of study, though here there is no stalk and it becomes necessary to plunge microelectrodes into the olfactory bulb or some other portion of the central tract to detect electrical changes associated with odor reception.

Adrian (3) has performed the most extensive experiments. Using fine wire electrodes, insulated except at the tips, he inserted them into various portions of the bulb to a level that would contact the axons of mitral cells. Bursts of action potentials accompanied each inspiration of odor-laden air, provided the right odorants were used and in sufficient concentration. In general the materials effective for human noses proved also to arouse olfactory reactions in cats, rabbits, and hedgehogs. Thus odorless air, carbon monoxide, and carbon dioxide were without effect. Compounds such as hydrogen sulfide, benzene, and acetylene produced trains of impulses. Some interesting species differences appeared. The rabbit gave the best potentials to fruity and aromatic smells, while the cat, unresponsive to floral odors, was especially sensitive to decaying animal material. The hedgehog is characterized by great olfactory versatility, a great range of substances evoking action potentials. Catfish responded strongly to foul materials, the most efficacious of Adrian's stimuli having been a kind of purée of decayed alligator head!

Records of electrical activity taken from electrodes embedded in the olfactory bulb necessarily represent the summed effect of many primary neurones. At best the projection involved is of a fairly general region of the olfactory epithelium, and the end organs contributing to the recorded potentials must be somewhat sparsely distributed throughout that region. It is a matter of considerable interest and no little theoretical importance, therefore, to find that some differences of discharge pattern can be detected by comparing the records taken from different portions of the olfactory bulb. In the cat the anterior-dorsal portion of the bulb shows its best response to amyl acetate and close chemical relatives. Such odors give an abrupt discharge which begins and ends with the intake of breath. Hydrocarbons, coal gas especially, make their strongest appeal to the posterior-ventral portion of the bulb. The potentials arising from their action are relatively slowly developing, rather than abrupt, and outlast somewhat the movement of air carrying the scent. A third area in the cat's olfactory lobe, having a posterior-dorsal location, gives its greatest effect when the stimulus is decayed meat or fish. Trimethylamine, which has a fishy odor, produces a large response in this area. There are thus at least three spatial-temporal patterns of excitation that can be shown to be connected with stimulus constitution. Perhaps a more thorough search will reveal additional ones.

Theories of Smell Sensitivity. Where facts are sparse, guesses are likely to abound. Lack of a sufficiently extensive body of established fact prevents the formation of a consistent and inclusive theory of smell. In its place there has accumulated a multiplicity of ideas, few of which can be dignified with the name "theory" or even "hypothesis."

Moncrieff (*214*, p. 314) catalogues 22 separate attempts at providing an odor theory, the earliest dating from 1870. Approximately half of them look to one or another chemical feature of odorants as the basic principle. Most of the remainder emphasize intramolecular vibrations and make of odors sources of wave motion which may arouse the olfactory epithelium to action.

The test of a theory, as we have had occasion to note several times previously while evaluating theories in other sense departments, is provided by (1) its ability to accommodate all relevant existing facts, or at least the better established of them, and (2) its fruitfulness in suggesting new hypotheses, in the experimental verification of which new facts will emerge. Theories of smell which meet these standards adequately are non-existent. Most of the possible candidates fall down on the first requirement. Not being broadly conceived, they are restricted to consideration of but a single chemical or physical property of odors. Other equally significant facts arise to embarrass them. Nearly all theoretical constructions in this field fail also to meet the second specification of acceptable theories, that they generate experimentally testable hypotheses. In this regard, however, one should not be too critical, for the failure may not be one of thought or ingenuity. The familiar barriers to olfactory research, difficulties of stimulus control and inaccessibility of receptors, may be more to blame.

The theoretical ideas thus far advanced are broadly classifiable into three categories, based on central emphasis: (1) those employing the notion of direct radiation from the odorous source; (2) those positing chemical reactivity as a necessary step in reception; and (3) those involving a radiation mechanism within the nostrils, once the odorous vapor has come into proximity with the olfactory epithelium.

The first of these need not detain us long; several simple considerations defeat it. The facts that odors travel with the wind, are not transmitted through transparent solids or reflected from mirrors, have their strength altered by temperature changes—to mention only a few —all speak against odor as a form of wave motion or corpuscular streaming from the source of scent to the nose.

What of the second class of theoretical constructions, those postulating the occurrence of chemical reactions between particles of the odorant and the tissues in the olfactory cleft? This type of theory has to be taken more seriously. That many of the changes characteristic of chemical reactions actually occur in the course of odor reception cannot be denied. The general facts concerning volatility and solubility we have already reviewed. It is a natural assumption that odor particles, having arrived at the cleft in vaporous form, enter into chemical combination with the substances there, whether aqueous or lipoid, protein or enzyme. A specific hypothesis based on the last-mentioned possibility is that of Kistiakowsky (185). He speculates that the olfactory nerve response may be set off by a system of reactions that are catalyzed by enzymes, as yet unidentified but present in the olfactory epithelium in a number related to that of "the number of basic smells." An odorant is pictured as inhibiting the action of one or more of the enzymes. This in turn causes shifts in the concentrations of the basic smell substances. Such changed concentrations are sufficient to set off appropriate impulses in the first cranial nerve. Kistiakowsky's hypothesis is in harmony with several salient features of the olfactory process and possesses, in addition, the real merit of being relatively simple in conception. The most important argument that can be urged against it applies with equal force to all other chemical hypotheses of odor stimulation, viz., it is difficult to picture a reaction based on sheer chemical change that observes the time schedule found in odor reception. Smell sensations are initiated practically coincidentally with the movement of odor-laden air in the nostrils. Moreover, in most instances there appears to be no perceptible lag in bringing the response to an abrupt termination. The sensation does not appreciably outlast the stimulus, so far as can be judged. How the slate can thus be wiped clean in the twinkling of an eye is not clear. Perhaps, if all the facts were known, we should find that there are greater delays than there appear to be. Perhaps the time relations are not inconsistent with the operation of substances as dilute as the olfactory enzymes need to be. Perhaps—and this seems not improbable— we are dealing with a mechanism not unlike that hypothesized by Bazett for temperature stimulation of the skin (see Chap. 11). Perhaps a "gradient" of absorption, regulated primarily by the velocity with which odor-laden air strikes the sensitive epithelium, is a necessary condition. Data on the rapidity with which successive odors can replace each other in sensation would be vital to such a hypothesis. Only more intimate studies of events transpiring at the cleft can provide the necessary answers.

The third type of hypothesis—that postulating vibrational interchange between odorous vapors in the nostrils and the sensitive tissue surface—exists in several different forms. Here belong Dyson's theory of the Raman shift, already alluded to, and Heyninx' belief that the molecules of odorous materials vibrate with a period equal to that of the ultraviolet light they absorb. Here also belongs the hypothesis, revived and elaborated by Miles and Beck (24), that odors are appreciated by way of their infrared absorbing characteristics. It has been known since the researches of Faraday that odorous substances strongly absorb energy from the infrared portion of the electromagnetic spectrum, waves varying roughly from 1 μ to 100 μ in length. The human body is, of course, an infrared radiator. At normal body temperature waves ranging from 4 μ to 20 μ, with a peak intensity at about 9 μ, are emitted. This being the case, so the theory goes, an odorous vapor in the nostrils can be expected to absorb infrared radiation in accordance with its own unique absorption spectrum, thus producing a transient local cooling of hair cells in the olfactory epithelium. A pattern of receptor elements, thrown out of dynamic equilibrium, discharges its fibers and reports the presence of the absorbent odorous substance.

Several serious objections to the infrared radiation theory have been offered. There are optical isomers of certain substances, limonene, e.g., that have precisely the same pattern of infrared absorption but which can be distinguished from each other on the basis of smell. The d-limonene form smells like freshly crushed lemon rind, while l-limonene resembles a moldy lemon. Another pair of isomers, hence with identical infrared lines, are d-carvone and l-carvone. The dextro-member is variously described as like dill or caraway, while the levo-form smells like spearmint. It is possible that the infrared absorption hypothesis can extricate itself from such embarrassments. Meanwhile, it is not apparent that the human nose is designed to do the work of an infrared spectrometer, which is substantially what this provocative but unconvincing theory demands.

15

The Sense of Taste

Taste is the "poor relation" of the family of senses. It is poor in having only a restricted set of qualities to contribute to the sum of human experience. It is also relatively poor as an object of productive scientific inquiry. The two things are not unrelated. Gustatory phenomena do not loom large in the world of human affairs, and few scientists have been attracted to their intensive study. However, fully as intriguing mysteries exist here as in other sense fields, as we shall see.

The Stimuli for Taste. To be tasted a substance must normally be soluble in water. This means that taste stimuli can initially be in solid, liquid, gaseous, or vaporous form, provided only that they will go into solution to some extent upon coming into contact with saliva. Their efficacy as taste stimuli then depends on a number of variables, among them solubility, concentration, ionization capacity, temperature, and their basic chemical composition. It is this last factor that has received the most attention. There is general agreement that there are but four basic taste qualities: salt, sour, bitter, and sweet. Curiosity as to the chemical foundation for these differences is natural.

Stimuli for the salty taste are best exemplified by table salt, NaCl. In fact, this is a common taste standard, all other substances being judged for the salty taste by comparison with it. NaCl, upon going into watery solution, immediately becomes ionized ($NaCl \rightarrow Na^+ + Cl^-$). Both the anion, Cl^-, and the cation, Na^+, have some responsibility for the salty taste, as can be judged by observing the effects of joining Cl^- with other cations and Na^+ with other anions. KCl, NH_4Cl, LiCl, $ZnCl_2$, and $CaCl_2$ all taste salty but not exactly alike, as would be the case if only the anion were responsible. Perhaps certain of these compounds make an appeal to other basic tastes, bitter or sweet, and thus acquire individuality of pattern through taste mixture or blending. One of this group, $ZnCl_2$, is an astringent and thus arouses a cutaneous component. A series of compounds made up of sodium joined with various anions is found to produce different strengths of the salty taste. The series goes like this, in order of diminishing strength: Na_2SO_4, NaCl, NaBr, NaI, $NaHCO_3$, $NaNO_3$. Since the sodium cation is common to all these salts it must be concluded that the various anions are responsible for the differential stimulating capacities displayed. Conspicuously salty cations, in addition to the commonly encountered Na and K, are Li, Mg, and NH_3. Anions are commonly the halides (Cl, Br, I, F), sulfates, nitrates, carbonates, and tartrates. One other generality about salty-tasting compounds seems possible, viz., all of them are of relatively low molecular weight. As salts get heavier there is a tendency for their taste to change from salty to bitter. Thus the chlorides, in general, are salty tasting, but cesium chloride, CsCl, which has a very high molecular weight, is bitter. Other heavy halides, CsI, KI, RbI, and RbBr, are also bitter tasting. Unfortunately, the generality concerning molecular weight may not be inverted, for it is not true that salts with light molecules are invariably salty tasting. Salts of beryllium (atomic weight, 9.02) are sweet; until recently beryllium was called *glucinum*, "the sweet element."

The sour taste, like the salty one, results from ionic action. Here it is possible to be quite specific. The ions concerned are always the cations resulting from acid dissociation, viz., hydrogen ions. That the hydrogen ion is the essential agent in the production of the sour taste is shown by the fact that all mineral or *inorganic* acids, such as HCl, H_2SO_4, or HNO_3, taste alike provided they are sampled in equal concentrations. To be sure, the same general statement cannot be made about weak *organic* acids such as acetic, tartaric, and citric. These have distinctive tastes, and they are, moreover, more sour than they should be if hydrogen-ion concentration were the sole principle at work. It is probable that the complex molecular structures found in the organic acids have an influence on more than a single basic taste mechanism and that their "flavor" really depends on gustatory blending. Much of the difficulty in arriving at a single, simple correlate for the sour taste seems to have come from the failure of experimenters to eliminate the chemical interactions between sour stimuli and saliva, the latter serving as a buffer solution in the ensuing stimulation of the gustatory receptors. Minimizing the effect of saliva by first clearing the tongue surface, then confining the acid stimulus to a mechanically isolated area of the tongue which saliva cannot invade, results in uniform threshold values for all acids of equal chemical combining capacity (233, p. 1149).

Salty and sour tastes are, then, essentially ionic; they are generated only after molecular dissociation has taken place. The stimuli for the remaining taste qualities, bitter and sweet, may also be ionic, though usually they are not. The most potent bitter materials are the alkaloids brucine, strychnine, and nicotine. A slightly less powerful alkaloid, quinine, is commonly used in taste experiments. These substances operate in the undissociated, molecular form. This is not to say that bitter tastes cannot be aroused by ionic solutions. On the contrary, in appropriate combination, ions of magnesium, silver, ferric iron, cesium, rubidium, and iodine all call forth the bitter taste.

Stimuli for sweetness exist in a profusion of forms and come from many different chemical families. Certain of the soluble lead and beryllium salts ionize to yield the sweet taste. Compounds containing the hydroxyl anion, $-OH^-$, are frequently sweet. The sweetest substances, however, have complex organic molecules which do not ionize. This is true of most of the sugars and of a host of compounds synthesized for use in the confectionery industry. Of recent years there have been concocted many new sweetening agents, some of them several thousand times as sweet as cane sugar. For the most part they are complex aromatics, all containing prominent nitro groups in their structure.

There is a suggestive relationship in the fact that many bitter and sweet stimuli have similar chemical and physical properties. Sweet materials, upon undergoing only a very slight chemical modification, merely an architectural rearrangement of atoms in the case of certain stereoisomers, may have their taste transformed to bitter. It is especially notable that a considerable number of sweet compounds falling in chemically related or "homologous" series tend to become bitter as the series is ascended. The effort to disclose generalities concerning chemical and physical properties of taste stimuli recalls the similar attempt in connection with smell. "Laws" of gustatory stimulation are as difficult to come by as are olfactory ones. If there are any altogether simple principles governing the relation between physicochemical composition and sensation quality they have until now eluded scientific detection.

The stimuli thus far considered are the normal or "adequate" ones for taste. Two forms of unusual or non-adequate stimulation are known. One involves, somewhat surprisingly, chemical stimulation by way of the blood stream; the other is what has come to be called "electric taste." The arousal of taste by substances transported by the blood has not been studied in any systematic way but has occasionally been reported as a kind of curiosity. A similar treatment has been afforded the somewhat more frequent production of smell sensations by the same route. In a few instances both smell and taste seem to have been aroused by a common agent in the blood (25). Thus patients taking the arsenical, Neosalvarsan, have reported tasting and smelling the substance only a few seconds after receiving it intravenously in the forearm. The average latency was somewhat under 8 sec, approximately the time required for the blood stream to transport it to the head region. Neither nasal obstructions nor cocainization of the olfactory epithelium diminished the sensation. Competition with the nasally presented odors of menthol and benzene produced no alteration, not even mixture. That the locus of action was not a cortical brain center is attested by the fact that patients having peripheral impairments, such as atrophy of the mucosa, were unable to appreciate the blood-borne material. The results were not confined to one substance; camphor and oil of turpentine had the same effect. Other investigators have reported that the intensely bitter substance, sodium dehydrocholate, and the peanut-like tasting Vitamin B_4 can be detected by "taste" only a few seconds after being injected into the arm. This is conceivably a very significant phenomenon, whatever its eventual explanation, for it suggests the possibility that the taste and smell mechanisms may be subject to a more or less uniform adaptation to the blood stream that nourishes them. Active stimulation would then have to be pictured as "breaking through" or being superposed on this constant background. The situation is reminiscent of the parallel one in vision, where "brain gray" may be thought of as the invariable uniform field on which colors put in their appearance.

The case of "electric taste" is a little less remarkable. Electric currents may be employed to arouse gustatory sensations, just as they may be used for non-adequate stimulation in most of the other senses, though the phenomena produced in this way are not as yet well understood. Direct and alternating currents give different results. With direct currents varying effects are produced, depending on the direction of flow. With alternating currents the taste aroused is dependent upon frequency of alternation. In both cases current strength is an important variable. With direct current as a source, a sour taste is evoked if the anode is applied to the tongue. Reversal of the current brings about a change to a "soapy" taste having a burning quality about it. With low-frequency alternating currents, of the order of 50 cycles, the sensation qualitatively resembles the anodal taste with the steady current, i.e., sour is evoked. Raise the frequency to the neighborhood of 1000 cycles, however, and the taste becomes predominantly bitter.   Frequencies midway between these give somewhat anomalous results.

Receptors and Neural Pathways for Taste.   Consideration of the receptor mechanism responsible for taste begins with the tongue and its papillae, though taste sensitivity is by no means confined to the

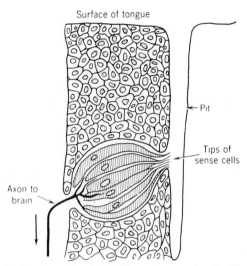

Surface of tongue

← Pit

Tips of
sense cells

Axon to
brain

FIG. 93.   A taste bud.   The individual cells comprising the "bud" are of two kinds, *gustatory* cells, spindle-shaped terminations of the nerve fibers subserving taste, and *sustentacular*, or supporting cells.   The tips of the sense cells protrude beyond the surrounding epithelium and are presumably stimulated through direct contact with taste solutions.   From Woodworth, *320*.   By permission of Henry Holt and Company, Inc., New York.

tongue.   Regions responsive to taste stimuli exist on the palate, in the pharynx and larynx, on the tonsils and epiglottis and, in some people at least, on the mucosa of the lips and cheeks, the underside of the tongue, and the floor of the mouth (*47*).   The areas of greatest responsiveness—and those most investigated by reason of relative ease of access—are the tip, sides, and rear of the dorsal tongue surface.   A region surrounding and including the middle of the tongue's upper surface is quite devoid of taste sensitivity.   The receptor organs, *taste buds* (see Fig. 93), comprise a group of individual gustatory cells, from two to a dozen or more of them forming an ovoid cluster, together with supporting (sustentacular) cells.   The gustatory cells are, in general, spindle-shaped, whereas the supporting cells, arranged around the taste cells somewhat in the manner of barrel staves, are more

columnar in form. Both kinds of structure have a common origin,
being modified epithelial cells, and there is some suspicion that sustentacular cells may develop into sense cells and replace the latter as
they "wear out." Each of the gustatory cells terminates distally in a
fine hair process which protrudes into a gustatory pore, the direct route
of access to taste solutions.

Whereas taste buds are distributed fairly generally over much of
the tongue's dorsal surface, they are most numerous in aggregates asso-

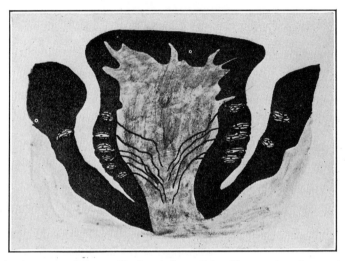

FIG. 94. A circumvallate papilla (semischematic). The structure is seen in cross
section with taste buds lining the walls and their pores opening on the "moat"
surrounding the papilla.

ciated with papillae, visible protuberances on the tongue's surface.
Four clearly different forms of papillae are to be found: *fungiform,
foliate, circumvallate,* and *filiform.* All but the filiform papillae contain taste buds. Fungiform papillae, mushroom-like in appearance as
the name implies, are found scattered somewhat irregularly over the
sides and forepart of the upper tongue surface. Foliate papillae derive from a series of grooves or folds in the midlateral border of the
tongue. The circumvallate papillae, most readily identifiable of all,
form a "chevron" near the back of the tongue, the apex toward the
throat. Each of these somewhat massive but low eminences is surrounded by a kind of "trench" or "moat" which forms a container for
taste solutions. Taste pores open into the moat (Fig. 94).

Papillae of this type have been most carefully studied histologically.
Data assembled from examination of well over 50,000 taste buds from

a total of several hundred circumvallate papillae (*14*) reveal that there are somewhat over 200 taste buds opening into the trench of the average papilla. There are many more in some; 865 were counted in one exceptional case. At birth there is apparently a full complement of taste buds on the sides of the papilla, but the far wall (beyond the moat) has few, if any, buds. The number on the papillae themselves remains fairly constant from early childhood until middle age. Meanwhile the trench wall becomes populated with buds. With the beginning of the atrophic changes of late maturity both groups of taste buds, those on the papilla and those on the wall, show a diminution in number. A typical count in old age shows less than a hundred buds to each circumvallate papilla, the far wall included. The papillae themselves, moreover, tend to become shrunken and wrinkled, and the surrounding trenches get filled up with squamous epithelial material. If there are sensitivity differences in taste correlated with age variations an anatomical basis for them would appear to be possible.

Unlike the olfactory receptor cell which, it will be remembered, is both generator and conductor of nerve impulses, the taste cell appears to be specially constructed to serve only the first of these functions. In this respect it more nearly resembles the encapsulated cutaneous receptors. Nerve fibers supplying taste cells terminate in arborizations on the cell surfaces; they do not enter the cell bodies proper. Two elements are thus present at the periphery of the gustatory afferent system: (1) a transducer, converting chemical changes to neural excitations; this is the taste cell, and (2) one or more centripetally conducting sensory fibers excited by action of the transducer; these are the gustatory afferents.

Another point of difference from the olfactory system has to do with the kind of nerve trunks involved. The olfactory cleft has a single sensory nerve, the first cranial, supplying it. The tongue and mouth region are innervated by no less than four cranial nerves, each of them of the mixed sensorimotor type. Two of these, the seventh (facial) and ninth (glossopharyngeal), are of undoubted importance for taste. Another, the tenth (vagus), is involved to the extent of supplying fibers for the taste buds of the pharynx and larynx. The remaining one is the fifth (trigeminal), which, it is now generally believed, is concerned in its sensory aspect exclusively with cutaneous functions. It is, of course, the trigeminal nerve that supplies the feeling patterns that complicate both olfactory and gustatory perceptions. In fact, current literature has come to speak of "the trigeminal component" in taste and smell.

The pathway to the brain from the anterior two-thirds of the tongue is over the *chorda tympani* branch of the facial nerve. This nerve trunk runs a devious course from the tongue to the medulla of the brain, at one point looping over the ossicles of the middle ear and passing near the eardrum, from which it derives its name. Taste cells of the posterior third of the tongue receive their nerve supply from the glossopharyngeal nerve, which likewise runs to the medulla and joins fibers of the facial nerve to form a well-defined bulbar center. From the medulla, through the optic thalamus, to the cortical projection areas the pathways conducting gustatory impulses seem to parallel those conveying cutaneous impulses from the face, mouth, and tongue. Apposite centers are involved at every stage in the ascent to the highest levels of the central nervous system, and the final projection areas in the cortex also border on each other. The center for taste is most probably near the lower end of the post-central gyrus, just above the fissure of Sylvius. The gustatory projection takes its place next to an orderly succession of somatic centers, the most proximal of which are those for the pharynx, mouth, and tongue. A chain of three neurones has carried the impulses from the taste bud to the cortex.

There would be reasons for supposing that gustatory and olfactory centers might lie in close association with each other, intimacy of functional connection between the two senses being what it is. In fact, the close liaison between smell and taste has more than once led to the mistaken belief that the central projection for taste must be in the rhinencephalon. Several lines of evidence combine to show that this is not the case. Thus, lesions created in the monkey's thalamus produce lowered taste sensitivity, as shown by elevated thresholds for preferred taste solutions (228). The effective lesions are those of the arcuate nucleus, a region which has no direct connections with the pyriform area or other possible olfactory centers. It will be remembered that the pathway for smell is exceptional among sense channels in that it does not pass through the thalamus on its way to the cerebrum. If smell and taste confusions are brought about by intimacy of brain connection the union would seem not to occur at or below the level of the thalamus. A second set of facts which speak against such an association comes from study of cerebral injuries. Börnstein (47) examined twelve patients with sensory disturbances brought about by gunshot wounds involving the parietal lobe of the brain. In each case displaying gustatory impairment there had been destruction of tissue at the base of the post-central gyrus. Finally, there is the testimony of patients whose brains were laid bare under local anesthetic and stimulated electrically in an effort either to define the limits of an area invaded by tumor or to reproduce the "warning" symptoms of epileptic attacks to which they were subject, and thus locate the focus of the difficulty causing them (230). Taste sensations could be aroused in this way only in a few instances but then always by stimulation of the parietal cortex, at the lower end of the central fissure. Even though the entire cortex was explored point by point, no other region ever gave a suggestion of gustatory sensation. The close association of smell and taste would seem to have nothing to do with proximity of brain centers but to stem from the accident of the peripheral placement of these two senses and the fact that both respond to chemical stimuli.

Absolute Taste Sensitivity. After all that has been learned concerning absolute sensitivity in the other sense departments it would be surprising indeed to discover that taste thresholds are fixed and immutable, that they are independent of a number of conditions surrounding their measurement. They are not, of course. A number of stimulus and receptor variables have to be taken into account, as do certain factors underlying individual differences in reactivity of the organism.

One of the important and interesting variables is temperature of the stimulus. As a practical matter it has long been known that the taste of food is partially determined by its temperature. Good cooks salt foods when they are neither too hot nor too cold. In making iced tea the sourness of added lemon is not apparent until the tea has cooled down. Confectioners know that candy made for use in the tropics must not be oversweetened lest it taste insipid.

The relation between temperature and taste sensitivity is not a simple one. Not all substances are affected alike by temperature changes. Measurements of gustatory thresholds for sodium chloride, hydrochloric acid, quinine, and dulcin, as made by Hahn (139) are presented in Fig. 95. The salt threshold increases steadily with a rise in temperature of the testing solution from 17° C. to 42° C. Sensitivity to the bitter stimulus, quinine sulfate, shows a generally similar trend, but the function connecting threshold with temperature, rather than being linear, is a positively accelerated curve. Thresholds for sweet are at a minimum in the neighborhood of 35° C. and increase if either warmer or cooler solutions are used. Sensitivity to HCl, the sour stimulus, is unaffected by temperature changes, at least in this concentration of the acid and over this temperature range. A number of other sweet stimuli used in the Hahn experiments gave curves midway between the inflected function for dulcin and the level line for hydrochloric acid. These varied results go some distance in discouraging any oversimplified interpretation of the taste mechanism. The stimulation process must consist of something more than a simple chemical reaction. Nearly all chemical processes are speeded up and made more effective when temperature is raised. In these threshold measurements only sweet solutions seem to behave as if they were entering into a chemical reaction, and even they do not do so in an entirely uniform manner.

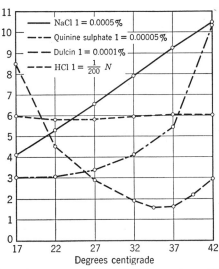

FIG. 95. The effect of temperature on taste sensitivity. The four curves, for four different substances, have been made comparable by assigning different ordinate values to them, as noted in the key. Sensitivity to NaCl and quinine declines with increasing temperature and that to HCl is uninfluenced, while dulcin gives an optimal response in the neighborhood of 35° C. From Hahn, 139.

A second and important variable affecting threshold determinations has to do with the particular area of the receptive surface used in making the measurements. Not all parts of the tongue's surface are equally responsive to all stimuli. In general, bitter solutions are most readily appreciated near the back of the tongue and sweet stimuli affect the tip of the tongue most strongly, while acids are most easily sensed along the edges about midway back from the tip. Except for ·the prominent zone on the tongue's top surface, where no taste sensations at all can be aroused, it is possible to evoke the salty taste pretty generally over the entire upper surface and edges, sensitivity being slightly better towards the front. The relative sensitivities of different portions of the tongue's edge to the four basic tastes are shown in

Fig. 96, which is derived from the early but careful explorations of Hänig (*142*). Whether or not individual papillae contain cells responsive to only a single kind of stimulus is still an unsettled point. The presumption is that a particular cell, perhaps even an aggregate of them forming a bud, is specialized in its function. But, by and large, the evidence does not suggest that all papillae contain only a single type of taste bud. On the contrary, a systematic exploration with taste solutions applied by a finely pointed camel's-hair brush finds

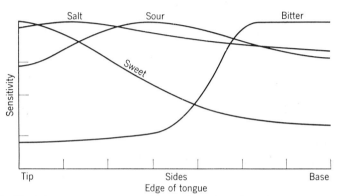

FIG. 96. Variations in gustatory sensitivity along the edge of the tongue. A plot of Hänig's data (*142*) by Boring, *45*. The sensitivity scale is one of threshold reciprocals. Figure reproduced by permission of Appleton-Century-Crofts, Inc., New York.

the great majority of papillae responsive to more than one kind of taste stimulus, though some do seem to be specialized in their function. Thus Kiesow (*184*), charting the sensitivities of 35 papillae, found 18 responsive to acid (3 exclusively so), 26 sensitive to sugar solution (7 exclusively), 18 responsive to salt (3 exclusively), and 13 sensitive to a bitter solution. There were none responding solely to the bitter stimulus. This kind of experiment has been repeated many times, always with similar results. Apparently the vast majority of papillae can mediate more than one sense quality. That those located near the base of the tongue are "biased" in the direction of bitter while those near the tip place the emphasis on sweet is evidenced not only by topographic studies; it is shown also by the tongue's response to several organic compounds falling in the "bittersweet" category. A single chemically pure (if somewhat complex) substance, para-brom-benzoic-sulfinide, tastes bitter to the back of the tongue and sweet to the tip. Magnesium sulfate (Epsom salts) also has a dual taste, bitter at the back and salty near the front of the tongue.

An especially critical determinant of the taste threshold is the matter of the technique used in applying the stimulus. It makes a difference whether a few drops of test solution are placed on the subject's tongue, the instruction being to identify the taste, or whether two 10-cc samples are presented in successive trials, one of test solution and the other of distilled water, the task being to discriminate between the two by sipping first one and then the other in a leisurely manner. Both of these methods, together with variants of them, were used by Richter and MacLean (246) to measure the threshold of the salty taste. Individual differences were large, a common finding in taste experiments, and these tended to obscure certain differences due to method. However, average thresholds for a large group of subjects ranged from a low concentration of 0.016% (water and NaCl discriminated, the two being sampled as frequently and in as large or small amounts as desired) to a high of 0.192% (NaCl being identified without comparison with any other solution, three drops being placed on the extended tongue). Individual thresholds, under the same circumstances, ranged from 0.007% to 0.350%, values which stand in a 1:50 ratio.

There are some other, generally less crucial, factors influencing the measurement of the absolute gustatory threshold. Enough has been said, however, to indicate that it is possible to tabulate sensitivities to taste stimuli only in a very gross way. Table 6, adapted from a

TABLE 6. ABSOLUTE THRESHOLDS FOR REPRESENTATIVE TASTE STIMULI

After Pfaffmann (233), p. 1152

Substance	Per Cent Concentration (Approx.)	Molar Concentration
Sugar (sucrose)	0.7	0.02
Sodium chloride	0.2	0.035
Hydrochloric acid	0.007	0.002
Saccharin (crystallose)	0.0005	0.00002
Quinine sulfate	0.00003	0.0000004

summary compiled by Pfaffmann (233), indicates the order of magnitude of thresholds to some representative stimuli. Two different ways of expressing threshold intensities have been used: (1) *Per cent concentration,* which is stated in terms of the number of grams of solute in 100 grams of solvent. Since water is ordinarily the solvent, this is tantamount to giving the weight, in grams, of the test substance in 100 cc of water. (2) *Molar concentration,* which is given by the gram-molecular weight (number of grams of solute divided by its molecular weight) per liter of total solution. Since equal volumes of solutions having the same molar concentration contain an equal number of molecules, regardless of the chemical constitution of the substances involved, there is a growing practice of specifying gustatory stimulus intensities in terms of *moles* (molar concentrations).

Differential Taste Sensitivity. While relatively large concentrations of stimulus solution are needed to reach the absolute threshold for taste, as compared with those required to arouse smell, the relative size of the increment (ΔI) to produce a just perceptible increase in sensation strength is no larger. That is to say, by and large, the Weber fraction ($\Delta I/I$) for taste is about the same size as that for smell. If we take the values ½ to ⅙ as the representative ones for the Weber fraction in smell (since these embrace the typical results for the middle span of intensities under a variety of conditions), a similar rough bringing together of the experimental data for taste would show fractions ranging from ½ to ⅒. But the measure of differential sensitivity, like that of absolute sensitivity, is affected by a number of experimental variables. Its magnitude is partially determined by the taste quality appealed to, whether salt, sour, sweet, or bitter. Moreover, the particular taste solution used seems to be critical. Kopera (*190*), testing with a variety of stimuli in intensity discrimination experiments, found differential sensitivity to sweet to be about twice as great as to bitter. The ΔI for salt fell between the two. But the size of the differential threshold was primarily a function of the composition of the test solution. Following are the values for the Weber fraction as obtained by Kopera: (bitter) quinine hydrochloride, 1/4.7; magnesium sulfate, 1/5.9; (salt) sodium chloride, 1/6.6; (sweet) glucose, 1/6.8; crystallose, 1/7.0; sucrose, 1/8.2; fructose, 1/9.6. The differences between the various sugars are reduced if sucrose, glucose, and fructose are first equated for estimated sweetness. However, there seems to be no possibility of bringing crystallose (sodium saccharin) into commensurate relation with the sugars. Its sweetness is judged to be several hundred times that of cane sugar, whereas the common sugars differ among themselves in this respect in less than a 3:1 ratio.

As in the other sense departments ΔI is not unaffected by the absolute intensity at which the determinations are carried out, just as it is not uninfluenced by temperature, by the prevailing state of adaptation, by the experimental procedure used in conducting the experiment and, in fact, by the whole host of conditions affecting the absolute threshold

itself. The systematic effect of intensitive changes has been determined carefully for one of the taste qualities, salt (*168*). The result
of plotting the Weber fraction against stimulus intensity, over the
range from absolute threshold to the point at which the salty taste gets
complicated by the introduction of a painful sting, is shown in Fig. 97.
Discriminability is poor at low intensities and improves up to a level

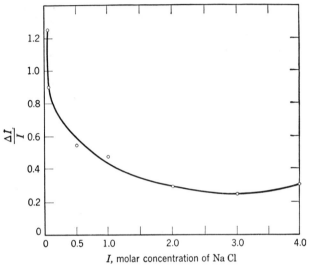

FIG. 97. Differential sensitivity to salt as a function of concentration. The Weber
fraction, $\Delta I/I$, becomes progressively smaller with an increase in absolute sensitivity, up to a concentration of about 3.0 mole, at which point gustatory sensation
begins to be complicated by the arousal of a painful sting from the chemical
action of salt. After Holway and Hurvich, *168*. Courtesy of the American
Journal of Psychology and Dr. Hurvich.

of about 3.0 moles. It should be said that the experiment establishing
this function was conducted by the "single-drop" technique, an estimate of sensation strength being given by the subject after the stimulation of the outstretched tongue by one drop of the test fluid. As has
been found for the absolute threshold, it is probable that larger quantities of salt solution, freely sipped, would yield somewhat different
results.

The question of sensitivity to relatively small changes in intensity is
connected with the further one of ability to estimate absolute levels of
taste intensity. To what extent is it possible to relate perceived
strength of taste sensation to physical concentration of gustatory stimulus? In an earlier day we should be said to be raising the question of
the adequacy of Fechner's "psychophysical law"; now we say we are

asking whether a "psychological scale" of taste intensity is possible. Lewis (*197; 116,* pp. 83–84) found that such a scale could be devised. He had subjects taste a standard solution, then select from a series of graded comparison solutions the one which tasted "half as strong" as the standard. Each of the four basic tastes was represented, the standard solutions being sodium chloride, sucrose, quinine sulfate, and tartaric acid. All were used in several concentrations, and the "halving" procedure was repeated with each. This is the so-called "fractionation" method for devising scales of observational intensity.

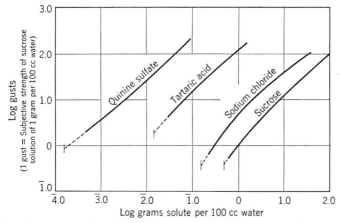

Fig. 98. The gust scale and the relation between observational intensity and stimulus strength for each of the four fundamental tastes. From Beebe-Center and Waddell, 27. By permission of the Journal Press.

Not only was it found possible to construct continuous scales from these data and to relate them to stimulus concentrations, but it was discovered that intensitive cross comparisons between different taste qualities could be made. Thus, it turns out to be possible for subjects to select, with satisfactory consistency, a salt solution that tastes just half as strong as a standard sugar solution. In a similar manner quinine and tartaric acid may be related to sugar (*27*). The strengths of all four basic tastes having thus been specified in terms of a common denominator, sugar, it is but one additional step to select a unit of measurement, define it, and generalize to a "psychological scale of taste strength." The fundamental unit chosen was the "gust," which is defined as the "psychological strength of a 1 per cent sucrose solution." Figure 98 shows the way in which observational intensity, in gusts, is related to stimulus concentration for the four fundamental tastes. The gust scale should recall the "dol" scale for pain (see Chap.

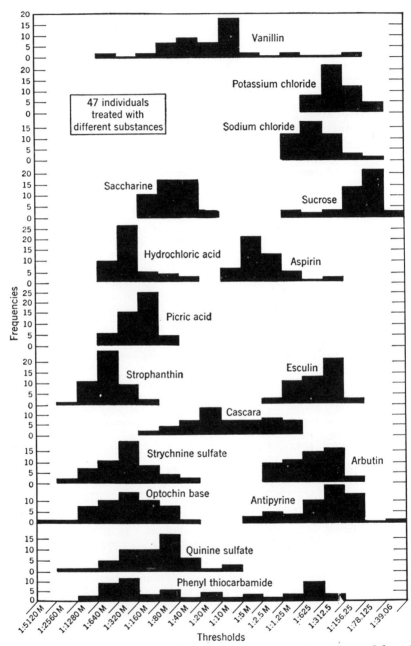

Fig. 99. Distributions of thresholds to 17 different taste stimuli. Variability of response is particularly evident in the case of vanillin (top) and PTC (bottom). From Blakeslee and Salmon, 39. Courtesy of the National Academy of Sciences.

10) which, as a matter of fact, has an identical logic underlying its construction.

Individual Differences in Taste Sensitivity: "Taste Blindness." It was noted earlier that individual differences in taste sensibility are likely to be of some magnitude. Gustatory thresholds are notoriously variable, not only from person to person, but in the same person from time to time. How much of the measured variation is traceable to crude-

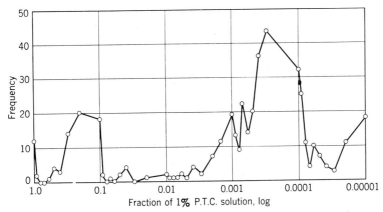

Fig. 100. Variation in sensitivity to PTC (phenylthiocarbamide). The occurrence of two modes in the distribution suggests why there originally seemed to be two gustatory "types": tasters and non-tasters. From the data of Setterfield, Schott, and Snyder (257) as charted by Cohen and Ogdon, 62. By permission of the *Psychological Bulletin* and the American Psychological Association.

ness of method and how much to constitutional factors has not been established, but it is clear that differences of the size encountered could not result exclusively from faulty techniques. There are displayed in Fig. 99 distributions of absolute thresholds of 47 subjects to 17 different test solutions. Two of the distributions, those for vanillin (top) and phenyl thiocarbamide (bottom), should especially pique our curiosity. Both show an extraordinarily large spread. The graph for phenyl thiocarbamide (PTC, as it has come to be called) embraces a particularly wide range of values. Moreover, in this distribution the great majority of cases do not cluster about a central value, as they do for vanillin. There is even a suggestion that the PTC curve is bimodal. This becomes a certainty when figures for a larger population are considered. Witness the curve in Fig. 100, plotted from results of testing several hundred subjects (62). This embraces an even larger range of thresholds than does the PTC graph of Fig. 99. There seems little doubt that two widely separated groups are involved, one of low, the other of high, sensitivity.

The phenomenon of two typically different reactions to PTC constitutes one of the major mysteries in the realm of human sensibilities. The effect was first noticed in 1931 by Dr. A. L. Fox, a chemist in the du Pont laboratories (97). Some PTC powder, while being transferred to a bottle, escaped into the laboratory air, and another chemist working nearby remarked on the bitter taste. Dr. Fox himself could get no taste whatever from the substance. The two chemists then tried crystals of the material on their tongues and got the same individual results; one was a "taster," the other a "non-taster." This incident precipitated an ever-widening series of investigations, extensive and intensive, on so-called "taste blindness," an effort which has not come to an end as yet. It was soon found that phenyl thiocarbamide is only one of a group of chemically related compounds, all of which behave in this way, though PTC has been the most widely used of the family and there are by now very extensive data on it. The responses of tens of thousands of cases are in the literature (62). The early investigators made the unfortunate mistake of regarding the phenomenon to be an all-or-nothing affair—either people could taste PTC or they couldn't. As soon as the commercially available product had been purified and higher concentrations could be used for testing it was found that the simple dichotomy, "taste blind" versus "taste normal," did not hold. Those who did not have their threshold in the "normal" range (less than 0.01% solution, say) were merely relatively insensitive, but their thresholds could be surpassed with sufficiently high concentrations of the stimulus.

One of the curious effects connected with the tasting of PTC has to do with the influence of saliva. Experiments, more scientific than esthetic, in which the saliva of a "taster" (low PTC threshold) is used by a "non-taster" (high PTC threshold), and vice versa, show that a non-taster cannot improve his sensitivity by substituting a taster's saliva for his own. However, a taster can reduce his sensitivity to PTC by using either water or the saliva of a non-taster in lieu of his own saliva. For a taster to retain his capacity to detect small concentrations of PTC he must have his own saliva at work. This circumstance has led to a certain amount of speculation about the role of saliva in tasting. Obviously it is not to be regarded as merely a source of moisture for putting taste stimuli into solution, though this is certainly one of its functions. The suggestion has been made that salivary constitution is a highly individual matter, and it may be that some people ("non-tasters") have a protein or colloid in their saliva that precipitates PTC as an insoluble product. Possibly further research on the biochemistry of saliva will provide the answer.

The Taste Qualities. Throughout our discussion of taste, thus far, there has been somewhat frequent and confident reference to the four basic taste qualities: salt, sour, sweet, and bitter. Without debate a fundamental questions seems to have been settled: What are the elementary tastes? There has not always been complete agreement on this subject, though currently there are few who would dissent from the common four-fold classification. The question of the elementary qualities in gustation is an old one (45, pp. 452–457), as is the analogous question in each of the other sense modalities. At the end of the sixteenth century there were nine basic tastes: sweet, sour, sharp, pungent, harsh, fatty, bitter, insipid, and salty. By the middle of the eighteenth century there were 11, if one followed Linnaeus (add astringent, viscous, aqueous, and nauseous, but drop pungent and harsh), or 12, if Haller were taken as the authority (add to the original list spirituous, aromatic, urinous, and putrid, but drop fatty). Some of these gradually disappeared, it being shown

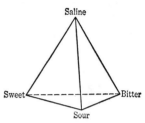

FIG. 101. Henning's taste tetrahedron. The figure is a solid, with gustatory sensations analyzable into two primaries located on the edges, into three primaries on the four triangular surfaces, and into four on the interior. After Henning, *166*.

that they really represented fusions of taste and touch. Others vanished for want of positive evidence to keep them alive. It was doubtless the demonstration, just about as the twentieth century was being ushered in, that salt, sour, sweet, and bitter have their own individual modes of distribution that tended to establish these four (which had always been present in all lists) as the fundamental taste qualities. The appearance of the four in the positions of "primacy," at the corners of Henning's taste tetrahedron (see Fig. 101), a geometrical figure devised to represent relations between taste qualities, strengthens the case for this analysis.

It is interesting that the taste tetrahedron should seem to place the stress on four different kinds of gustatory sensation, with the implication that four separate physiological processes and possibly four different kinds of receptor cells are involved, because Henning views taste as one, not as four, senses. It is membership in a common modality that he is trying to emphasize in bringing the four qualities together in a single figure. All tastes are "unitary" in the same sense

that visual orange, purple, and blue-green are unitary. While resembling two other qualities they do not break up spontaneously into
these components. However, as in vision and olfaction, some gustatory qualities are outstanding and serve as convenient reference points
for the description of other, related tastes. Thus, the taste of sodium
bicarbonate is most readily described as lying on the line of the taste
tetrahedron connecting salt with sour. Potassium bromide lies between salt and bitter. Lead acetate is on the line between sour and
sweet. Acetone is the representative of a large number of compounds having both sweet and bitter components and therefore falls
on the line connecting these two qualities. Some tastes have more
than a dual reference and so occupy positions either on a surface of
the tetrahedron, if there are three qualities concerned, or in the interior of the figure, if there are four. Thus, the "metallic" taste simultaneously has resemblances to sweet, bitter, and salt and must, therefore, take up its position on ·the appropriate triangular face of the
tetrahedron.

Most tastes encountered in foods would presumably yield an analysis with all four fundamental taste qualities present in some degree.
The entire internal area of the tetrahedron should consist of such col-
locations of four qualities, each discriminably different locus representing a unique, if complex, taste.

That food products may be subject to just such an analysis is the
import of some preliminary work by Beebe-Center (26). He was
prompted by very much the same considerations as those that led
Crocker and Henderson to their system of odor specification, described
in the previous chapter. Four qualitative standards were set up—aqueous solutions of sucrose for sweet, of quinine sulfate for bitter, of
tartaric acid for sour, of sodium chloride for salty—and each of these
was prepared in nine graded concentrations. The intensive steps
ranged from 1 gust (see above) to 100 gusts in steps of 0.25 log gusts.
About 2 j.n.d. are represented by each of the 8 steps on the scale of
intensity. The result of analyzing 14 different food products by direct
comparison with the taste standards is given in Table 7.

There are some surprising emphases in this listing. The most significant one does not immediately meet the eye. It is that nearly all
these foods, selected for their flavor, have relatively low ratings on the
various taste scales. The intensities of the standards, after all, extended
up to 100 gusts. There is only one food on the list, honey, which ex-
ceeds the halfway point (50 gusts) on any of the scales of psychological intensity. This circumstance indicates the relative blandness

TABLE 7.   ANALYSIS OF CERTAIN FOOD PRODUCTS, IN GUSTS

Data from J. G. Beebe-Center (26)

	Sweet	Bitter	Sour	Salt
Cola drink	11.2	2.2	5.0	1.3
Ale	2.5	28.2	10.0	1.3
Unsweetened grapefruit juice	3.2	2.0	35.5	2.0
Consommé	1.4	1.3	4.5	7.9
Tokay wine	10.0	4.2	4.2	1.8
Riesling wine	1.0	7.5	6.7	1.3
"Root" tonic	4.2	1.3	3.2	1.3
Coffee, unsweetened	1.0	42.3	3.2	1.0
Coffee, 5% sucrose	3.2	23.8	3.2	1.3
Anchovy fillet	1.3	23.8	5.6	10.0
Sweet pickles	3.2	3.2	13.4	3.2
Sour pickles	1.0	1.8	18.0	3.2
Raspberry jam	23.8	1.8	10.0	1.3
Honey	56.4	2.4	1.8	1.3
Means	8.8	10.4	8.9	2.7

of many foods notable for distinctive "flavor" and points up a conclusion, arrived at much earlier on the basis of other considerations, that flavor is largely a matter of odor, not taste.

Taste Mixtures. If one can make an analytic dissection, so to speak, of the gustatory components of flavor it should also be possible, knowing the elements, to synthesize complex tastes by suitable mixing of the appropriate solutions. If the four primary taste qualities merely go together in an additive fashion to create various blends, then accurate predictions of the mixture products can be based on the most elementary arithmetic. If, on the other hand, there are mutual interactions, whether of suppression or enhancement, between the four systems of sensitivity, the desired predictions cannot be made without further knowledge of the combining principles at work.

Unfortunately, the current evidence is somewhat equivocal. Few thoroughgoing experiments have been conducted in the area of taste mixture, and those that have been performed differ so radically among themselves as to discourage conclusions of any real degree of generality. However, this much seems certain—there are clear instances of interaction effects. Whether presented simultaneously to two different parts of the tongue or combined in a single physical mixture, two stimulus solutions, each appealing to a different taste quality, are not likely to function independently of each other.

Both facilitatory and inhibitory phenomena have been reported. Thus Kiesow, who is responsible for some of the earliest experiments on "taste contrast" (183), found sweet, sour, and salt all to interact with each other in the direction of mutual enhancement. Bitter neither influenced nor was influenced by the others. Kiesow applied his solutions to individual papillae with a pointed brush and either stimulated opposite sides of the tongue simultaneously ("simultaneous contrast") or the same place successively, the first stimulus being washed away before the second was delivered ("successive contrast"). All results are in the form of observed increases in sensation intensity of one taste as a result of the action of another. If a subliminal sugar solution were applied to one side of the tongue the simultaneous presentation of salt to the other side would cause sweet sensitivity to surge upward and make the sugar perceptible. Reversal of the solutions would do the same for salt. Similar results obtained for combinations of sour and salt and, less certainly, for sweet and sour.

Interactions involving gross stimulation of the gustatory receptors, as contrasted with the "punctiform" approach of Kiesow, are less well understood. Recent experiments fail to agree. On the one hand, Hahn and Ulbrich (140), stimulating an area 1.5 cm in diameter near the tip of the tongue, find small but definite reductions in thresholds to saccharin, e.g., as a result of adding to the test solution just subliminal concentrations of quinine sulfate, sodium chloride, or hydrochloric acid. However, exactly the opposite direction of interaction, mutual inhibition, is found by Anderson (11) in some careful experiments conducted by the "sipping" method. Threshold concentrations of sucrose, quinine hydrochloride, or tartaric acid were combined with sodium chloride solutions in measuring the absolute threshold to the latter. Salt thresholds were uniformly raised in the presence of the sweet, bitter, or sour stimulus. Less definite but generally inhibitory relations came out of other pairings of stimuli.

The foregoing results are for stimuli operating in the neighborhood of the absolute threshold. What about the combining of qualitatively different taste solutions of higher concentrations? This is a research area of great interest to those concerned with food processing. Apparently there are some complex relations to be considered. Some acids increase the saltiness of salt, yet salt reduces the sourness of acids (89). The presence of salt also increases the sweetness of sugar. Whereas all sugars seem to reduce the sourness of all acids, acids do not uniformly suppress the sweet taste of all sugars. Two of the common acids, hydrochloric and acetic, have no effect on the sweetness of sucrose, while the action of citric acid, one of the least sour-tasting of the acids, is actually to increase the observed sweetness of sucrose. The sweet taste of fructose, contrariwise, is reduced by acetic and some other acids, but not by hydrochloric and citric acids. Obviously, there is yet much to be learned about taste interactions at the levels of intensity encountered in foods and beverages.

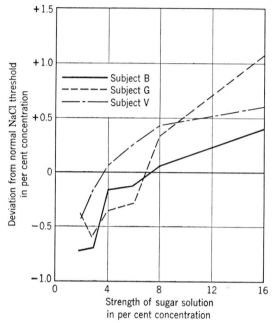

FIG. 102. Taste interaction at different intensity levels. The results obtained by Bujas (51) in an experiment testing the effect on the threshold for NaCl, applied to one side of the tongue, of simultaneous stimulation of the other side with a sugar solution. Low concentrations of sugar enhance, and high concentrations depress, saline sensitivity.

A suggestive relationship which, if borne out by more extensive work, might go far toward harmonizing the seemingly diverse results of interaction experiments, was found by Bujas (51). He used Hahn's technique of letting taste solutions flow over the tongue, stimulating through a 1.5-cm diameter opening in a U tube. In fact, two such stimulators were used, the areas contacted being 1 cm apart and 3 cm back from the tip of the tongue. Salt and sugar solutions at 32° C. were presented, salt to one side of the tongue, sugar to the other. All exposures were uniformly 7 sec in duration. First, sensitivity to salt solution was established, the absolute threshold being measured in one system while water flowed through the other. Then sugar, in one of six concentrations, replaced the water, and the salt threshold was redetermined. As can be seen in Fig. 102, Bujas found evidence for both enhancement and depression of saline sensitivity through the simultaneous action of a neighboring sweet stimulus. At low concentrations of sugar, intensities not far above threshold strength, the result is like that originally gotten by Kiesow; the effort is a facilitatory one, the salt threshold being lowered. At higher sugar concentrations there is a reversal of effect. Sweetness now interferes with detection of the salt stimulus and the salty taste is "masked." In passing from one phenomenon to the other there must, of course, be a neutral point; there must be some concentration of sugar which neither depresses nor heightens salt sensitivity. It is apparent from these data that fairly high intensities of the sweet stimulus are in effect when neutrality is realized. Bujas' three subjects, showing individual differences in this respect, as in absolute sensitivity itself, gave values of 3.75%, 7.00%, and 8.5% for the neutral concentrations. This kind of experiment could well serve as the pattern for a set of much-needed, completely systematic ones which would embrace all taste qualities and extend over the full intensity range for each. Indeed, until we are in possession of the kind of facts such an inquiry would yield we are not in a strong position to make predictions concerning the probable results of mixing taste stimuli.

Gustatory Adaptation. Taste receptors have their sensitivity automatically reduced by being exposed to a continuous, unvarying stimulus, just as olfactory end organs do under analogous conditions. In fact, the addition of the sense of taste completes the catalogue of sense departments displaying adaptation; this had been found to be an entirely universal phenomenon in the world of sensation.

It was clear, from Kiesow's early experiments (184), that individual papillae display the adaptation phenomenon. Application of taste solutions to isolated papillae would, in some instances, eventually make them totally unresponsive. It has not always been equally clear that more general stimulation of the tongue and mouth would result in total abolition of taste sensitivity. This was shown to be the case, however, in a series of experiments by Dallenbach and his students (1, 191). Five different concentrations of NaCl (0.84 mole to 3.93 moles) were employed as adapting solutions and the tongue and mouth were continuously irrigated, an entrance tube carrying the solution in at mouth temperature and an exit tube serving as a drain after the fluid had circulated. Typically, the salty taste declined gradually in intensity until it finally disappeared altogether. Adaptation was complete. The time between onset of the stimulus and total cessation of gustatory sensation ("adaptation time") proved to be a function of NaCl concentration. Low intensities gave relatively short adaptation times, less than 20 sec on the average; high intensities took longer to adapt, nearly 2 min for the highest concentration used. Individual differences were marked, and after-effects were prominent. However, it was demonstrated that the taste sensations persisting after the stimulus flow had been stopped were due to the action of traces of salt lingering in crevices of the tongue and cheeks, in the interstices between the teeth, etc. Similar siphoning into the mouth of solutions of sour (tartaric acid in three strengths: from 0.0022 mole to 0.013 mole), sweet (sucrose in five concentrations: from 0.066 mole to 1.26 moles), and bitter (quinine hydrochloride in three intensities: from 0.000013 mole to 0.000083 mole) led to entirely comparable results for these qualities. In all cases adaptation continued to completion, time to extinction being primarily a function of stimulus intensity. Average adaptation times were, approximately: sour, 1.5 min (weak) to 3.0 min (strong); sweet, 1.0–5.0 min; bitter, 1.5–2.5 min. After-tastes were present in all instances and were traceable to the same general cause as that operating with salt. Sugar could be washed away fairly promptly, but quinine was dislodged only with difficulty.

Whereas these studies tell us much about the nature of gustatory adaptation, they naturally do not inform us as to the exact course of the adaptation process. Extensive experiments by Hahn, employing his familiar U-tube arrangement, provide not only a picture of the course of adaptation but one of the recovery process as well (138). Figure 103 charts the rise of the thresholds throughout an adaptation period of 40 sec and their subsequent decline during a 30-sec recovery interval. The sensitivity alterations for a single saline stimulus (5% NaCl solution) and two different sweet stimuli (10% cane sugar and 1% glycocol solutions) are represented. It is apparent that the changes produced by adaptation are prompt and extensive, and also that the course of adaptation is in part dependent on the nature of the substance producing it.

Another important variable, the effect of which is not shown in Fig. 103 but which entered into Hahn's experiments, is temperature. The effect of warming a 10% sucrose solution from 17° C. to 32° C. is not only to reduce the absolute threshold, prior to adaptation, but to shift the entire adaptation curve downward so that after 5 sec of continuous stimulation the warmer solution has elevated the threshold only half as much as has the cooler one. Within 15 sec the entire

process is complete in both instances, however. The influence of
temperature on the rapidity of adaptation is important for us to know
about because this effect can only be interpreted to mean that adaptation has a peripheral, rather than a central, locus. The differential
effect of temperature must be exerted at the tongue surface, of course.

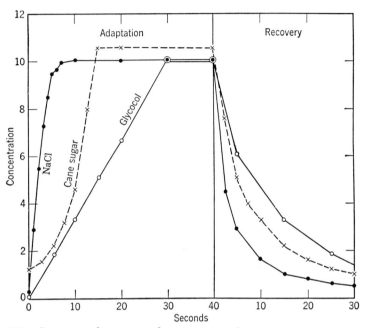

FIG. 103. Gustatory adaptation and recovery. Ordinates give threshold concentrations, the units being arbitrary ones with the value 10 representing the adapting
concentration. The three substances, salt, sugar, and glycocol, show different
courses of adaptation and different rates of recovery. From Pfaffmann (*233*) after
Hahn, Kuckulies, and Taeger, 1938.

That the influence of temperature is on the adaptation process rather
than on the stimulation process itself—and these are two different
things—is demonstrated with glycocol. This substance, though tasting
sweet, is an organic acid (amino-acetic acid, $CH_2NH_2 \cdot COOH$; also
known as "glycine"). As with its distant inorganic relative, HCl, its
absolute taste threshold depends not at all on temperature. However,
the speed with which adaptation to glycine proceeds is definitely a
function of temperature. Hahn has shown (*139*, p. 934) that adaptation to a 0.1% solution of glycine at 17° C. produces about the same
elevation of threshold in 20 sec that is brought about by a 22° C. solution of the same strength in a whole minute.

The Electrophysiology of Taste. Attention to the changes occurring in afferent nerves belonging to other sense modalities has uniformly been found to be profitable. There are also some things to be learned from the fibers carrying gustatory impulses. Experiments have been made on several different animal preparations in an effort to discover the nature of gustatory afferent impulses and their relation to the stimulation process. Action potentials in nerves supplying the tongue have been successfully recorded in the frog, cat, dog, and rat. The findings in the cat are interesting (231). Here it develops that single fibers of the chorda tympani and glossopharyngeal nerves show a certain degree of specificity. At least, single fibers can be found which will discharge only in response to a single stimulus, acid. Other fibers are activated indiscriminately by either acid or salt, while still others signal the presence of either acid or quinine. Sugar was rarely capable of exciting any fiber to activity. Thus, it appears that the only neural response mechanism tuned exclusively to a particular form of stimulus is the "acid fiber." Mixed types, acid-salt- and acid-quinine-sensitive, can be accounted for on the basis that many gustatory fibers send branches to more than one taste cell. At the same time it seems strange that no fibers specific to salt or quinine ever put in an appearance despite an extensive sampling of fibers terminating in all parts of the tongue.

Sugar and its failure to arouse nerve responses are also of interest. The cat, of course, does not have a "sweet tooth." The dog does have, and subsequent experiments by Zotterman and his colleagues (12) show that the dog also possesses fibers in his chorda tympani which respond only to sweet stimuli. There are also in the dog fibers specific to acid and others of a mixed variety (acid-salt-sensitive). Acids and salt arouse to activity fibers which, judging from the size of the potentials recorded from them, must be of the order of 6.0 μ in diameter. Bitter and sweet stimuli lead to the discharge of somewhat smaller fibers.

Except for the stimulus specificities displayed by them, the gustatory fibers behave like all other afferents. Their response is "all or none"; changes in stimulus intensity bring about characteristic changes in discharge frequency in individual fibers and variation in the number of fibers active at any one time; and they display the "equilibration" phenomenon. The latter consists of a high initial impulse rate and a smooth frequency decline in the presence of an unchanging stimulus; this would seem to be the direct correlate of adaptation. All these features can be observed in the oscillographic records displayed in

322 The Sense of Taste

Fig. 104, taken from Pfaffmann's study of single gustatory fibers in the cat.

As has not infrequently happened in the brief but busy history of electrophysiology, some phenomena connected with the functioning of gustatory nerves have turned up which seem not to have any experiential counterpart and which, therefore, appear difficult of interpretation. There have been discovered, e.g., some fibers in the glossopharyngeal nerve of the frog which respond to distilled water as they might to a potent taste stimulus (*13*). The fibers are relatively big

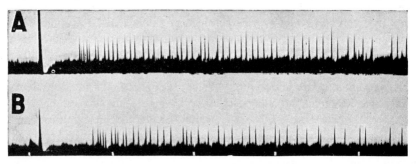

FIG. 104. Action potential record from a single nerve fiber in response to acid on the tongue. In *A* the stimulus was 0.5 *N* acetic acid, in *B* 0.01 *N* hydrochloric acid. In each case the first large upward deflection signals the application of the drop of acid. Time marks are 0.1 sec. From Pfaffmann, *231*. From original of Fig. 4, C. Pfaffmann, *J. cell. comp. Physiol.*, 1941, *17*, 248.

ones and thus give large potentials which are long lasting and slowly adapting. Salt solutions of any strength (0.025% or more) fail to discharge these fibers, though they do excite smaller-diameter ones in the same bundle. Acids also fail to arouse the "water receptors," though they, like salt, are able to stimulate a still different set of small fibers. Apparently the frog is in possession of a gustatory mechanism which permits him to make discriminations among salt, acid, and pure water; nor is appreciation of the water based merely on an absence of stimulation. There seems to be a positive "water taste" for him.

Theories of Taste Sensitivity. This chapter was introduced with the characterization of taste as the poor relation of the family of senses. Nowhere is its poverty more manifest than in the realm of theory. Gustatory theory, in general, is lacking in ideas and vague in the elaboration of the few it possesses. Only one general principle ever seems to assert itself. It is that tastes are generated through interaction of sapid substances and some material or materials, as yet unidentified, on the sensitive surfaces of the tongue, palate, etc., or perhaps housed in the cellular confines of the papillae. This is the burden of Crozier's hypothesis (66, p. 1029) that "the qualitative differentiation of the taste-buds might be due to the fact that there are four separate receptive substances, appropriately segregated in distribution, corresponding to the four conspicuous gustatory qualities." It is the idea underlying the taste theories of Lasareff, Hahn, and others (214, p. 125), which postulate chemical reactions yielding decomposition products which, in turn, ionize and stimulate the appropriate papillae.

It is only one step from this type of theory to the assumption that tastes might be generated through interference with one or more enzymes existing in the gustatory tissues. Indeed, there is some good evidence that such enzymes do exist and that they may have their balance disturbed through the action of substances having gustatory properties. El-Baradi and Bourne (87) have found two different enzymes to be present in the foliate papillae of the rabbit. These have been identified by histochemical methods as a phosphatase and another, unknown esterase. The reactions of both are strongly inhibited by sapid substances but not the same ones in the two cases. The phosphatase (or, possibly, group of related phosphatases) is readily affected by vanillin, capsicum, and infusions of tea; to a lesser extent it responds to the presence of oil of peppermint, oil of aniseed, and coffee infusions. However, sugar, salt, and quinine have no effect on it. On the other hand the unknown esterase, found to be present in high concentration in the taste buds and in smaller amounts in the neighboring epithelial tissue of the tongue, has its histochemical reaction strongly inhibited by quinine but remains unaffected by salt and sugar. It seems quite probable that further search will reveal other, similar catalysts to be present in the gustatory system. If so, we shall have some of the necessary building blocks for an eventual theory of taste.

References

1. Abrahams, H., Krakauer, D., and Dallenbach, K. M. Gustatory adaptation to salt. *Amer. J. Psychol.*, 1937, *49*, 462–469.
2. Adrian, E. D. Rod and cone components in the electrical response of the eye. *J. Physiol.*, 1946, *105*, 24–37.
3. Adrian, E. D. Olfactory discrimination. *Année psychol.*, 1951, *50*, 107–113.
4. Adrian, E. D., Cattell, McK., and Hoagland, H. Sensory discharges in single cutaneous nerve fibres. *J. Physiol.*, 1931, *72*, 377–391.
5. Adrian, E. D., and Matthews, B. H. C. The interpretation of potential waves in the cortex. *J. Physiol.*, 1934, *81*, 440–471.
6. Adrian, E. D., and Matthews, R. The interaction of retinal neurones. *J. Physiol.*, 1928, *65*, 273–298.
7. Adrian, E. D., and Zotterman, Y. The impulses produced by sensory nerve-endings. Part II. The response of a single end-organ. *J. Physiol.*, 1926, *61*, 151–171.
8. Allers, R., and Halpern, F. Wechselwirkungen gleichzeitiger Erregung mehrerer Hautsinne. I. Die Beeinflussung der Tastschwelle durch die Hauttemperatur. *Pflüg. Arch. ges. Physiol.*, 1921, *193*, 595–609.
9. Allison, A. C., and Warwick, R. T. T. Quantitative observations on the olfactory system of the rabbit. *Brain*, 1949, *72*, 186–197.
10. Alston, J. H. The spatial condition of the fusion of warmth and cold in heat. *Amer. J. Psychol.*, 1920, *31*, 303–312.
11. Anderson, R. J. Taste thresholds in stimulus mixtures. *Microfilm Abstr.*, 1950, *10(4)*, 287–288.
12. Andersson, B., Landgren, S., Olsson, L., and Zotterman, Y. The sweet taste fibres of the dog. *Acta physiol. scand.*, 1950, *21*, 105–119.
13. Andersson, B., and Zotterman, Y. The water taste in the frog. *Acta physiol. scand.*, 1950, *20*, 95–100.
14. Arey, L. B., Tremaine, M. J., and Monzingo, F. L. The numerical and topographical relations of taste buds to human circumvallate papillae throughout the life span. *Anat. Rec.*, 1935, *64*, 9–25.
15. Aronoff, S., and Dallenbach, K. M. Adaptation of warm spots under continuous and intermittent stimulation. *Amer. J. Psychol.*, 1936, *48*, 485–490.

16. Baker, H. D. The course of foveal light adaptation measured by the threshold intensity increment. *J. opt. Soc. Amer.*, 1949, *39*, 172–179.
17. Bartley, S. H. *Vision*. New York: Van Nostrand, 1941.
18. Bazett, H. C. Temperature sense in man. Pp. 489–501 in *Temperature, its measurement and control in science and industry*. New York: Reinhold, 1941.
19. Bazett, H. C., and McGlone, B. Studies in sensation: II. The mode of stimulation of cutaneous sensations of cold and warmth. *Arch. Neurol. Psychiat., Chicago*, 1932, *27*, 1031–1069.

20. Bazett, H. C., McGlone, B., and Brocklehurst, R. J. The temperatures in the tissues which accompany temperature sensations. *J. Physiol.*, 1930, *69*, 88–112.

21. Bazett, H. C., McGlone, B., Williams, R. G., and Lufkin, H. M. Sensation. I. Depth, distribution and probable identification in the prepuce of sensory end-organs concerned in sensations of temperature and touch; thermometric conductivity. *Arch. Neurol. Psychiat., Chicago*, 1932, 27, 489–517.

22. Beasley, W. C. Discriminations based on varying the relative amplitudes of four frequencies in combination. Pp. 350–354 in Valentine's *Readings in experimental psychology.* New York: Harper, 1931.

23. Beasley, W. C. Normal hearing for speech at each decade of life. *Publ. Hlth. Rep., Wash.*, 1938, Hearing Study Ser., No. 5.

24. Beck, L. H. Osmics: olfaction. Pp. 658–664 in Glasser's *Medical physics,* Vol. II. Chicago: Year Book Publishers, 1950.

25. Bednár, M., and Langfelder, O. Ueber das intravenöse (hämatogene) Riechen. *Mschr. Ohrenheilk.*, 1930, *64*, 1133–1139.

26. Beebe-Center, J. G. Standards for the use of the gust scale. *J. Psychol.*, 1949, *28*, 411–419.

27. Beebe-Center, J. G., and Waddell, D. A general psychological scale of taste. *J. Psychol.*, 1948, *26*, 517–524.

28. Beitel, R. J. Spatial summation of subliminal stimuli in the human retina. *J. gen. Psychol.*, 1934, *10*, 311–327.

29. Békésy, G. von. Ueber die Hörschwelle und Fühlgrenze langsamer sinusförmiger Luftdruckschwankungen. *Ann. d. Phys.*, 1936, *26*, 554–566.

30. Békésy, G. von., and Rosenblith, W. A. The mechanical properties of the ear. Chap. 27 (pp. 1075–1115) in Stevens (ed.), *Handbook of experimental psychology.* New York: Wiley, 1951.

31. Belonoschkin, B. Ueber die Kaltreceptoren der Haut. *Z. Biol.*, 1933, *93*, 487–489.

32. Bentley, M. The synthetic experiment. *Amer. J. Psychol.*, 1900, *11*, 405–425.

33. Bernhard, C. G., and Granit, R. Nerve as model temperature end organ. *J. gen. Psychol.*, 1946, *29*, 257–265.

34. Berry, W., and Imus, H. Quantitative aspects of the flight of colors. *Amer. J. Psychol.*, 1935, *47*, 449–457.

35. Bigelow, N., Harrison, I., Goodell, H., and Wolff, H. G. Studies on pain: quantitative measurements of two pain sensations of the skin, with reference to the nature of the "hyperalgesia of peripheral neuritis." *J. clin. Invest.*, 1945, *24*, 503–512.

36. Bishop, G. H. Responses to electrical stimulation of single sensory units of skin. *J. Neurophysiol.*, 1943, *6*, 361–382.

37. Bishop, G. H. Neural mechanisms of cutaneous sense. *Physiol. Rev.*, 1946, *26*, 77–102.

38. Bishop, G. H. Relation of pain sensory threshold to form of mechanical stimulator. *J. Neurophysiol.*, 1949, *12*, 51–57.

39. Blakeslee, A. F., and Salmon, T. H. Genetics of sensory thresholds: individual taste reactions for different substances. *Proc. nat. Acad. Sci., Wash.*, 1935, *21*, 84–90.

40. Boeke, J. Nerve endings, motor and sensory. Pp. 243–315 in Penfield (ed.), *Cytology and cellular pathology of the nervous system,* Vol. I. New York: Hoeber, 1932.
41. Boring, E. G. The sensations of the alimentary canal. *Amer. J. Psychol.,* 1915, *26,* 1–57.
42. Boring, E. G. The thermal sensitivity of the stomach. *Amer. J. Psychol.,* 1915, *26,* 485–494.
43. Boring, E. G. *The physical dimensions of consciousness.* New York: Appleton-Century, 1933.
44. Boring, E. G. The size of the differential limen for pitch. *Amer. J. Psychol.,* 1940, *53,* 450–455.
45. Boring, E. G. *Sensation and perception in the history of experimental psychology.* New York: Appleton-Century, 1942.
46. Boring, E. G., and Stevens, S. S. The nature of tonal brightness. *Proc. nat. Acad. Sci., Wash.,* 1936, *22,* 514–521.
47. Börnstein, W. S. Cortical representation of taste in man and monkey. II. The localization of the cortical taste area in man and a method of measuring impairment of taste in man. *Yale J. Biol. Med.,* 1940, *13,* 133–156.
48. Brecher, G. A. Die untere Hör- und Tongrenze. *Pflüg. Arch. ges. Physiol.,* 1934, *234,* 380–393.
49. Bremer, J. L., and Weatherford, H. L. *A textbook of histology* (6th ed.). Philadelphia: Blakiston, 1944.
50. Brown, R. H., and Page, H. E. Pupil dilatation and dark adaptation. *J. exp. Psychol.,* 1939, *25,* 347–360.
51. Bujas, Z. Quelques remarques sur le contraste et l'inhibition à la suite d'excitations gustatives simultanées. *C. R. Soc. Biol., Paris,* 1934, *116,* 1304–1306.

52. Cannon, W. B. *Bodily changes in pain, hunger, fear, and rage* (2nd ed.). New York: Appleton-Century, 1934.
53. Cannon, W. B. Hunger and thirst. Chap. 5 (pp. 247–263) in Murchison (ed.), *Handbook of general experimental psychology.* Worcester: Clark Univ. Press, 1934.
54. Cannon, W. B., and Washburn, A. L. An explanation of hunger. *Amer. J. Physiol.,* 1912, *29,* 441–454.
55. Carr, H. Head's theory of cutaneous sensitivity. *Psychol. Rev.,* 1916, *23,* 262–268.
56. Chapanis, A. How we see: a summary of basic principles. Chap. 1 (pp. 3–60) in *Human factors in undersea warfare.* Washington: National Research Council, 1949.
57. Chapanis, A., Garner, W. R., and Morgan, C. T. *Applied experimental psychology.* New York: Wiley, 1949.
58. Clark, B., and Graybiel, A. Linear acceleration and deceleration as factors influencing nonvisual orientation during flight. *J. Aviat. Med.,* 1949, *20,* 92–101.
59. Clark, W. E. LeG. Anatomical basis of colour vision. *Nature, Lond.,* 1940, *146,* 558–559.

60. Clark, W. E. LeG. Projection of the olfactory epithelium on to the olfactory bulb: a correction. *Nature, Lond.*, 1950, *165*, 452–453.

61. Clark, W. E. LeG., and Warwick, R. T. T. The pattern of olfactory innervation. *J. Neurol. Psychiat.*, 1946, *9*, 101–111.

62. Cohen, J., and Ogdon, D. P. Taste blindness to phenyl-thio-carbamide and related compounds. *Psychol. Bull.*, 1949, *46*, 490–498.

63. Creed, R. S., Denny-Brown, D., Eccles, J. C., Liddell, E. G. T., and Sherrington, C. S. *Reflex activity of the spinal cord.* Oxford: Clarendon Press, 1932.

64. Crocker, E. C. *Flavor.* New York: McGraw-Hill, 1945.

65. Crowe, S. J., Guild, S. R., and Polvogt, L. M. Observations on the pathology of high-tone deafness. *Johns Hopk. Hosp. Bull.*, 1934, *54*, 315–379.

66. Crozier, W. J. Chemoreception. Chap. 19 (pp. 987–1036) in Murchison (ed.), *Handbook of general experimental psychology.* Worcester: Clark Univ. Press, 1934.

67. Culler, E. A. In Symposium on tone localization in the cochlea. *Ann. Otol., etc., St. Louis,* 1935, *44*, 807–813.

68. Culler, E., Coakley, J. D., Lowy, K., and Gross, N. A revised frequency-map of the guinea-pig cochlea. *Amer. J. Psychol.*, 1943, *56*, 475–500.

69. Cutolo, F. A preliminary study of the psychology of heat. *Amer. J. Psychol.*, 1918, *29*, 442–448.

70. Dallenbach, K. M. The temperature spots and end-organs. *Amer. J. Psychol.*, 1927, *39*, 402–427.

71. Dallenbach, K. M. The temperature spots and end-organs. Pp. 496–516 in Wheeler's *Readings in psychology.* New York: Crowell, 1930.

72. Dallenbach, K. M. A method of marking the skin. *Amer. J. Psychol.*, 1931, *43*, 287.

73. Dallenbach, K. M. Pain: history and present status. *Amer. J. Psychol.*, 1939, *52*, 331–347.

74. Dallenbach, K. M. Smell, taste, and somesthesis. Chap. 19 (pp. 600–626) in Boring, Langfeld, and Weld (eds.), *Introduction to psychology.* New York: Wiley, 1939.

75. Davis, H. Psychophysiology of hearing and deafness. Chap. 28 (pp. 1116–1142) in Stevens (ed.), *Handbook of experimental psychology.* New York: Wiley, 1951.

76. Davis, H. *Hearing and deafness: a guide for laymen.* New York: Murray Hill, 1947.

77. Davis, H., Fernández, C., and McAuliffe, D. R. The excitatory process in the cochlea. *Proc. nat. Acad. Sci., Wash.*, 1950, *36*, 580–587.

78. Detwiler, S. R. Some biological aspects of vision. *Sigma Xi Quart.*, 1941, *29*, 112–129 and 142.

79. Dimmick, F. L. Vision. Chap. 12 (pp. 269–296) in Boring, Langfeld, and Weld (eds.), *Foundations of psychology.* New York: Wiley, 1948.

80. Dimmick, F. L., and Hubbard, M. R. The spectral location of psychologically unique yellow, green, and blue. *Amer. J. Psychol.*, 1939, *52*, 242–254.

81. Dimmick, F. L., and Hubbard, M. R. The spectral components of psychologically unique red. *Amer. J. Psychol.*, 1939, *52*, 348–353.

82. Dohlman, G. Some practical and theoretical points in labyrinthology. *Proc. roy. Soc. Med.*, 1935, *28*, 1371–1380.

83. Dohlman, G. Investigation in the function of the semicircular canals. *Acta oto-laryng., Stockh. Suppl.*, 1944, *51*, 211–219.
84. Donaldson, H. H. On the temperature sense. *Mind*, 1885, *10*, 399–416.
85. Dusser de Barenne, J. G. The labyrinthine and postural mechanisms. Chap. 4 (pp. 204–246) in Murchison (ed.), *Handbook of general experimental psychology*. Worcester: Clark Univ. Press, 1934.

86. Egan, J. P. The effect of noise in one ear upon the loudness of speech in the other ear. *J. acoust. Soc. Amer.*, 1948, *20*, 58–62.
87. El-Baradi, A. F., and Bourne, G. H. Theory of tastes and odors. *Science*, 1951, *113*, 660–661.
88. Elsberg, C. A., and Levy, I. The sense of smell. I. A new and simple method of quantitative olfactometry. *Bull. neurol. Inst. N. Y.*, 1935, *4*, 5–19.

89. Fabian, F. W., and Blum, H. B. Relative taste potency of some basic food constituents and their competitive and compensatory action. *Food Res.*, 1943, *8*, 179–193.
90. Feindel, W. H., Weddell, G., and Sinclair, D. C. Pain sensibility in deep somatic structures. *J. Neurol. Psychiat.*, 1948, *11*, 113–117.
91. Ferree, C. E., and Rand, G. Chromatic thresholds of sensation from center to periphery of the retina and their bearing on color theory. *Psychol. Rev.*, 1919, *26*, 16–41; 150–163.
92. Fick, A. Zur Theorie der Farbenblindheit. *Pflüg. Arch. ges. Physiol.*, 1896, *64*, 313–320.
93. Fitts, P. M. Engineering psychology and equipment design. Chap. 35 (pp. 1287–1340) in Stevens (ed.), *Handbook of experimental psychology*. New York: Wiley, 1951.
94. Fletcher, H. *Speech and hearing*. New York: Van Nostrand, 1929.
95. Fletcher, H. A space-time pattern theory of hearing. *J. acoust. Soc. Amer.*, 1930, *1*, 311–343.
96. Foster, D., Scofield, E. H., and Dallenbach, K. M. An olfactorium. *Amer. J. Psychol.*, 1950, *63*, 431–440.
97. Fox, A. L. The relationship between chemical constitution and taste. *Proc. nat. Acad. Sci., Wash.*, 1932, *18*, 115–120.
98. Frey, M. von. Ueber die zur ebenmerklichen Erregung des Drucksinns erfordlichen Energiemengen. *Z. Biol.*, 1919, *70*, 333–347.
99. Frey, M. von, and Kiesow, F. Ueber die Function der Tastkörperchen. *Z. Psychol.*, 1899, *20*, 126–163.
100. Fry, G. A., and Bartley, S. H. The effect of steady stimulation of one part of the retina upon the critical frequency in another. *J. exp. Psychol.*, 1936, *19*, 351–356.
101. Fulton, J. F. *Physiology of the nervous system*. (2nd ed.) New York: Oxford, 1943.

102. Galambos, R., and Davis, H. The response of single auditory-nerve fibers to acoustic stimulation. *J. Neurophysiol.*, 1943, *6*, 39–57.
103. Galambos, R., and Davis, H. Action potentials from single auditory-nerve fibers? *Science*, 1948, *108*, 513.

104. Galileo Galilei. *Dialogues concerning two new sciences* (Trans. H. Crew and A. de Salvio). Evanston, Ill.: Northwestern Univ. Press, 1950.
105. Gardner, E. *Fundamentals of neurology.* Philadelphia: Saunders, 1947.
106. Gatti, A., and Dodge, R. Ueber die Unterschiedsempfindlichkeit bei Reizung eines einzelnen, isolierten Tastorgans. *Arch. ges. Psychol.*, 1929, *69*, 405–425.
107. Geldard, F. A. The measurement of retinal fatigue to achromatic stimulation. I, II. *J. gen. Psychol.*, 1928, *1*, 123–135; 578–590.
108. Geldard, F. A. Brightness contrast and Heymans' Law. *J. gen. Psychol.*, 1931, *5*, 191–206.
109. Geldard, F. A. Foveal sensitivity as influenced by peripheral stimulation. *J. gen. Psychol.*, 1932, *7*, 185–189.
110. Geldard, F. A. The description of a case of total color blindness. *J. opt. Soc. Amer.*, 1933, *23*, 256–260.
111. Geldard, F. A. Flicker relations within the fovea. *J. opt. Soc. Amer.*, 1934, *24*, 299–302.
112. Geldard, F. A. The perception of mechanical vibration. I. History of a controversy. *J. gen. Psychol.*, 1940, *22*, 243–269.
113. Geldard, F. A. The perception of mechanical vibration. II. The response of pressure receptors. *J. gen. Psychol.*, 1940, *22*, 271–280.
114. Geldard, F. A. The perception of mechanical vibration. III. The frequency function. *J. gen. Psychol.*, 1940, *22*, 281–289.
115. Geldard, F. A. The perception of mechanical vibration. IV. Is there a separate "vibratory sense"? *J. gen. Psychol.*, 1940, *22*, 291–308.
116. Geldard, F. A. Somesthesis and the chemical senses. *Ann. Rev. Psychol.*, 1950, *1*, 71–86.
117. Gernandt, B. Response of mammalian vestibular neurons to horizontal rotation and caloric stimulation. *J. Neurophysiol.*, 1949, *12*, 173–185.
118. Gibson, K. S., and Tyndall, E. P. T. The visibility of radiant energy. *Sci. Pap. U. S. Bur. Stand.*, 1923, *19*, No. 475.
119. Gilmer, B. von H. The relation of cold sensitivity to sweat duct distribution and the neurovascular mechanisms of the skin. *J. Psychol.*, 1942, *13*, 307–325.
120. Gilmer, B. von H. The glomus body as a receptor of cutaneous pressure and vibration. *Psychol. Bull.*, 1942, *39*, 73–93.
121. Gilmer, B. von H., and Haythorn, S. R. Cutaneous pressure-vibration spots and their underlying tissues. *Arch. Neurol. Psychiat., Chicago*, 1941, *46*, 621–648.
122. Goldscheider, A. Untersuchungen über den Muskelsinn. I. Ueber die Bewegungsempfindung. Pp. 97–200 in *Gesammelte Abhandlungen von A. Goldscheider*, Vol. II. Leipzig: Barth, 1898.
123. Goldscheider, A. Untersuchungen über den Muskelsinn. II. Ueber die Empfindung der Schwere und des Widerstandes. Pp. 201–281 in *Gesammelte Abhandlungen von A. Goldscheider*, Vol. II. Leipzig: Barth, 1898.
124. Graham, C. H. Vision. III. Some neural correlations. Chap. 15 (pp. 829–879) in Murchison (ed.), *Handbook of general experimental psychology.* Worcester: Clark Univ. Press, 1934.

125. Graham, C. H., and Granit, R. Comparative studies on the peripheral and central retina. VI. Inhibition, summation, and synchronization of impulses in the retina. *Amer. J. Physiol.*, 1931, *98*, 664–673.

126. Granit, R. Comparative studies on the peripheral and central retina. I. On interaction between distant areas in the human eye. *Amer. J. Physiol.*, 1930, *94*, 41–50.

127. Granit, R. The components of the retinal action potential in mammals and their relation to the discharge in the optic nerve. *J. Physiol.*, 1933, *77*, 207–239.

128. Granit, R. The retinal mechanism of color reception. *J. opt. Soc. Amer.*, 1941, *31*, 570–580.

129. Granit, R., and Harper, P. Comparative studies on the peripheral and central retina. II. Synaptic reactions in the eye. *Amer. J. Physiol.*, 1930, *95*, 211–228.

130. Graybiel, A., Kerr, W. A., and Bartley, S. H. Stimulus thresholds of the semicircular canals as a function of angular acceleration. *Amer. J. Psychol.*, 1948, *61*, 21–36.

131. Grindley, G. C. The variation of sensory thresholds with the rate of application of the stimulus. I. The differential threshold for pressure. *Brit. J. Psychol.*, 1936, *27*, 86–95.

132. Grindley, G. C. The variation of sensory thresholds with the rate of application of the stimulus. II. Touch and pain. *Brit. J. Psychol.*, 1936, *27*, 189–195.

133. Gross, N. B., and Thurlow, W. R. Microelectrode studies of neural auditory activity of cat. II. Medial geniculate body. *J. Neurophysiol.*, 1951, *14*, 409–422.

134. Guild, S. R., Crowe, S. J., Bunch, C. C., and Polvogt, L. M. Correlations of differences in the density of innervation of the organ of Corti with differences in the acuity of hearing. *Acta oto-laryng., Stockh.*, 1931, *15*, 269–308.

135. Guilford, J. P., and Lovewell, E. M. The touch spots and the intensity of the stimulus. *J. gen. Psychol.*, 1936, *15*, 149–159.

136. Häggqvist, G. Histophysiologische Studien über die Temperatursinne der Haut des Menschen. *Anat. Anz.*, 1913, *45*, 46–63.

137. Hahn, H. Die physiologische Konstanten und Variablen des Temperatursinnes. *Z. Psychol.*, 1929, *60*, 162–232.

138. Hahn, H. Die Adaptation des Geschmacksinnes. *Z. Sinnesphysiol.*, 1934, *65*, 105–145.

139. Hahn, H. Ueber die Ursache der Geschmacksempfindung. *Klin. Wschr.*, 1936, *15*, 933–935.

140. Hahn, H., and Ulbrich, L. Eine systematische Untersuchung der Geschmacksschwellen. *Pflüg. Arch. ges. Physiol.*, 1948, *250*, 357–384.

141. Hallpike, C. S., and Rawdon-Smith, A. F. The Helmholtz resonance theory of hearing. *Nature, Lond.*, 1934, *133*, 614.

142. Hänig, D. P. Zur Psychophysik des Geschmacksinnes. *Philos. Stud. (Wundt)*, 1901, *17*, 576–623.

143. Hardy, A. C. *Handbook of colorimetry.* Cambridge, Mass.: Technology Press, 1936.

144. Hardy, J. D., and Oppel, T. W. Studies in temperature sensation. III. The sensitivity of the body to heat and the spatial summation of the end organ responses. *J. clin. Invest.*, 1937, *16*, 533–540.

145. Hardy, J. D., Wolff, H. G., and Goodell, H. Studies on pain; a new method for measuring pain threshold: observations on spatial summation of pain. *J. clin. Invest.*, 1940, *19*, 649–657.

146. Hardy, J. D., Wolff, H. G., and Goodell, H. Studies on pain: discrimination of differences in intensity of a pain stimulus as a basis of a scale of pain intensity. *J. clin. Invest.*, 1947, *26*, 1152–1158.

147. Hartline, H. K. The nerve messages in the fibers of the visual pathway. *J. opt. Soc. Amer.*, 1940, *30*, 239–247.

148. Hartline, H. K., and Graham, C. H. Nerve impulses from single receptors in the eye. *J. cell comp. Physiol.*, 1932, *1*, 277–295.

149. Head, H. *Studies in neurology.* London: Oxford, 1920.

150. Hecht, S. On the binocular fusion of colors and its relation to theories of color vision. *Proc. nat. Acad. Sci., Wash.*, 1928, *14*, 237–240.

151. Hecht, S. The retinal processes concerned with visual acuity and color vision. *Bull. Howe Lab. Ophthal. (Harvard)*, 1931, *No. 4*, 1–88.

152. Hecht, S. The interrelations of various aspects of color vision. *J. opt. Soc. Amer.*, 1931, *21*, 615–639.

153. Hecht, S. A quantitative formulation of colour vision. Pp. 126–156 in *Report of a joint discussion on vision.* London: The Physical and Optical Societies, 1932.

154. Hecht, S. The instantaneous visual threshold after light adaptation. *Proc. nat. Acad. Sci., Wash.*, 1937, *23*, 227–233.

155. Hecht, S. The nature of the visual process. *Bull. N. Y. Acad. Med.*, 1938, *14*, 21–45.

156. Hecht, S., and Mandelbaum, J. Dark adaptation and experimental human vitamin A deficiency. *Amer. J. Physiol.*, 1940, *130*, 651–664.

157. Hecht, S., and Shlaer, S. Intermittent stimulation by light. V. The relation between intensity and critical frequency for different parts of the spectrum. *J. gen. Physiol.*, 1936, *19*, 965–977.

158. Hecht, S., and Shlaer, S. An adaptometer for measuring human dark adaptation. *J. opt. Soc. Amer.*, 1938, *28*, 269–275.

159. Hecht, S., Shlaer, S., and Pirenne, H. Energy at the threshold of vision. *Science*, 1941, *93*, 585–587.

160. Hecht, S., and Williams, R. E. The visibility of monochromatic radiation and the absorption spectrum of visual purple. *J. gen. Physiol.*, 1922, *5*, 1–34.

161. Heiser, F. Stimulus-duration and sensations of warmth. *Amer. J. Psychol.*, 1937, *49*, 58–66.

162. Heiser, F., and McNair, W. K. Stimulus-pressure and thermal sensation. *Amer. J. Psychol.*, 1934, *46*, 580–589.

163. Helmholtz, H. L. F. von. *Physiological optics* (Trans. J. P. C. Southall), Vol. II. Rochester, N. Y.: Optical Society of America, 1924.

164. Helmholtz, H. L. F. von. *Sensations of tone* (Trans. A. J. Ellis), 5th ed. New York: Longmans, Green, 1930.

165. Henney, K. *Principles of radio* (3rd ed.). New York: Wiley, 1938.

166. Henning, H. Die Qualitätenreihe des Geschmacks. *Z. Psychol.*, 1916, *74*, 203–219.

167. Henning, H. *Der Geruch* (2nd ed.). Leipzig: Barth, 1924.
168. Holway, A. H., and Hurvich, L. M. Differential gustatory sensitivity to salt. *Amer. J. Psychol.*, 1937, *49*, 37–48.
169. Hsü, E. H. A factorial analysis of olfaction. *Psychometrika*, 1946, *11*, 31–42.
170. Huddart, J. An account of persons who could not distinguish colours. *Philos. Trans.*, 1777, *67*, 260–265.

171. Jenkins, W. L. Adaptation in isolated cold spots. *Amer. J. Psychol.*, 1937, *49*, 1–22.
172. Jenkins, W. O. The tactual discrimination of shapes for coding aircraft-type controls. Chap. 14 (pp. 199–205) in P. M. Fitts (ed.), *Psychological research in equipment design*. Washington: U. S. Government Printing Office, 1947.
173. Johnson, E. P. The electrical response of the human retina during dark-adaptation. *J. exp. Psychol.*, 1949, *39*, 597–609.
174. Jones, L. A. The fundamental scale of pure hue and retinal sensibility to hue differences. *J. opt. Soc. Amer.*, 1917, *1*, 63–77.
175. Jones, L. A., and Lowry, E. M. Retinal sensibility to saturation differences. *J. opt. Soc. Amer.*, 1926, *13*, 25–34.
176. Judd, D. B. Facts of color blindness. *J. opt. Soc. Amer.*, 1943, *33*, 294–307.
177. Judd, D. B. Current views on colour blindness. *Documenta Ophthalmologica*, 1949, *3*, 251–288.

178. Katz, D. The vibratory sense and other lectures. *Univ. Maine Bull.*, 1930, *32*, 90–104.
179. Keller, M. The relation between the critical duration and intensity in brightness discrimination. *J. exp. Psychol.*, 1941, *28*, 407–418.
180. Kemp, E. H. A critical review of experiments on the problem of stimulation deafness. *Psychol. Bull.*, 1935, *32*, 325–342.
181. Kemp, E. H., Coppée, G. E., and Robinson, E. H. Electrical responses of the brain stem to unilateral auditory stimulation. *Amer. J. Physiol.*, 1937, *120*, 304–315.
182. Kemp, E. H., and Johnson, P. Localization of response in the cochlea as determined by electrical recording. *Science*, 1939, *90*, 405.
183. Kiesow, F. Beiträge zur physiologischen Psychologie des Geschmacksinnes (Fortsetzung). *Philos. Stud.* (*Wundt*), 1894, *10*, 523–561.
184. Kiesow, F. Contribution à la psycho-physiologie de la cavité buccale. *Arch. ital. Biol.*, 1898, *30*, 377–398.
185. Kistiakowsky, G. B. On the theory of odors. *Science*, 1950, *112*, 154–155.
186. Knudsen, V. O. Hearing with the sense of touch. *J. gen. Psychol.*, 1928, *1*, 320–352.
187. Köhler, W. Akustische Untersuchungen. II. *Z. Psychol.*, 1910, *58*, 59–140.
188. Kolbe, H. Die zeitliche Veränderung der Unterschiedsschwelle während der Einwirkung eines stetigen Dauerdruck- oder Dauerlichtreizes. *Z. Sinnesphysiol.*, 1936, *67*, 53–68.
189. Komuro, K. Le minimum perceptible de l'odorat dans une enceinte absolument inodore. *Arch. neérl. Physiol.*, 1921, *6*, 20–24.
190. Kopera, A. Untersuchungen über die Unterschiedsempfindlichkeit im Bereiche des Geschmacksinns. *Arch. ges. Psychol.*, 1931, *82*, 273–307.

191. Krakauer, D., and Dallenbach, K. M. Gustatory adaptation to sweet, sour, and bitter. *Amer. J. Psychol.*, 1937, *49*, 469–475.

192. Laidlaw, R. W., and Hamilton, M. A. A study of thresholds in apperception of passive movement among normal control subjects. *Bull. neurol. Inst. N. Y.*, 1937, *6*, 268–273.

193. Lanier, L. H. An experimental study of cutaneous innervation. *Proc. Ass. Res. nerv. ment. Dis.*, 1934, *15*, 437–456.

194. Laurens, H., and Hamilton, W. F. The sensibility of the eye to differences in wave-length. *Amer. J. Physiol.*, 1923, *65*, 547–568.

195. Lashley, K. S. The problem of cerebral organization in vision. In H. Klüver (ed.), *Biological symposia*, Vol. VII. Lancaster, Pa.: Jacques Cattell Press, 1942.

196. Levine, H. A., and Dallenbach, K. M. Adaptation of cold spots under continuous and intermittent stimulation. *Amer. J. Psychol.*, 1936, *48*, 490–497.

197. Lewis, D. R. Psychological scales of taste. *J. Psychol.*, 1948, *26*, 437–446.

198. Lewis, T. *The blood vessels of the human skin and their responses.* London: Shaw, 1927.

199. Lewis, T. Pain. New York: Macmillan, 1942.

200. Lickley, J. D. *The nervous system.* New York: Longmans, Green, 1931.

201. Licklider, J. C. R. Basic correlates of the auditory stimulus. Chap. 25 (pp. 985–1039) in Stevens (ed.), *Handbook of experimental psychology.* New York: Wiley, 1951.

202. Licklider, J. C. R., and Miller, G. A. The perception of speech. Chap. 26 (pp. 1040–1074) in Stevens (ed.), *Handbook of experimental psychology.* New York: Wiley, 1951.

203. Löwenstein, O., and Sand, A. The mechanism of the semicircular canal. A study of the responses of single-fibre preparations to angular accelerations and to rotation at constant speed. *Proc. roy. Soc.*, 1940, *129B*, 256–275.

204. Luft, E. Ueber die Unterschiedsempfindlichkeit für Tonhöhen. *Philos. Stud. (Wundt)*, 1888, *4*, 511–540.

205. MacCorquodale, K. Effects of angular acceleration and centrifugal force on nonvisual space orientation during flight. *J. Aviat. Med.*, 1948, *19*, 146–157.

206. McDougall, W. The sensations excited by a single momentary stimulation of the eye. *Brit. J. Psychol.*, 1904, *1*, 78–113.

207. Matthews, B. H. C. The response of a muscle spindle during active contraction of a muscle. *J. Physiol.*, 1931, *72*, 153–174.

208. Matthews, B. H. C. Nerve endings in mammalian muscle. *J. Physiol.*, 1933, *78*, 1–53.

209. Maxwell, J. C. On the theory of three primary colours. Paper XXII (pp. 445–450) in *The scientific papers of James Clerk Maxwell*, Vol. I. Cambridge: Cambridge Univ. Press, 1890.

210. Mettler, F. A., Finch, G., Girden, E., and Culler, E. Acoustic value of the several components of the auditory pathway. *Brain*, 1934, *57*, 475–483.

211. Meyer, M. F. The hydraulic principles governing the function of the cochlea. *J. gen. Psychol.*, 1928, *1*, 239–265.

212. Meyer, M. F. *How we hear: how tones make music.* Boston: Branford, 1950.

213. Miller, D. C. *Anecdotal history of the science of sound.* New York: Macmillan, 1935.

214. Moncrieff, R. W. *The chemical senses.* New York: Wiley, 1944.

215. Morgan, C. T., and Stellar, E. *Physiological psychology.* New York: McGraw-Hill, 1950.

216. Mountcastle, V., and Henneman, E. Pattern of tactile representation in thalamus of cat. *J. Neurophysiol.,* 1949, *12*, 85–100.

217. Mueller, C. G., and Lloyd, V. V. Stereoscopic acuity for various levels of illumination. *Proc. nat. Acad. Sci., Wash.,* 1948, *34*, 223–227.

218. Nafe, J. P. The pressure, pain, and temperature senses. Chap. 20 (pp. 1037–1087) in Murchison (ed.), *Handbook of general experimental psychology.* Worcester: Clark Univ. Press, 1934.

219. Nafe, J. P., and Wagoner, K. S. The insensitivity of the cornea to heat and pain derived from high temperatures. *Amer. J. Psychol.,* 1937, *49*, 631–635.

220. Nafe, J. P., and Wagoner, K. S. The nature of pressure adaptation. *J. gen. Psychol.,* 1941, *25*, 323–351.

221. Newhall, S. M., Nickerson, D., and Judd, D. B. Final report of the OSA subcommittee on the spacing of the Munsell colors. *J. opt. Soc. Amer.,* 1943, *33*, 385–422.

222. Newman, E. B., Stevens, S. S., and Davis, H. Factors in the production of aural harmonics and combination tones. *J. acoust. Soc. Amer.,* 1937, *9*, 107–118.

223. Nickerson, D., and Newhall, S. M. A psychological color solid. *J. opt. Soc. Amer.,* 1943, *33*, 419–422.

224. Ogden, R. M. *Hearing.* New York: Harcourt, Brace, 1924.

225. Østerberg, G. Topography of the layer of rods and cones in the human retina. *Acta ophthal., Kbh., Suppl.,* 1935, *61*, 1–102.

226. Parker, G. H., and Stabler, E. M. On certain distinctions between taste and smell. *Amer. J. Physiol.,* 1913, *32*, 230–240.

227. Pattle, R. E., and Weddell, G. Observations on electrical stimulation of pain fibres in an exposed human sensory nerve. *J. Neurophysiol.,* 1948, *11*, 93–98.

228. Patton, H. D., Ruch, T. C., and Walker, A. E. Experimental hypogeusia from Horsley-Clarke lesions of the thalamus in *Macaca mulatta. J. Neurophysiol.,* 1944, *7*, 171–184.

229. Pendleton, C. R. The cold receptor. *Amer. J. Psychol.,* 1928, *40*, 353–371.

230. Penfield, W., and Boldrey, E. Somatic motor and sensory representation in the cerebral cortex of man as studied by electrical stimulation. *Brain,* 1937, *60*, 389–443.

231. Pfaffmann, C. Gustatory afferent impulses. *J. cell. comp. Physiol.,* 1941, *17*, 243–258.

232. Pfaffmann, C. Studying the senses of taste and smell. Chap. 10 (pp. 268–288) in Andrews (ed.), *Methods of psychology.* New York: Wiley, 1948.

233. Pfaffmann, C. Taste and smell. Chap. 29 (pp. 1143–1171) in Stevens (ed.), *Handbook of experimental psychology.* New York: Wiley, 1951.

234. Polyak, S. L. *The retina.* Chicago: Univ. Chicago Press, 1941.

235. Priest, I. G. Note on the relation between the frequencies of complementary hues. *J. opt. Soc. Amer.,* 1920, *4,* 402–404.

236. Priest, I. G., and Brickwedde, F. G. The minimum perceptible colorimetric purity as a function of dominant wavelength with sunlight as a neutral standard. *J. opt. Soc. Amer.,* 1926, *13,* 306–307.

237. Purdy, D. M. Spectral hue as a function of intensity. *Amer. J. Psychol.,* 1931, *43,* 541–559.

238. Purdy, D. M. The Bezold-Brücke phenomenon and contours for constant hue. *Amer. J. Psychol.,* 1937, *49,* 313–315.

239. Ramón y Cajal, S. *Histology* (Trans. M. Fernán-Núñez). Baltimore: William Wood, 1933.

240. Ranson, S. W. *The anatomy of the nervous system* (7th ed.). Philadelphia: Saunders, 1943.

241. Rasmussen, A. T. *Outlines of neuro-anatomy.* Dubuque, Ia.: Brown, 1943.

242. Ratliff, F., and Riggs, L. A. Involuntary motions of the eye during monocular fixation. *J. exp. Psychol.,* 1950, *40,* 687–701.

243. Reeves, P. Rate of pupillary dilation and contraction. *Psychol. Rev.,* 1918, *25,* 330–340.

244. Rein, H. Ueber die Topographie der Warmempfindung. *Z. Biol.,* 1925, *82,* 513–535.

245. Rich, G. J. A study of tonal attributes. *Amer. J. Psychol.,* 1919, *30,* 121–164.

246. Richter, C. P., and MacLean, A. Salt taste threshold of humans. *Amer. J. Physiol.,* 1939, *126,* 1–6.

247. Riesz, R. R. Differential intensity sensitivity of the ear for pure tones. *Phys. Rev.,* 1928, *31,* 867–875.

248. Riggs, L. A., Berry, R. N., and Wayner, M. A comparison of electrical and psychophysical determinations of the spectral sensitivity of the human eye. *J. opt. Soc. Amer.,* 1949, *39,* 427–436.

249. Riggs, L. A., and Johnson, E. P. Electrical responses of the human retina. *J. exp. Psychol.,* 1949, *39,* 415–424.

250. Rinde, C. A. Retinal chromatic fields as a function of wave-length. *J. opt. Soc. Amer.,* 1932, *22,* 333–356.

251. Rivers, W. H. R. *Instinct and the unconscious.* Cambridge: Cambridge Univ. Press, 1920.

252. Rosenblith, W. A. Auditory masking and fatigue. *J. acoust. Soc. Amer.,* 1950, *22,* 792–800.

253. Rosenblith, W. A., Miller, G. A., Egan, J. P., Hirsh, I. J., and Thomas, G. J. An auditory afterimage? *Science,* 1947, *106,* 333–335.

254. Schoen, Z. J., and Wallace, S. R. Ocular dominance: its independence of retinal events. *Arch. Ophthal., N. Y.,* 1936, *15,* 890–897.

255. Schumacher, G. A., Goodell, H., Hardy, J. D., and Wolff, H. G. Uniformity of the pain threshold in man. *Science,* 1940, *92,* 110.

256. Senders, V. L. The physiological basis of visual acuity. *Psychol. Bull.,* 1948, *45,* 465–490.

257. Setterfield, W., Schott, R. G., and Snyder, L. H. Studies in human inheritance. XV. The bimodality of the threshold curve for the taste of phenyl-thio-carbamide. *Ohio J. Sci.*, 1936, *36*, 231–235.
258. Sherrington, C. S. *The integrative action of the nervous system.* London: Constable, 1906.
259. Shower, E. G., and Biddulph, R. Differential pitch sensitivity of the ear. *J. acoust. Soc. Amer.*, 1931, *3*, 275–287.
260. Sivian, L. J., and White, S. D. On minimum audible sound fields. *J. acoust. Soc. Amer.*, 1933, *4*, 288–321.
261. Skramlik, E. von. Psychophysiologie der Tastsinne. *Arch. ges. Psychol.*, Ergänzungsbd. *4*, 1937.
262. Sloan, L. L., and Wollach, L. A case of unilateral deuteranopia. *J. opt. Soc. Amer.*, 1948, *38*, 502–509.
263. Smith, F. O. An experimental study of retinal sensitivity and discrimination for purple under different degrees of intensity of stimulation. *J. exp. Psychol.*, 1925, *8*, 381–397.
264. Smith, J. R. Spatial and binocular effects in human intensity discrimination. *J. gen. Psychol.*, 1936, *14*, 318–345.
265. Southall, J. P. C. *Introduction to physiological optics.* New York: Oxford, 1937.
266. Steindler, O. Die Farbenempfindlichkeit des normalen und farbenblinden Auges. *S. B. Akad. Wiss. Wien*, 1906, *115*, 39–62.
267. Steinhardt, J. Intensity discrimination in the human eye. I. The relation of $\Delta I/I$ to intensity. *J. gen. Physiol.*, 1936, *20*, 185–209.
268. Steinhausen, W. Ueber den experimentellen Nachweis der Ablenkung der Cupula terminalis in der intakten Bogengangsampulle des Labyrinths bei der thermischen und adäquaten rotatorischen Reizung. *Z. Hals- Nas.- u. Ohrenheilk.*, 1931, *29*, 211–216.
269. Stevens, S. S. The attributes of tones. *Proc. nat. Acad. Sci., Wash.*, 1934, *20*, 457–459.
270. Stevens, S. S. The relation of pitch to intensity. *J. acoust. Soc. Amer.*, 1937, *8*, 191–195.
271. Stevens, S. S. Machines cannot fight alone. *Amer. Scientist*, 1946, *34*, 389–400.
272. Stevens, S. S., and Davis, H. Psychophysiological acoustics: pitch and loudness. *J. acoust. Soc. Amer.*, 1936, *8*, 1–13.
273. Stevens, S. S., and Davis, H. *Hearing.* New York: Wiley, 1938.
274. Stevens, S. S., Davis, H., and Lurie, M. H. The localization of pitch perception on the basilar membrane. *J. gen. Psychol.*, 1935, *13*, 297–315.
275. Strughold, H. Ueber die Dichte und Schwellen der Smerzpunkte der Epidermis in der verschiedenen Körperregionen. *Z. Biol.*, 1924, *80*, 367–380.
276. Strughold, H., and Karbe, M. Vitale Färbung des Auges und experimentelle Untersuchung der gefärbten Nervenelemente. *Z. Biol.*, 1925, *83*, 297–308.
277. Strughold, H., and Porz, R. Die Dichte der Kaltpunkte auf der Haut des menschlichen Körpers. *Z. Biol.*, 1931, *91*, 563–571.

278. Thomas, G. J. Equal-volume judgments of tones. *Amer. J. Psychol.*, 1949, *62*, 182–201.
279. Thurlow, W. R. Binaural interaction and the perception of pitch. *J. exp. Psychol.*, 1943, *32*, 13–36.

280. Thurlow, W. R., Gross, N. B., Kemp, E. H., and Lowy, K. Microelectrode studies of neural auditory activity of cat. I. Inferior colliculus. *J. Neurophysiol.*, 1951, *14*, 289–304.

281. Tice, F. G. Individual differences in fusion frequency correlated with other visual processes. Unpublished Ph.D. dissertation. Univ. of Virginia, 1941.

282. Titchener, E. B. Psychology: science or technology? *Pop. Sci. Mon.*, 1914, *84*, 39–51.

283. Tower, S. S. Pain: definition and properties of the unit for sensory reception. Chap. II (pp. 16–43) of *Pain*. Baltimore: Williams and Wilkins, 1943.

284. Travis, R. C. The effect of varying the position of the head on voluntary response to vestibular stimulation. *J. exp. Psychol.*, 1938, *23*, 295–303.

285. Troland, L. T. The psychophysiology of auditory qualities and attributes. *J. gen. Psychol.*, 1929, *2*, 28–58.

286. Troland, L. T. The Hering theory in modern form. Para. 332 in *The principles of psychophysiology*, Vol. II. New York: Van Nostrand, 1930.

287. Tunturi, A. R. A study on the pathway from the medial geniculate body to the acoustio cortex in the dog. *Amer. J. Physiol.*, 1946, *147*, 311–319.

288. Verrier, M. L. La morphologie comparée des cellules visuelles et la théorie de la dualité de la vision. *C. R. Acad. Sci., Paris*, 1935, *200*, 261–263.

289. Wald, G. The photochemistry of vision. *Documenta ophthalmologica*, 1949, *3*, 94–137.

290. Wald, G., and Clark, A. B. Visual adaptation and the chemistry of the rods. *J. gen. Physiol.*, 1937, *21*, 93–105.

291. Wallace, S. R. Studies in binocular interdependence. I. Binocular relations in macular adaptation. *J. gen. Psychol.*, 1937, *17*, 307–322.

292. Wallace, S. R. Studies in binocular interdependence. II. Some qualitative phenomena. *J. gen. Psychol.*, 1938, *19*, 169–177.

293. Wallace, S. R. Studies in binocular interdependence. III. An active principle. *J. gen. Psychol.*, 1939, *20*, 33–45.

294. Wallace, S. R. The effect of foveal stimulation on peripheral sensitivity. *Psychol. Bull.*, 1938, *35*, 496.

295. Walls, G. L. Factors in human visual resolution. *J. opt. Soc. Amer.*, 1943, *33*, 487–505.

296. Walshe, F. M. R. The anatomy and physiology of cutaneous sensibility: a critical review. *Brain*, 1942, *65*, 48–112.

297. Wangensteen, O. H., and Carlson, A. J. Hunger sensations in a patient after total gastrectomy. *Proc. Soc. exp. Biol., N. Y.*, 1931, *28*, 545–547.

298. Waterston, D. Observations on sensation: the sensory functions of the skin for touch and pain. *J. Physiol.*, 1933, *77*, 251–257.

299. Weddell, G. The multiple innervation of sensory spots in the skin. *J. Anat., Lond.*, 1941, *75*, 441–446.

300. Weddell, G. The anatomy of pain sensibility. *J. Anat., Lond.*, 1947, *81*, 374.

301. Weddell, G., Sinclair, D. C., and Feindel, W. H. An anatomical basis for alterations in quality of pain sensibility. *J. Neurophysiol.*, 1948, *11*, 99–109.

302. Wegel, R. L., and Lane, C. E. The auditory masking of one pure tone by another and its probable relation to the dynamics of the inner ear. *Phys. Rev.,* 1924, *23,* 266–285.

303. Weinberg, M., and Allen, F. On the critical frequency of pulsation of tones. *Phil. Mag.,* 1924, *47,* 50–62.

304. Weitz, J. Vibratory sensitivity as affected by local anesthesia. *J. exp. Psychol.,* 1939, *25,* 48–64.

305. Weitz, J. Vibratory sensitivity as a function of skin temperature. *J. exp. Psychol.,* 1941, *28,* 21–36.

306. Weitz, J. The coding of airplane control knobs. Chap. 13 (pp. 187–198) in P. M. Fitts (ed.), *Psychological research in equipment design.* Washington: U. S. Government Printing Office, 1947.

307. Wendt, G. R. Vestibular functions. Chap. 31 (pp. 1191–1223) in Stevens (ed.), *Handbook of experimental psychology.* New York: Wiley, 1951.

308. Wenzel, B. M. Differential sensitivity in olfaction. *J. exp. Psychol.,* 1949, *39,* 129–143.

309. Wever, E. G. *Theory of hearing.* New York: Wiley, 1949.

310. Wever, E. G., and Bray, C. W. Present possibilities for auditory theory. *Psychol. Rev.,* 1930, *37,* 365–380.

311. Wever, E. G., and Bray, C. W. The perception of low tones and the resonance-volley theory. *J. Psychol.,* 1937, *3,* 101–114.

312. Wever, E. G., and Bray, C. W. Distortion in the ear as shown by the electrical responses of the cochlea. *J. acoust. Soc. Amer.,* 1938, *9,* 227–233.

313. Wever, E. G., Bray, C. W., and Lawrence, M. A quantitative study of combination tones. *J. exp. Psychol.,* 1940, *27,* 469–496.

314. Wilska, A. Eine Methode zur Bestimmung der Hörschwellenamplituden des Trommelfells bei verschiedenen Frequenzen. *Skand. Arch. Physiol.,* 1935, *72,* 161–165.

315. Wingfield, R. C. An experimental study of the apparent persistence of auditory sensations. *J. gen. Psychol.,* 1936, *14,* 136–157.

316. Wolf, H. Exakte Messungen über die zur Erregung des Drucksinnes erforderlichen Reizgrössen. Inaugural dissertation, Jena, 1937.

317. Wolff, H. G., and Wolf, S. *Pain.* Springfield, Ill.: Thomas, 1948.

318. Wood, A. G. A quantitative account of the course of auditory fatigue. Unpublished Master's thesis. Univ. of Virginia, 1930.

319. Woodworth, R. S. *Experimental psychology.* New York: Holt, 1938.

320. Woodworth, R. S. *Psychology* (4th ed.). New York: Holt, 1940.

321. Woollard, H. H., Weddell, G., and Harpman, J. A. Observations on the neurohistological basis of cutaneous pain. *J. Anat., Lond.,* 1940, *74,* 413–440.

322. Woolsey, C. N., Marshall, W. H., and Bard, P. Representation of cutaneous tactile sensibility in the cerebral cortex of the monkey as indicated by evoked potentials. *Johns Hopk. Hosp. Bull.,* 1942, *70,* 399–441.

323. Woolsey, C. N., Marshall, W. H., and Bard, P. Note on the organization of tactile sensory area of the cerebral cortex of the chimpanzee. *J. Neurophysiol.,* 1943, *6,* 285–291.

324. Woolsey, C. N., and Walzl, E. M. Topical projection of nerve fibers from local regions of the cochlea to the cerebral cortex of the cat. *Johns Hopk. Hosp. Bull.,* 1942, *71,* 315–344.

325. Worchel, P., and Dallenbach, K. M.   The vestibular sensitivity of deaf-blind subjects. *Amer. J. Psychol.,* 1948, *61,* 94–99.
326. Wright, W. D.   A re-determination of the trichromatic coefficients of the spectral colours. *Trans. Opt. Soc., Lond.,* 1928–1929, *30,* 141–164.

327. Zigler, M. J.   Pressure adaptation time: a function of intensity and extensity. *Amer. J. Psychol.,* 1932, *44,* 709–720.
328. Zigler, M. J., and Holway, A. H.   Differential sensitivity as determined by amount of olfactory substance. *J. gen. Psychol.,* 1935, *12,* 372–382.
329. Zwaardemaker, H.   *L'odorat.* Paris: Doin, 1925.
330. Zwaardemaker, H.   An intellectual history of a physiologist with psychological aspirations. Pp. 491–516 in Murchison (ed.), *A history of psychology in autobiography,* Vol. I.   Worcester: Clark Univ. Press, 1930.

Index

362 Index

Synapses of auditory tract, time delay, 146
Synthesis, as test of analysis, 190
of complex tastes, 315
of "heat," 223, 224
"Synthetic" angina, 242
Syringomyelia, 175
Systems of sensitivity, in skin, 159
of taste, 315

Tactile discs, 168
Tactile papillae, 191
Tactual discrimination of shapes, 11
Taeger, H., 320
Talbot's Law, 21
Tartini, G., 129
"Tartini's tone," 129
Taste, adaptation to blood stream, 298
electrophysiology of, 321–323
qualities of, 295, 297, 313
Taste analysis of foods, 314–315
"Taste blindness," 311–313
Taste bud, 299–300
diagram of, 299
Taste cells, nerve fibers supplying, 301
Taste contrast, 316
Taste intensity, psychological scale of, 309
Taste interaction in foods and beverages, 317
Taste mixtures, 315–318
at high concentration, 316
Taste pores, 300
Taste receptors, 299–303
Taste sensitivity, absolute, 303–307
differential, 307–311
individual differences in, 311–313
theories of, 322–323
variations along edge of tongue, 305
Taste stimulator, 317
Taste stimuli, 295–299
Taste tetrahedron, 313, 314
Taste threshold, drop method, 306
single-drop technique, 308
sipping method, 306
"Tasters" versus "non-tasters," 312
Tectorial membrane, 110, 152
Telephone theory of hearing, 146, 151–152, 154
Temperature, and taste sensitivity, 303, 304
effect of on taste adaptation, 319
effect of on taste threshold, 319
Temperature cylinder, 162–163

Temperature economy of skin, 229
of taste stimuli, 295
receptor, nerve as, 231–232
sensations, as kinesthetic, 228
sensitivity, loss in syringomyelia, 175
classical theory of, 224–227
"Temperature sense," 218
Temporal cortex, 145
Temporal pressure patterns, 184–188
Temporal visual acuity, 87–90
Tench, electrical response of retina, 77
Tendinous sense, 235
Tendons, pain sensitivity of, 199
Tension, and differential pressure sensitivity, 183
as stimulus for pressure, 179
Tension recorders, Golgi tendon organs as, 239
Tensor tympani, 107
Terminal cylinders (Ruffini), 171
Tests, color vision, 70
Tetartanopia, characteristics of, 72
Thalamus, cutaneous pathways through, 175
Thallium green in color mixing, 56
Theories of hearing, 146–157
Theory, test of a, 292
Theory of duplex retina, 31
Thermal adaptation, 206, 218–222, 229
as stimulus failure, 221–222
complete, 221
course of, 220
punctiform stimulation, 220
Thermal changes in skin, 214–218
Thermal gradient theory, 216
Thermal senses, 211–214
Thermal sensitivity of stomach, 241
Thermal stimulation, and pain, 195–198
of colon, 241
of skin, 161
role of vascular system in, 214
Thermocautery, 162
Thermocouples, subcutaneous, 214, 215
Thermoesthesiometer, 207
Thermometer, skin as, 219
Thirst, 240, 246–248
appetitive, 247, 248
as sensory pattern, 247, 248
induced by atropine, 246
in polyuria, 247
in stage fright, 247